THE FERTILE CRESCENT

W9-AEB-216

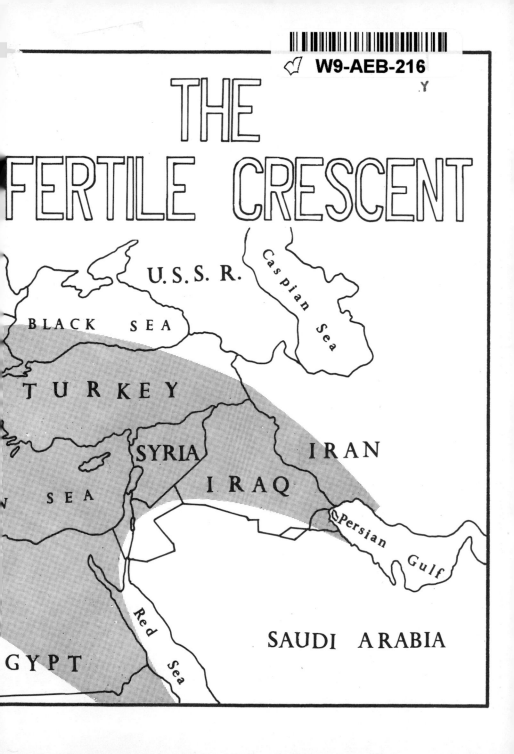

THE FERTILE CRESCENT

Travels in the Footsteps

of

Ancient Science

By Clifford N. Anderson

The Solar System and the Constellations

The Fertile Crescent

Travels in the Footsteps of Ancient Science

THE FERTILE CRESCENT

CLIFFORD N. ANDERSON

Illustrated

CARL A. RUDISILL LIBRARY
LENOIR RHYNE COLLEGE
HICKORY, N. C. 28601

SYLVESTER PRESS
FORT LAUDERDALE, FLORIDA

509.3
An2f
90012
Oct/1974

SYLVESTER PRESS
2605 Castilla Isle, Fort Lauderdale, Florida 33301

SECOND EDITION (REVISED)

© 1968, 1972 by Clifford N. Anderson. *All rights reserved, including the right of reproduction in whole or in part in any form except for short quotations in critical essays and reviews.* Manufactured in the United States of America.

LIBRARY OF CONGRESS CATALOGUE CARD NUMBER: 72-75821

To

my parents

PETER *and* CARRIE ANDERSON

whose sacrifices can never be repaid

EASTERN
MEDITERRANEAN
AND THE
NEAR EAST

FOREWORD

A WIDE sweeping arc starting at the Persian Gulf and swinging northward along the valleys of the Tigris and Euphrates rivers, along the areas adjacent to the Aegean and Eastern Mediterranean seas, and continuing southward to include the Nile Valley, might be said to be the spawning grounds of Western civilization. The term "The Fertile Crescent" has been applied to part of this arc[1] and is being used in this volume in a somewhat broader sense. Here written language developed; our alphabet had its beginnings; philosophers discussed the nature of the universe; mathematics, physics, biology, astronomy, geography, medicine, and other sciences had their beginnings; different forms of government were tried without finding any ideal solution; literature blossomed and the arts flourished. Unfortunately, so did war!

Viewing these lands today, one wonders how they could support the large populations and invading armies and still attain the cultural levels they did. Iraq, Southern Iran and Syria are mainly deserts; Turkey is mountainous with only occasional valleys inland and limited arable coastal areas. Only 20 percent of Greece is arable and in Egypt the only arable land is the Nile Delta and a few miles on each side of the Nile, less than one-half of one percent. However, though it may have lacked in agricultural fertility, the Crescent certainly was fertile culturally. There was ceaseless warfare with depopulated, plundered, and razed cities, and enslavement for the survivors. Life was difficult and precarious. Yet, not only did people survive but cities were rebuilt, arts flourished, and knowledge advanced in unprecedented steps. It was as if "Daily with souls that cringe and plot, we Sinais climb and know it not."[2]

The horizons of knowledge five or six centuries before the Christian era were extremely limited in both time and space. In

[1] J. H. Breasted, *Ancient Times* (Boston, 1916).
[2] James Russell Lowell, *The Vision of Sir Launfal.*

the preceding millennia, Mesopotamia had developed a written language, a system of gods and goddesses, a literature of myths and epics, arithmetical processes, depicted constellations, and formulated an empirical method for predicting eclipses. The bases for the Greek pantheon and the constellations can be traced to this source. The myths of Creation and the Flood and the codified laws of Hammurabi reappear in the Bible. But the crude maps of 500 B.C., on which one can hardly recognize the Mediterranean Sea, attest to their meager knowledge. Science groped its way through the mass of bewildering impressions until, suddenly, it found itself mature enough to ask questions and endeavor to explain man, nature, and the interrelationships. The people of that time can be forgiven for the vague and faltering steppingstones. Put yourself in their place and see what sort of model of the universe you would envision. The greatest activity was between 500 and 200 B.C., with a few stragglers as late as 400 A.D. But the results were astounding. From then on for a thousand years, science lay more or less dormant in the schools of the Arab scholars.

The climate in which science developed was one of ceaseless, gruesome warfare waged for the usual reasons: greed, power lust, plunder, slaves, envy, revenge, glory, and just the adventure of killing and destroying. Campaigns were sometimes rationalized as defensive wars or religious wars, but it was booty and tribute that made them attractive. Combatants were often so weakened that both the victor and the conquered fell prey to a previously unobtrusive nation. Sometimes when a nation felt itself too weak to attack a potential enemy, it tried the slower but safer method of fostering revolts among the stronger's vassals. The results were always the same: lands devastated, cities razed and property destroyed or damaged, tribute exacted, massacres, cruelty, torture, murder, plunder, enslavement, and populations deported.

The events of the 20th century, unfortunately, do not seem to be too different. Wars have ever been on the increase and have reached a new high in recent years. One need only be reminded of the Spanish Civil War, World War II ushering in the atomic bomb, the Korean War, purges in Russia, China, and Indonesia, torture schools in Indonesia and elsewhere, the genocide of Jews in Germany and Poland, the mass deportation of Arabs from Palestine, mass population transplants in India and Pakistan, the establishment of a Communist state in Cuba with accompanying purges and a fleeing population, the war in Viet Nam, and the general "cold war" for decades which occasionally waxes lukewarm.

One is inclined to ask, why this inherent urge for savagery, warfare and destruction? The trait seems to be shared with the rest of the animal kingdom and, to a lesser extent, with plant life as well. Among animals in the wild, there are many confrontations between members of the same specie but they always end without bloodshed unless retreat is blocked. Except for rats, man is the only animal that practices agression and mass murder of one community by another of his own specie.

Nature's pattern is one of promiscuous and bountiful production of innumerable forms. Then, instead of making it easy to survive, Nature makes it difficult. Life is a struggle. The species that survive are those that can cope with the environment. Over 90% have failed and are extinct. Those that have survived are endowed with an intense instinct for survival and nearly all of man's decisions and reactions are manifestations of this instinct. Primarily this is for survival of the species, but of course this has to be served by the survival of individuals. Yet the osprey deliberately starves the weak fledgling lest the entire strain be weakened; a bee may sacrifice its life in stinging, though it serves notice that bees in general should not be molested; a parent may sacrifice his or her life to save the life of their child; in war, a man may sacrifice his life to save the lives of his comrades. The hero complex is an important factor in the survival of the species.

Survival of the species depends upon the fitness of the individuals. When Nature is allowed to function, it destroys the unfit and the misfit, and combat was one of Nature's ways in the dim and distant past when combat was hand to hand with simple weapons. Today's wars circumvent Nature's plan in that the unfit are left behind to procreate the race. Warfare is therefore a genetic tragedy and in addition there is the loss of life, maimed survivors, suffering

and broken homes by both victor and vanquished alike. Nevertheless, the instincts remain: to fight, to destroy the weaker antagonist,
to be considered superior, to be a hero, to achieve recognition and
glory. Some individuals can channel those instincts into productive
achievements; for others it means acts of violence, vandalism,
crime, and disregard for the rights of others. On the national level,
it spells war.

In studying the history of science, one cannot help but be impressed by the tremendous strides made by science in the last 25
centuries and, in contrast, the relatively meager improvements in
government. Are there no lessons that can be learned from history,
or is it so difficult for civilization to benefit from the past? Assuming survival of the species to be the basic aim of Nature, what can
be done to maintain the vigor of the human race? Nature's way of
eliminating the unfit and the misfit was by combat, pestilence,
famine, and other natural disasters. Modern warfare destroys the
fit and hence does not seem to serve Nature's purpose. Furthermore, the military with or without war, is no permanent solution.
Nations justify increased armament in order to increase security.
This results in continuing escalation as other nations catch up. As
a result there is the paradox of steadily *increasing armament* and
steadily *decreasing security*. With proper safeguards, warfare,
therefore, can probably be classed as unessential, although it may
be too presumptive to expect that a substitute can be found for
what has been ingrained in our genes from time immemorial.
Military forces will still be needed for defense against recalcitrant
nations, but forces larger than necessary foster "power diplomacy,"
arrogant rulers, and restless armies that seek activity and glory.

Unfortunately, nations are not prepared to forego warfare.
There are ideological wars, wars started by rulers seeking power
and fame, and wars by "have-not" nations in order to acquire living space or the accumulated wealth of nations that "have". Then
there is the reluctance to reduce armament because of distrust of
their neighbor's intentions. Arms reduction conferences are praise-
worthy but each nation wants to bargain from strength. As no nation will agree to being second-rate, such efforts are not likely to

be fruitful. Until there is a certain amount of stabilization among nations, agreement of fundamentals, and potential causes of war eliminated, or at least subdued, there is little chance of wars being abolished. It will take a long time, possibly a century or more, before the futility of warfare is fully realized by all nations and they unanimously truly desire and agree to outlaw war and settle international differences by judicial means. It should be emphasized that *all* nations are necessary to support such an agreement as only one holdout nation capable of waging war against a neighbor will defeat the plan.

To achieve a world of self-reliant nations, each willing to respect the boundaries and the way of life of others, is certainly a Utopia devoutly to be wished. Judging from the past, the outlook is not bright. Self-reliance is a prime requirement for a nation and that entails, among other things, the productivity potential, the cultural level, and a population that can be supported at that level. The tasks are formidable and universal cooperation is a necessity. The matter of populations is a world problem that will take centuries to stabilize. It is fraught with danger. Given a section of Society subsisting at a sub-marginal level; provide medical aid and food relief; there is a temporary improvement in conditions; more people survive and the birth rate increases; the result, more people subsisting at a sub-marginal level and living in misery. The lesson is that *providing aid without controlling the birth rate is no solution.* Populations should be limited to that which can be supported without outside help. That too must be practiced with caution lest the talented practice control leaving the population to be dominated by the offspring of the less able. The less cultured nations and those with less assets have to realize that any improvement in their status has to be earned. False prosperity due to funds supplied by other nations leads to degeneracy and trouble when the bounty stops. Nations must realize they must live within their means. To "empire builders", this idea is distasteful.

Plato and Aristotle analyzed governments 24 centuries ago and, although they had in mind the various city-states of Greece, the analyses still apply in large part to governments of today. In general, governments were classified into Monarchies, Oligarchies, and Democracies. The best form depends a good deal on circumstances, including the cultural attainment and the temperament of the people governed. It is necessary, of course, to get the right kind of people to head the government, but there is no safe way of selecting a ruler. Aristotle listed five different kinds of monarchies, of which four may be acceptable under proper circumstances, and the fifth, tyranny, unacceptable, as it is the lawless rule over unwilling subjects. In oligarchies, wealth, property, the church, or the military determines the ruler, and this is subject to some dangers. An oligarchal government may actually rule under the guise of a democracy. Four different kinds of democracies are listed depending upon the degree of freedom. One form in which a relatively small faction rule by their own decree contrary to law and the good of the nation, as in labor strikes and riots, can hardly be dignified by calling it a democracy. Extreme abuses in any of these forms of government generally lead to another form. Too much freedom leads to mob rule followed by a dictatorship or a military takeover.

All forms of government have their weaknesses, with neither the despotic rule of tyranny nor the mob rule of too much freedom in a democracy acceptable. Aristotle felt that *no ruler should be given too much power, so that if mistakes are made, the damage is not too extensive.* The United States Constitution endeavors to do just that by recognizing State Rights and dividing the ruling responsibility into Legislative, Judicial, and Executive departments, one to be a brake upon the other. The present trend seems to circumvent that plan with the Judiciary appointed to satisfy election debts instead of superlative judicial ability and Congress relegated to a rubber stamp. Large appropriations distributed by the Executive Department serve as blackmail to sway Congress to accede to the Executive Department's wishes.

Stoic philosophy championed freedom but *with responsibility* and maintained that the individual's own ends must be subordinate to the ends and needs of Society. The individual has no inherent rights contrary to the rights of Society. Laws and rules of conduct are for the purpose of protecting Society and, to the extent that one is a conformist, they protect the individual as well. This fact is lost sight of these days with all the agitation for individual freedom. Some day Society will have to be given the benefit of the doubt instead of the individual and avoid setting criminals free on technicalities, who then resume their life of crime.

Looking to the immediate future, it is unlikely things will be much different from the past. The lapse in moral and ethical values among people in general and those in government in particular, and the indiscriminate use of the concept of freedom to justify most any kind of action but without any reference to responsibility, may be Man's version of the survival of the fittest but Nature may decide it is decay. As a guide, the administration of justice and legislative programs should be considered in the light of the survival of the more fit as being Society's criterion. Since this involves decisions by a ruler or ruling group, temper their powers so that if mistakes are made, the damage may not be too great.

There are many lessons to be learned from history. Each generation feels that its era is unique and the events of the past have no bearing on the present. The details are different, but the general trend and results are much the same. The same unethical conduct in individuals, in government, and among nations exists today as over 2,000 years ago. Wars are more frequent and more severe; reasons for justifying them are much the same. One cannot help but note, therefore, the contrast between the little or no progress made in government and the great strides made in science.

CONTENTS

PART ONE

MESOPOTAMIA

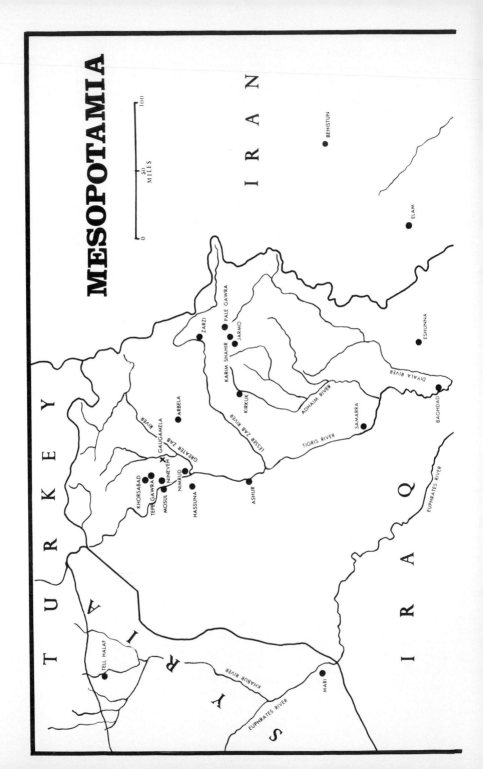

MESOPOTAMIA

IRAN

TURKEY

SYRIA

IRAQ

IRAN

100

50
MILES

0

BEHISTUN

ELAM

ESHUNNA

DIYALA RIVER

BAGHDAD

SAMARRA

ADHAIM RIVER

TIGRIS RIVER

LESSER ZAB RIVER

ZARZI

PALE GAWRA

KARIM SHAHIR

JARMO

KIRKUK

ARBELA

GREATER ZAB RIVER

GAUGAMELA

KHORSABAD

TEPE GAWRA

NINEVEH

MOSUL

NIMRUD

HASSUNA

ASHUR

EUPHRATES RIVER

TELL HALAF

KHABUR RIVER

MARI

EUPHRATES RIVER

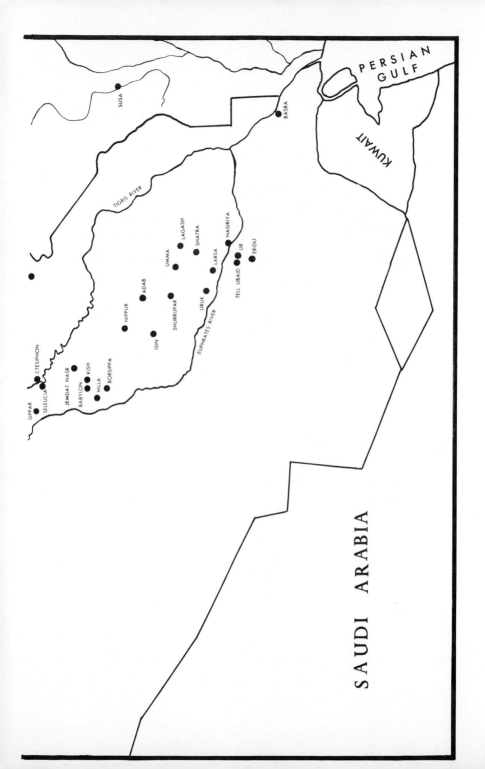

AT THE eastern end of the Fertile Crescent is a structural basin between the plateau of Iran and the tableland and desert of Arabia. Almost all lies within the boundaries of Iraq and is generally known as Mesopotamia, the Land Between the Rivers, the rivers being the Tigris and the Euphrates. In the glacial period, the Persian Gulf extended as far north as Baghdad, some 400 miles inland from the present shore line. The southern half of the area is therefore a delta plain. Baghdad is only 113 feet above sea level and the gradient along the river is less than three inches per mile. Rain occurs only in the winter months and that is less than ten inches a year. June to October are rainless. The rivers are fed mainly from mountain streams in the Kurdistan section of eastern Turkey. A section of the same basin, but in southwestern Iran, is fed by rivers from the Zagros Mountains. This was the region of Elam with its capital at Susa, a section which, at times, has figured in the political history of the area.

With such aridity, natural vegetation is limited to plants adjusted to scanty and periodic moisture. Trees are absent except along the rivers and the upper mountains. Evaporation is so great that the volume of water in the Euphrates diminishes toward its mouth. In the soil, the water rises to the surface and evaporates, leaving mineral deposits in the form of crusts of salts and alkalies. Because of this, large areas are unsuitable for cultivation, and, without drainage, irrigation often aggravates the situation.

The lower reaches constitute the Land of the Reeds, where people live in reed huts on unstable islands in the swampland in primitive conditions with domesticated water buffalos. These animals supply meat, milk, and dung for fuel. They have even been described as patient machines for processing reeds into suitable fuel. The marshes are infested with snakes, sandflies, scorpions, gnats, typhus, malaria, dysentery and vicious tusked boars as large as a small donkey. Since the inhabitants are Moslems, the hogs have no food value.

Agriculture has always been the basis of general economy and where irrigation is feasible, crops are dependable. Beans, onions, cabbages, sesame oil, olive oil, and wine are produced. Barley and wheat are grown in the north, and rice, corn, and cotton are grown in the south. But dates is the most important crop with one-third of all the date trees in the world, most of them in a 100-mile stretch north of Basra. These furnish three-fourths of the world supply. Wool is an important commodity in the highlands. Today, of course, oil is the main source of national income and for Iraq this will mean a new era.

Nevertheless, one can't help but wonder how this land was at one time the site of Biblical Eden; how this land supported cultures which were fought over time after time; how this land, in spite of wars, fostered the development of a written language, mathematics, astronomy, civil codes, pioneered irrigation, produced literature about Creation and the Flood, myths of their pantheon, and other tales which their successors and neighbors adopted as their own. Was the physical situation different from what it is today? Climatic conditions are undoubtedly about the same. The Persian Gulf did extend further upstream to Eridu, a seaport on an island, and possibly as far as Lagash. That means 30 feet less silt and a steeper river gradient with less likelihood that the canals would silt up. It also means the saline concentration was less than now. Ineffective irrigation due to changes in the river beds and to the destruction of the irrigation canals by the Mongols (1258 A.D.) might be a contributing factor.

The earliest traces of inhabitants in this region seem to be in the northeast corner of Iraq, east of the Tigris River and the city of Mosul. Several cave sites dating from the Old Stone Age (10,000 B.C.) have been found. The earliest settled village revealed thus far is Jarmo (7000-5000 B.C.). The houses were of mud brick and similar in construction to countryside houses of today. The floors were of dried mud over reeds. Pottery dated about 5000 B.C. has been found at Hassuna (20 miles south of Mosul) and at Samarra* (70 miles north of Baghdad). Documentary history begins, however, with the inhabitants near the southern confluence of the Tigris and Euphrates rivers. This was the land of SUMER.

---

*Samarra is the site of a tapered spiral minaret with an outside ramp.

SUMER

ALTHOUGH it is believed that Sumerian people came from the Persian highlands, it is not known definitely where they originated or what their linguistic affiliation was. Their language was of the agglutinative type, in which compounded words are used for new ideas. For example, instead of a single word to designate "rain," the symbols for "water" and "heaven" were used. This is distinctly different from the Semitic languages which dominated the later history of Mesopotamia. Most of the Semitic root words have a core of three consonants with internal vowel changes. The uniqueness of the Sumerian language would normally render its solution impossible. Its decipherment started with decoding the Persian cuneiform inscriptions at Persepolis and Behistun. Bilingual inscriptions enabled the Akkadian versions to be solved, after which bilingual Akkadian-Sumerian inscriptions and dictionaries led to the final solution. By means of pottery, pictured cylinder seals, their cuneiform literature, and commercial records, a surprising amount of information is available about these people who lived 4,000-6,000 years ago. They were first overthrown by the Semite Akkadians, about 2300 B.C., and later by the Amorites. But they left a legacy to succeeding cultures which extends down to our own.

By 4000 B.C. there were well-established cities, of which the city of Eridu is traditionally the oldest. At that time the city was on an island near the head of the Persian Gulf. Today it lies buried under a mound, Abu-Shahrain, 10 miles upstream from the sea. Plain or simply decorated brownish-red and gray pottery characterizes the early culture called *al Ubaid* after the Tell-el-Obeid site about 12 miles north of Eridu and adjacent to Ur. Decorative clay pins reinforced the mud walls and formed primitive mosaics.

Sumerian king lists note seven kings prior to the Flood. The capital was at Nunki. An *En,* or lord, was chosen for administrative duties in each city and a *Lugal* (Lu = man; Gal=great; Lugal=

great man, or king) was chosen for war. The kingships changed from city to city depending upon which city could dominate, though at times kings reigned concurrently. After the Flood, the king list indicates: Kish, 23 kings; Uruk, 12 kings; Ur, 4 or 5; Awan, 3; Kish II, 8; Hamash, 1; Uruk II, 3; Ur, 4; Adab, 1; Mari, 6; Kish III, 1; Aksak, 6; Lagash, 10; Kish IV, 7; Uruk III, 1. Other Sumerian cities during this early period include Nippur, Umma, Larsa, Shuruppak, Sippar, and Jemdat Nasr. Taking advantage of the interdynastic feuds, the Akkadians under Sargon I overthrew the Sumerians (2334-2154 B.C.), but the rule ended in disaster when Mesopotamia was overrun by barbaric tribes from Iran called Guti. Political chaos followed, except in Lagash, which for some reason was spared. Finally (c 2120 B.C.) the Sumerians, under the leadership of Uruk and Ur, were able to regain control. The century that followed under the 3rd dynasty of Ur was prosperous at first, but general decay and famine caused an economic collapse and the land fell prey to the Amorites, a nomadic people of Semite origin. It was the end of Sumer as a political entity.

Uruk

Pottery styles at the Uruk site show 18 different levels, with the historic era beginning about 3600 B.C By that time the city was already mature and it continued to be occupied for 2,000 years. The city, near modern Warka, was the Biblical Erech. By 3000 B.C. the 1100-acre city was fully developed and enclosed by a double wall, six miles in length and with 800 watchtowers. The bread-loaf type of mud bricks had been introduced and irrigation projects had been initiated. Uruk is the site of the earliest known ziggurat, on top of which, 40 feet above the plain, are the remains of a 60-by-80 foot temple. It was probably dedicated to the sky-god An, as Uruk was his main seat of worship. Nearby, on the plain below, are the remains of the Pillar Temple, dated about 2000 B.C. and dedicated to Inanna, the tutelary goddess of the city. It must have been a beautiful structure with eight columns of palm logs covered with mother-of-pearl, pink limestone, and shells on an asphalt base and binder. Engaged columns in the side walls, eight feet in diameter,

PILLARS FROM THE TEMPLE AT URUK (c 3000 B.C.)
The pillars are studded with small red, black, and white cones of fired
clay. (Pergamon Museum, East Berlin)

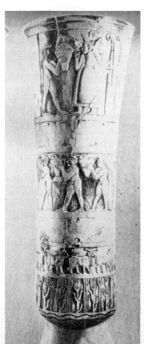

WARKA ALABASTER VASE
The vase is three feet high with three
bands of relief. (Baghdad Museum)

are the earliest example of columnar architecture on a grand scale. Small baked black, red, and gray cones were inserted to form a mosaic-like decorative and protective surface.

Stone had to be imported, so it is not surprising that examples of sculpture, other than cylinder seals, are few. Diorite, a hard black stone capable of taking a high polish, was a favorite. The outstanding example of sculpture is the Warka gypsum vase in the Baghdad Museum. It is three feet high with three bands of relief depicting men carrying gifts to goddess Inanna. Figures of painted clay bulls and lions, representing the crescent and full moon respectively, were found in the deepest excavations.

Gilgamesh, the legendary king of Uruk and a hero of Sumerian mythology and Babylonia's greatest epic, may have been an actual historical figure from the early Uruk period.

Nippur

Nippur was an intellectual and religious center and from the earliest times, the Sumerians believed their kingships had to be sanctioned by this holy city. In mythology, Nippur was inhabited by Gods alone before the creation of man. It was the home of the air-god Enlil, the most important deity in the Sumerian pantheon and the deity who gave rulers the kingship of the land.

Excavations by the University of Pennsylvania (1889-1900) uncovered 20 strata extending over a period of 3,000 years. A collection of 30,000 clay tablets was found, over 90 percent of which are economic in character. About 2,000 literary tablets and fragments dating from about 2000 B.C. are the source of much of what is known of Sumerian literature. A map of Nippur at the University of Jena, Germany, is probably the oldest city map in history. It is inscribed on a 5-by-8-inch clay tablet and is believed to be dated about 1500 B.C. The city was in the shape of an irregular square about 3,600 feet on a side. The west side was bounded by the Euphrates River, called Buranum in Sumerian. Through the center of the city, from northwest to southeast, ran a river now known as Shatt-en-Nil. The city's most renowned temple, Ekur, was on the east side of town. The temple area appears to be about 600 feet square. With the growth in importance of Babylon and its god Marduk, Nippur gradually deteriorated. Although Assurbanipal rejuvenated the city in the 7th century B.C. and built a ziggurat measuring 128 by 190 feet, it never regained any prominence.

In view of the hundreds of thousands of tablets which have been unearthed, the demand for scribes must have been great. Consequently, there were a number of schools for scribes throughout the area, such as the ones excavated at Nippur. Practice tablets show various degrees of proficiency from the crude scratches of the beginners to the perfection of those about to graduate. Duplication of the exercises has materially facilitated the study of Sumerian literature, as damaged portions of one tablet can often be found intact on others. Translations of the various languages using the cuneiform script would have been impossible without bilingual dictionaries and bilingual inscriptions.

Lagash

Lagash was one of the most important cities of Sumer. The ruins are located about 11 miles north of the town of Shatra and are now called Tello. There are a number of mounds spread out over an area two and a half miles long and a mile wide. The largest mound covers the temple of Ninurta, a warrior god who was the son of the air-god Enlil. It is believed to date from about 2500 B.C. Nearby is "Tablet Hill", where over 100,000 tablets have been excavated. Among the artifacts found are stone images of bulls with human faces, horned heads with ears like those of oxen, silver vases, serpents coiled around a staff, and images of the crescent moon in the shape of the horns of a bull.

The city was competely destroyed by Lugal-Zaggisi of Umma in about 2340 B.C. It was rebuilt but never regained its independence following the invasions of the Akkads (2300 B.C.) It was spared devastation by the Gutians (2150 B.C.) but ceased to be inhabited at about the time of Hammurabi (1750 B.C.).

The outstanding feature of Lagash's history is the social reform initiated by a ruler called Urukagina. Due to wars in which Lagash was involved with other city-states, the citizens of Lagash found themselves deprived of political and economic freedom. Confiscatory taxes to support the army and enrich the ruling coterie under Lugal Banda (2353-2348 B.C.), who were reluctant to relinquish controls, incited the people to revolt and install Urukagina, from another family, as ruler. He ended government inspection, forbade seizing of property, abolished fees of the governor and clergy, cleared the city of usurers, thieves, and murderers, and restored temple property. However, the reforms during his ten-year rule came too late and Lagash succumbed to Umma. Nevertheless, the social implications of the reforms were reflected in civil codes of Ur-Nammu (2112-2095 B.C.), Lipit-Ishtar (c 1930 B.C.), Hammurabi (1792-1750 B.C.), and others.

Ur

The remains of the ancient city of Ur are located about 200 miles south of Baghdad, near the Baghdad-Basra railway, and 15 miles west of the city of Nasirya. The site is on a wide arid plain and it is hard to reconcile the prosperity of ancient Ur with the brown desert of today. However, in those days, the Persian Gulf extended as far north as Eridu, 15 miles to the south, with the Euphrates River along the west wall of the city and the mouth of the Tigris nearby. The city was in the shape of an irregular oval, about three-quarters of a mile long and half a mile wide, and was surrounded by a 25-foot wall of mud bricks. In the northwest quadrant was a walled rectangular enclosure, about 800 by 1200 feet, within which was a temple dedicated to Nannar, the moon-god and patron deity of Ur, a temple to his consort Ningal, the palace of the ruler Ur-Nammu, and the well-preserved ziggurat. The ziggurat is pictured by artists as being a three-tiered 68-foot structure capped with a shrine. The structure at present consists of a massive base, 210 by 140 feet and possibly 50 feet high, with a stairway complex of one grand stair flanked by two others. On top is a small platform.

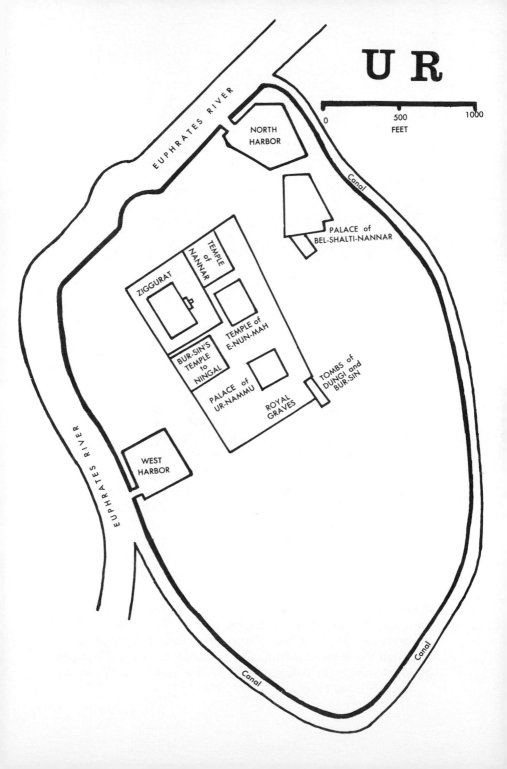

UR

0   500   1000
           FEET

EUPHRATES RIVER

NORTH HARBOR

Canal

PALACE of
BEL-SHALTI-NANNAR

TEMPLE of NANNAR

ZIGGURAT

TEMPLE of E-NUN-MAH

BUR-SIN'S TEMPLE to NINGAL

PALACE of UR-NAMMU

ROYAL GRAVES

TOMBS of DUNGI and BUR-SIN

EUPHRATES RIVER

WEST HARBOR

Canal

Canal

THE ZIGGURAT AT UR
The structure was built during the reign of Ur-Nammu (c 2100 B.C.) and is believed to have consisted of three tiers with a temple on top.

Contiguous with the southeast corner of the enclosure are the tombs from which the joint British Museum - University of Pennsylvania excavation project in 1922-1934 unearthed beautiful works of art in gold, silver, and semi-precious stones. Most of these came from the royal tombs of King Adar-gi and Queen Shub-ad* (c 2600 B.C.). The list of the exquisite things is long and varied: fluted gold goblets and bowls, a gold dagger with a single piece of lapis lazuli studded with gold nails together with an openwork gold sheath, a helmet of Prince Mes-kalam-shar hammered from a single sheet of gold-silver alloy with the ears and a knot of hair in relief and details of the hair chased, necklaces of gold and lapis lazuli, necklaces of shells and red limestone, a bull's head from a lyre with the hair and beard made of lapis lazuli and the wooden core head covered by gold leaf, a ram in a thicket, women's head ornaments with carnelian, lapis lazuli and gold beech leaves, bracelets, rings and anklets.

Land areas in the vicinities of large rivers are subject to great floods. Some of these may be beneficial, as in the case of the Nile, some may be destructive, and some may be the subject matter of literature, as in the Biblical story of Noah. The name of the Sumerian Noah was Ziusadra. The Sumerian version is incomplete but does state, "The deluge raged over the surface of the earth—

*Recently called Pu-abi.

RAM IN THICKET FOUND IN THE ROYAL GRAVES AT UR
(c 2600 B.C.) (University of Pennsylvania Museum, Philadelphia)

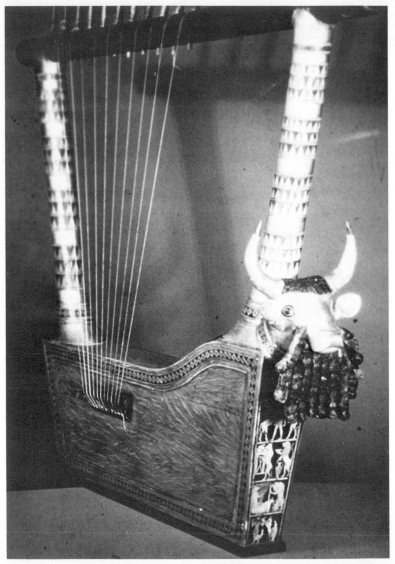

LYRE FOUND IN THE ROYAL GRAVES AT UR (c 2600 B.C.)
(University of Pennsylvania Museum, Philadelphia)

BULL'S HEAD ORNAMENT ON THE LYRE
The wooden form is covered with gold leaf; the hair
and beard are of lapis lazuli.
(University of Pennsylvania Museum, Philadelphia)

for seven days and seven nights, the deluge raged over the land
and the huge boat tossed about on the great waters." Excavations
in various Sumerian cities do show evidences of great floods, thick

alluvial deposits which could only have been laid down under conditions of long and deep sustained flooding. In Ur there is such a deposit which varies from 9 to 12 feet, but it seems to have occurred about 3500 B.C. This is earlier than the Biblical flood, which is assumed to have been about 2900 B.C. There are other evidences of floods, such as one at Ur about 2700 B.C., two at Kish, one in 2900 B.C. and a 16-inch deposit about 2600 B.C., and a 2-foot deposit at Shurappak about 2850 B.C. The occurrences of floods seem to provide ample basis for the Flood stories of the Bible and the Gilgamesh Epic, but it is difficult to associate them with any specific event. Possibly the storytellers exercised a certain amount of literary license.

King Utu-Hegal of the 5th dynasty of Uruk (2120-2113 B.C.) was mainly responsible for the defeat of the Gutians. He named Ur-Nammu to be governor of Ur. Ur-Nammu was loyal at first but later proclaimed himself "King of Sumer and Akkad" and initiated the 3rd dynasty of Ur (2113-2004 B.C.). It was his title which gave the clue that the land should be called "Sumer." During his 18-year reign and the 47-year reign of his son Shulgi, Ur flourished, trade brought prosperity, the large ziggurat was built, as well as temples and palaces. He promulgated a law code to establish justice, regulate weights and measures, and punish criminals. The last three kings of the dynasty had Semitic names: Bur-Sin, Gimil-Sin, and Ibbi-Sin. Decline set in toward the end of the 25-year reign of Ibbi-Sin. Nomadic peoples of Semitic origin called Amorites (Westerners) invaded the empire and controlled the countryside. Famine and complete economic collapse followed. The Elamites captured Ur in 2005 B.C. and carried Ibbi-Sin off to Susa in captivity. The political center moved upstream through Isin and Larsa to Babylon, and with it the Akkadian language replaced the Sumerian except for sacred and learned purposes.

Ur was the birthplace of Abraham and his ancestors, although there is no record in Ur of his having lived there. Genesis 11:31 states that Terah took Abram, Lot, and Sarai "and brought them out of Ur of the Chaldees to go to the land of Canaan and they came to Harran and dwelt there." This was about 1600 or 1500 B.C.

AKKAD

THE dynasty of Akkad (2334-2154 B.C.) was founded by an out-standing personality of that era, Sharrukin, better known as Sargon I. The latter name was associated with him because an Assyrian king of a much later date, also named Sharrukin, was called Sargon in the Bible. Apparently he was the illegitimate son of a priestess and, like Moses a thousand years later, was laid in a basket and abandoned in the river. He was a sort of dependent prince under the Kish IV and Uruk III dynasties and ruled in Kish after a palace revolt. He felt that control of the trade routes was essential to security and campaigned up north as far as the Taurus Mountains and the Mediterranean Sea. Lugal Zaggisi in Uruk felt that Sargon was too ambitious and marched north to subdue him but was him-self beaten. Sargon moved south and captured Uruk, Lagash, Umma, and Nippur. He was crowned King-of-the-Land, from Persia to the Mediterranean.

He established his capital at Agade, or Akkad, probably near Babylon. The city has never been located definitely, although its ruins were mentioned in the 5th century B.C. His reign (2334-2279 B.C.) was one of continuous warfare and revolts. There was a general decline under his ten successors, ending in invasion by the Guti barbarians and general destruction throughout the land. Uruk, Ur, and other cities were subdued and the destruction of the capital, Agade, was complete.

From the cultural standpoint, the feature of this dynasty was the accelerated shift from the Sumerian language to the Semitic Akkadian. The cuneiform script was adopted, as well as many Sumerian words; but, although Sumerian rule was restored in the Ur III dynasty, the Sumerian language was on the way out except for inscriptions, legal forms, rituals, and literature.

BABYLON

AFTER the fall of Ur III (2000 B.C.), the Sumerian cities were governed by contemporary dynasties of Isin (2017-1794 B.C.) and Larsa (2025-1763 B.C.), but, except for a legal code in the Sumerian language promulgated in the reign of the Isin King Lipit-Ishtar (c 1930 B.C.), history has little to report. Their end was foreshadowed by the rising power of Babylon, and from then on the history of that city is also the history of Mesopotamia.

The beginning of Babylon is obscure. The earliest reference seems to be about 2300 B.C. with the Sumerian name of Ka-dingr, or Ka-dingr-Ra, the Gate of God. The Akkadians translated this literally as Bab-ilu, or, later, Bab-ilani. The Greeks rendered this as Babylon.

Babylon is situated on a barren sandy plain about 60 miles south of Baghdad, amidst desolate sandy mounds, low hills, and ridges. The only green is that of the palm trees along the Euphrates, now some distance away, and the few patches of cultivated land which are green after winter rains. There is an irrigation project under way between Babylon and Baghdad which may reclaim some of the desert. The view of the roofless mud-brick remains of the excavated city is saddening and depressing. Here once was "the most magnificent city of the world"; the city of the Hanging Gardens, one of the ancient Seven Wonders of the World; a fountainhead of ancient astronomy, mathematics, and literature; the city to which inhabitants of Jerusalem were brought as captives (597-539 B.C.) and treated as colonists rather than slaves. Here Alexander the Great came to conquer and to die.

It was also a city of sorrow, misery, war, and atrocities. Once a mighty city, it is now only a whistle stop on the Baghdad-Basra railway. *Sic transit gloria mundi*—Thus passes the glory of the world.

Early Babylonian Dynasties

The 1st dynasty of Babylon (1894-1595 B.C.) was founded by an Amorite sheik called Sumuabum. The rise in power apparently began with the fifth in line, Sin-muballit, the last of the rulers to have an Akkadian name. The most illustrious personality was his son, Hammurabi, who reigned for 43 years (1792-1750 B.C.). It was a very productive reign from the standpoints of literature and mathematics but is best known for the Hammurabi Civil Code.

Hammurabi promulgated his code near the end of his reign and included in it customs and Sumerian usage already common in the area. There had been other civil codes in Mesopotamia: a Sumerian code (c 2000 B.C.) during the reign of Ur-Nammu, a reform code (c 1930 B.C.) of 38 laws on seven tablets during the reign of Lipit-Ishtar of the Isin dynasty, and a code of King Balalama (1884-1863 B.C.) of Eshnunna. Hammurabi's code was apparently less legal practice than to indicate the ruler's awareness of existing and desirable practices. It starts out with an elaborate preamble telling of his own greatness and that Marduk commissioned him to govern the people. This is followed by 282 paragraphs of enactments prescribing barbarous punishments for even slight offenses. It includes such statements as "an eye for an eye, a tooth for a tooth, a hand for a hand, a foot for a foot." It lists legal procedures, offenses against property, temple property, property settlement, sale of property, theft, false charges, perjury, assault and battery, robbery, arson, money loans, irrigation, cultivation of land and dates, trade and commerce, building codes, slaves, marriage and divorce, and the like. The code was undoubtedly one source for the Mosaic law, as much of the phrasing is repeated word for word. Instead of being recorded on clay tablets, the code is inscribed in the Akkadian language with cuneiform script on a seven-foot, five-inch diorite stele. The top portion shows the king receiving the code of laws from Shamash, the sun-god. It was originally set up in the temple of Shamash at Sippar, north of Babylon, but was taken away to Susa as war booty by the Elamites in the middle of the 12th century B.C. A French mission to Persia in 1901-1902

TOP PORTION OF
THE CODE OF
HAMMURABI STELE

CODE OF
HAMMURABI
STELE

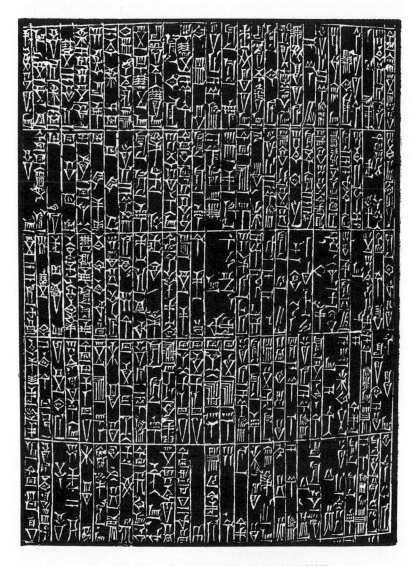

PART OF THE INSCRIPTION ON THE
CODE OF HAMMURABI STELE

discovered the monument and it is now in the Louvre in Paris.
Fragments of two other stelae have been found in Susa.

During the reign of Hammurabi's son, Samsu-iluna (1749-1712
B.C.), the provinces revolted. The walls of Uruk and Ur were
destroyed in 1740 B.C. to prevent refuge for the rebels, and by the
time of his death the Babylonian empire was reduced to a small
area around the city. It struggled along until 1595 B.C., when the
Hittites took Babylon and plundered it. They made no effort to
retain control but returned home with their booty. The Kassites
from the Zagros Mountain region in Persia took over and more or
less controlled Babylon for over 400 years until 1157 B.C. Circumstances of their rise in power are hidden in the unprecedented
blackout of the Dark Ages,* which lasted until the middle of the
Kassite dynasty (c 1375 B.C.).

The Assyrians invaded Babylonia in 1174 B.C., but the conquerors were so weakened that they fell prey to the Elamites, who
plundered Babylon as it had never been plundered before. They in
turn were ousted by a resistance movement developed primarily in
Isin, and that dynasty managed to retain control for 130 years
(Isin II, 1156-1025 B.C.). In the meantime, pressure in the north
from the Semitic Aramaean nomads and from the Chaldeans in the
south, together with famine and plague, threatened survival for
both Babylonia and Assyria.

Assyrian Era

Toward the end of the 10th century B.C., Babylonia was half
ruined and occupied with Aramaeans. Assyria was at her lowest
ebb and the only thing that saved her was the lack of unity among
her enemies. Her territory was no more than about 100 miles long
and 50 miles wide. But she was still intact, the strongest of her
neighbors, and from about 900 B.C. she was the dominant kingdom
in Mesopotamia. Even though they may have considered them
preventive wars, they waged them year after year with booty and
tribute. In order to get support, they considered them religious
wars to protect their god Ashur; to an unbiased observer, they
were simply massacre and robbery.

*It may also have been an unprecedented period of peace. "Happy is the
land that has no history."

Their kings were noted for their cruelty and Ashurnasirpal II (883-859 B.C.) surpassed them all. He flayed the conquered rulers, spread their skins on the city walls, and sadistically tortured the inhabitants, men, women, and children alike. He reoccupied the city of Kalah (modern Nimrud, 22 miles south of Mosul), built a new palace and, in connection with the opening ceremony in 879 B.C., feasted 70,000 inhabitants for ten days. There is little left of the site but a few figures and inscriptions. The Metropolitan Museum of Art in New York City has two large winged, human-headed lion and bull guardians and a large alabaster relief of a winged genie from Nimrud. The large collection in the British Museum includes the Black Stone, a monument to Shalmaneser III (858-824 B.C.), six feet high of basalt with the four sides decorated with fine reliefs and cuneiform inscriptions. The museum in Mosul has among its collections the throne base and a stone describing Ashurnasirpal's achievements and a description of the feast for the 70,000 guests.

Shalmaneser III spent 31 years of his 34-year reign at war. In one campaign his army slew 14,000 warriors and used their corpses as a bridge across the Orontes. The end of his reign was marked with revolts, even by one of his own sons, and a period of stagnation set in which lasted for nearly a century. In the meantime, Babylon was too weak to attack the Assyrians and too strong to be attacked by them. Shalmaneser's successor was a son, Shamshi-Adad V (823-811 B.C.), whose queen was a Babylonian princess called Shammuremat. After his death, she acted as regent for six years until her son, Adad-nirari V, became of age. The Greeks called her Semiramis and she had the reputation of being the most beautiful, the most cruel, the most powerful, and the most lustful of the Oriental queens. Tiglath-Pileser III, Hebraic form of Tukulti-apal-escharra (745-727 B.C.), reorganized the army, put administrative reforms into effect and provided internal peace. One means of discouraging revolts was to transplant inhabitants on foot to other regions of the empire in groups of 18,000, 30,000, 65,000, and 154,000 at a time. In the meantime, Babylon had 250 years of uncertain rule, relying more or less on the protection of Assyria.

GATEWAY GUARDIAN FROM NIMRUD
Colossal winged human-headed figures graced the palace of Ashur-nasirpal. Note the five legs so that the figure appears normal when viewed from either the front or the side. (British Museum)

THE BLACK STONE MONUMENT TO SHALMANESER III
Sculptured scenes represent the tribute from subject princes. (British Museum)

When Nabu-nasir, the last of these rulers, died in 734 B.C., an Aramaean chieftain usurped the throne. He was defeated in 729 B.C. by Tiglath-Pileser, who then decided to rule Babylon under the name of Pulu. He died two years later.

His successor, except for one, was Sargon II (Biblical name for Sharru-kin), who ruled in Assyria from 721 to 705 and in Babylon from 709 to 705 B.C. He may have been a usurper. Shortly after he was enthroned, Elam and Egypt, the avowed enemies of Assyria, decided that since they were too weak to attack that kingdom directly, they would try the slower and safer method by fostering revolts among Assyria's vassals. Sargon's reign was a long struggle against such rebellions. In Babylonia, the Chaldean ruler Marduk-apal-iddina (Merodach-Baladan II) ascended the throne supported by Elam and it took Sargon 12 years to unseat him.

In the meantime, Sargon had founded a new Assyrian capital called Dur Sharrukin (Khorsabad) about 12 miles northeast of Mosul. The city was laid out as a rectangle with an area a little over a square mile. There was a large temple dedicated to the moon-god Sin. The moon's crescent looks somewhat like the horns of a bull, so there were many statues and reliefs of bulls, some winged and some with human heads. They were called cherubs. There were more than 200 rooms and 30 courtyards in the palace, the walls of which were decorated with blue, green, and yellow bricks. The large audience chamber and the corridors were decorated with statuary and alabaster reliefs. However, death overtook Sargon about the time the capital was finished and it is doubtful if it was occupied very much. P. E. Botta, the French consular agent in Mosul, excavated the site in 1843. He was looking for Nineveh but found Dur Sharrukin instead. In shipping the material down to Basra in reed boats, most of the material was lost overboard. The Oriental Institute of the University of Chicago excavated at the site during the 1930's, finding several winged bulls. There is little to show the vistor at Khorsabad except a little mound representing the remains of the ziggurat, the throne room, excavator's trenches, and the mounds outlining the city walls.

Sargon's son Sennacherib (Sin-ahe-eriba, ruled 704-681 B.C.) made Nineveh his capital. *Nineveh* appears to be a compounded form of the name of the Assyrian deity Nina, or Ninua, the founder of the city some time before 2000 B.C. It is situated on the eastern bank of the Tigris River opposite the city of Mosul. It was about three miles long and a mile wide with an area about 1,850 acres. The city was much embellished during Sennacherib's reign and enlarged from about two miles in circumerence to about eight. The city walls were of limestone, as were the wide paved streets. The palace was built on a 50-foot platform of stone masonry. It had roof beams of cedar and doors of cypress bound with shining copper. The rooms and corridors were decorated with slabs of limestone on which were sculptured beautiful bas-reliefs of winged lions and bulls with human heads, lion hunts, siege scenes, battles and religous ceremonies. The temple enclosure to the Assyrian deity Ashur was in the center of the city. The outstanding library in Mesopotamia was that of Assurbanipal found by A. H. Layard and Hormuzd Rassam in 1850-1853. It consisted of two large chambers piled foot-high with over 30,000 tablets covering literature, science, grammars, dictionaries, Sumerian texts with Assyrian translations, and even an autobiography of Assurbanipal.

Today's visitor is impressed by the expanse of the city as outlined by the mounds of the city walls. But that is all, as the area within is now cultivated farmland. Even two centuries after its destruction by the Medes, when Xenophon and his mercenaries passed the site (400 B.C.), no one knew what city the mounds represented. A new museum graces a mound at the entrance of one of the city gates, with several large carved bulls and other items excavated on the site.

The reign of Sennacherib was marked by a series of bitter wars, chiefly against Babylon, which city he destroyed; against Elam, which ended with the sack of Susa; and against Judea and Sidon, which ended disastrously. His reign over Babylon was interrupted by the return of Elamite puppet rulers. Finally in 689 B.C. the city was attacked by Assyrian troops, set on fire and totally destroyed. Houses, temples, palaces, and city walls were razed and the rubble was thrown in the canals. The site was flooded and remained a wasteland until the end of his reign. He was assassinated by one, or possibly two, of his sons in 681 B.C. because of jealousy of the brother, Essarhaddon, who was the king-designate and at that time in exile. Essarhaddon (Ashur-akh-iddin) was occupied principally with two projects during his reign, 681-669 B.C. One was the reconstruction of Babylon, which went on during his entire reign. The other was the conquest of Egypt, which finally succeeded in 671 B.C. when he captured Memphis. He appointed local kings and officials, but revolts required that he return to suppress them. He died on the way.

Assurbanipal (668-631 B.C.) had previously been designated to be king of the realm and another son, Shamash-shum-ukin, was to be king of Babylon. One of Assurbanipal's early tasks was to suppress the Egyptian revolts. His armies plundered Thebes in 663 B.C. and the city never recovered. By 655 B.C., however, the Egyptians were strong enough to throw off the Assyrian yoke. The uneasy peace between Nineveh and Babylon lasted 17 years. Shamash-shum-ukin was jealous of his brother's rule and joined with Elam in 651 B.C. against Assurbanipal. By 648 B.C. the streets in Babylon were piled high with those who had died of hunger and pestilence; survivors ate human flesh; Shamash-shum-ukin set fire to his palace and died in the flames. Susa was again sacked and by 639 B.C. Elam practically ceased to exist. A Chaldean noble, Kandalanu, was installed as puppet king of Babylon.

Assurbanipal was a ruthless monarch and when he died in 631 B.C. he left behind two accomplishments: ruined cities and devastated nations from the Persian Gulf to Thebes on the upper Nile in Egypt; and secondly, an immense library and art collection at Nineveh. The empire had already started to decline during his reign and was easy prey to the Medes under King Cyaxares, who took Assur in 614 B.C. and Nineveh in 612.

It was the end of an empire with a 2,000-year history and an unbroken line of 117 kings. All its cities and settlements had been plundered, battered down, and destroyed. A century later, even their names were unknown.

Chaldean Era

About the 9th century B.C. a number of Aramaean tribes called Chaldeans settled in the lower regions of the Tigris and Euphrates rivers, a section which became known as Kaldu, or Chaldea. They were destined 300 years later to provide Babylon with one of its greatest monarchs. They endeavored to remain independent from Assyria, refused to pay taxes, and practiced guerrilla warfare against supply routes and Assyrian garrisons operating midst a population of doubtful loyalty. Adjacent anti-Assyrian Elam provided refuge for pursued rebels and supplied the tribes with supplies and weapons. They supported Merodach-Baladin II (Marduk-apal-iddin) as king of Babylonia in 721 B.C. until he was unseated by Sargon II twelve years later. In 648 B.C., during an uneasy peace between Assyria, Akkad, and Sumer, a Chaldean noble called Kandalanu was appointed viceroy of Babylon. Taking advantage of Assyria's weakness during the last years of Assurbanipal's reign, the puppet king Kandalanu revolted. Both Assurbanipal and Kandalanu died in 627 B.C. and the governor of Sea Land, Nabu-apal-usur (Nabopolasser), an Aramaean of the Kaldu tribe, was able to win the throne of Babylon. Sporadic warfare between Assyria and Babylon took place during the period between his accession and the intervention of the Medes in 615 B.C. From then on, Babylon remained in full possession of Mesopotamia, taking over all the Assyrian provinces from the Persian Gulf to the Mediterranean. The one threat, Egypt, was attacked by Nabopolasser's son Nebuchadnezzar* II at Carchemish, who routed her troops and pushed them back to the Egyptian border. In the meantime, some districts in Syria refused to pay tribute, among them Judah. Jerusalem was besieged and taken (586 B.C.), looted, Solomon's temple was burned, and thousands of Jews were deported to Babylon. The last years of his reign are obscure, apparently ending in disorders. During his 43-year reign (605-562 B.C.) he brought Babylon up to a state of magnificence not theretofore approached.

The general plan of the 2500-acre city was rectangular, stra-

*Hebraic form of Nabu-kudurri-usur, "Nabu protect my boundary mark."

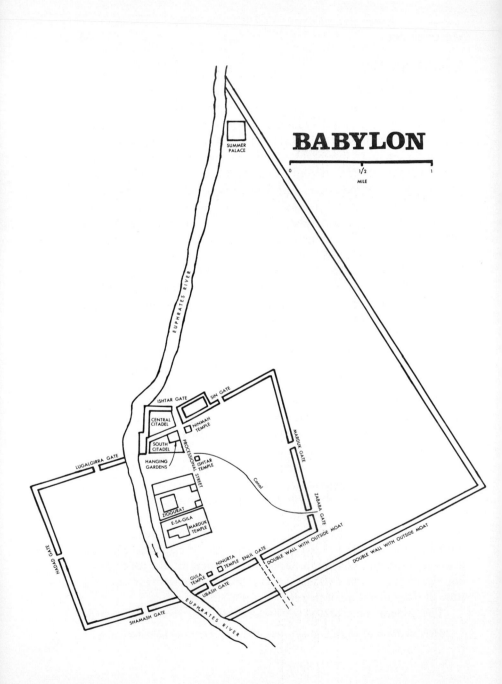

dling the Euphrates River, with two-thirds on the east bank and called Old Town. A double wall, with brass gates, and a moat surrounded the city.* The Old Town had an additional rampart extending two miles eastward from the river and then three miles northwestward to the river. Between the double walls was a 37-foot roadway. There was no evidence of an outer rampart on the west side of the river. The moats resulted from digging clay for the walls. The clay was made into bricks and then, in constructing the walls, they used hot bitumen (a natural asphalt derived from oil seepage) for cement.

On the north wall next to the river was the famous arched Ishtar Gate built by Nebuchadnezzar II. It was 40 feet high, with 152 figures of bulls, dragons, and other hybrid animals in high relief of enameled bricks. The walls facing the 600-foot Processional Way had 120 six-foot figures of lions, some yellow with red manes and some white with yellow manes. The background was blue.

Just inside the gate was the citadel and a palace with the terraced Hanging Gardens. A description of the Gardens is given by a Greek court physician, Ctesias (c 450 B.C.). It was a 400-foot square wooded enclosure sloped like a hillside with terraces. The walls were 22 feet thick separated by ten-foot passages. The galleries were roofed with beams over which was a layer of reeds set in bitumen, two layers of baked bricks, and a cover of lead. Earth was piled on top, deep enough to contain the roots of the trees. The galleries were open in places to provide light for the royal apartments. One gallery had shafts so that great quantities of water could be raised from the river to the top. There is a story that Nebuchadnezzar built the Gardens for his Queen Amytis, a Median princess, to console her for enforced residence on the plain.

*	City Wall	Outer Rampart
Height	60 feet	60 feet
Width, inner	21 feet	23 feet
Width, outer	12 feet	40 feet
Moat width	250 feet	300 feet
Length		
Old City	3 miles	2 miles E. and 3 miles N.W.
New City	2¼ miles	
Gates	8	
Towers	Every 65 feet	Every 130 feet

MODERN GATE AT THE RUINS OF BABYLON
SIMILAR TO THE ISHTAR GATE
The original gate has been reassembled in the East Berlin Pergamon
Museum. Some of the excess tiles were purchassd by the Oriental
Institute of the University of Chicago and built into a doorway.

RUINS IN THE VICINITY OF THE HANGING GARDENS

VIEW OF THE SIDE OF THE
PROCESSIONAL WAY

ORIGINAL FIGURES IN COLORED TILE
FROM THE ISHTAR GATE (c 580 B.C.)
(Pergamon Museum, East Berlin)

PART OF THE THRONE ROOM FACADE FROM
NEBUCHADNEZZAR'S PALACE IN BABYLON
(Pergamon Museum, East Berlin)

The throne room of Nebuchadnezzar was 170 feet long, 56 feet wide, and about as high. The walls were blue-enameled and 20 feet thick. There were yellow columns with blue capitals spaced three feet apart. Near the ceiling, on all four walls, was a multicolored frieze.

Across from the palace was the Temple of Ninmah, the mother-goddess.

In the center of the Old Town, near the river, was the seven-tiered tower *Etemenanki,* the 150-foot ziggurat with an outside stairway which was the traditional Tower of Babel. On top was a temple. Across the street was the E-sa-gila, the Temple of Marduk. The sanctuary was 1,350 feet by 1,650 feet and included a chapel called E-kua. The marble walls were adorned with gold and lapis lazuli. The cedar doors were sheathed with bronze plaques with emblems of Marduk. A large gold figure of the god rested on the golden throne. The figure was reported as weighing three tons. There were two altars outside, on one of which full-grown animals were sacrificed.

In the early history of the city, it was necessary to use a boat to cross from the Old City to the New City. Herodotus reported that during the reign of Queen Nitocris, the banks were lined with quays of burnt bricks with landing places opposite the city gates and a stone bridge was built near the center of the city with blocks bound together with iron and lead. Queen Nitocris was married to Labynetus, the son of Nebuchadnezzar, and reigned about 560 B.C. She had her tomb constructed in the upper part of one of the city gates with this inscription: "If there be one of my successors on the throne of Babylon who is in want of treasure, let him open my tomb and take as much as he chooses—not, however, unless he be truly in want, for it will not be for his good." The tomb remained un-touched until Darius came to the kingdom. In his greed he opened the tomb, but instead of treasure, he found only the dead body with a note which said: "Hadst thou not been insatiate of self and care-less how thou gottest it, thou wouldst not have broken open the sepulchres of the dead."

Babylon no doubt gave the traveler the impression of enormous wealth with its magnificent walls, the 53 temples, the palaces, and other superb structures of royalty.* The dwellings of the great mass

---

* The ruins were excavated by R. Koldewey of the Deutsche Orient Gesell-schaft (1899-1917). A reconstructed Ishtar Gate and facade of the throne room are built into the Pergamon Museum in East Berlin. Some excess tiles of the Ishtar Gate were purchased by the Oriental Institute of the University of Chicago and built into a doorway.

of the people were, however, little better than wretched hovels. The whole of Babylon was intersected with canals, one of which connected the Euphrates and Tigris rivers. The boats in the rivers were similar to some now in use, circular with skins stretched over willow frames. The chief freight was wine stored in casks made of wood of the palm tree. Wheat and barley were plentiful, commonly yielding 200- or even 300-fold. Sesame plants provided oil and the palm trees yielded bread, wine, and honey. When the boats reached Babylon, the cargoes and the frames of the boats were sold. The skins were then loaded on their asses and they returned to Armenia.

The last king of the Chaldean dynasty was Nabonidus (556-539 B.C. He was the son of an official of the government and a priestess of the temple of Sin at Harran. When the Medes were threatening Harran, Nabonidus and his mother fled to Babylon. He was in his sixties when he ascended the throne and seemed particularly interested in restoring the Sin temple in Harran. This, together with his slighting of Marduk, canceling the New Year festivals for several years, and his absence for ten or more years in the distant oasis of Tema in western Arabia, made him unpopular. His son Belshar-usur (Belshazzar), who was left in charge during the absence of Nabonidus, was equally unpopular. The Bible (Dan. 5), though a little inaccurate in the genealogy, tells of Belshazzar's feasting, seeing the handwriting on the wall, and getting Daniel to explain the meaning of the three words:

> *Mane:* God hath numbered thy kingdom and hath finished it.
> *Thecal:* Thou are weighed in the balance and found wanting.
> *Phares:* Thy kingdom is divided and given to the Medes and
> the Persians.

And so it was!

Persian Era

About the end of the 2nd millennium, an Indo-European people moved into what is now southern Persia in a district called
Parsa; hence the name Persia. It was from this group that Cyrus
(Kurush = sun), the son of a Persian prince and a daughter of the
king of the Medes, found himself the king of an expanding empire.
He defeated Croesus of Sardis in 546 B.C. Croesus had been told by
the Delphic oracle that if he attacked Cyrus, he would destroy a
mighty empire. He did not realize that it would be his own. Croesus
later commented, "No one is so foolish as to prefer war to peace
in which, instead of sons burying their fathers, fathers bury their
sons."

Cyrus kept on expanding his empire and looked covetously on
Babylonia. When Nabonidus returned home from Tema to find
famine and revolt widespread, the time seemed opportune. Within
a month of the start of his campaign (September, 539 B.C.), he
entered Babylon by diverting the Euphrates and marching into the
city via the old, now dry, river bed. The city was spared, buildings
were restored, forced labor was abolished, former gods were reinstated, and private lives remained unaltered. But it marked the end
of the city's greatness. Jews exiled by Nebuchadnezzar when Jerusalem fell in 586 B.C. were told they could go back to Palestine.
Now that they could go back, many decided they were fairly well
off and did not leave.

Cyrus' son, Cambyses, was recognized as the king of Babylonia and the empire. Herodotus reported that he was an epileptic,
subject to committing deeds of savage violence, including the secret
murder of his brother Bardiya (Smerdis). On his way back to Susa
after a campaign in Egypt, Cambyses died, either by his own hand
or, according to Herodotus, by an accident. A Persian Magus,
called Gaumata, impersonated the dead Smerdis and usurped the
throne. By the eighth month, a group of high-ranking Persians were
convinced of the deceit and had the usurper murdered. The group
decided that one of them was to be chosen successor and the choice
was to be determined by a unique method. They were to ride out

the following morning into the outskirts of the city and he whose steed first neighed after the sun was up should have the kingdom. Darius, the son of Hystapes, was one of the group. During the night, his groom brought a mare, the favorite of the horse Darius was to ride, out to the suburb and tied it. He then led the horse of Darius around and around the mare and finally brought them together. In the morning as the group neared the spot where the equine rendezvous had taken place the night before, the horse of Darius sprang forward and neighed.

Is it possible that the course of history of the world could depend on anything so trivial as a horse's neigh?

Revolts were prevalent, including Babylon. Herodotus describes the measures Darius took to subdue the city. The besieged city strangled most of the women to lessen the demands on their stores. Zopyrus, a son of one of Darius' generals, disfigured himself by cutting off his nose and ears and came to Darius with a plan. He proposed to desert to the Babylonians with his disfigurement as proof to the Babylonians of his justification. After a week or two to enable Zopyrus to gain the confidence of the Babylonians, Darius was to send an expendable force of 1,000 practically unarmed soldiers to camp near the city gate. Zopyrus would attack and kill them. A week or so later, a second force, this time 2,000 men, was to be sent to a similar fate. Later, a force of 4,000 was similarly wiped out. By this time, Zopyrus had the complete confidence of the Babylonians. He then opened the city gates and the army of Darius took the city. Darius destroyed the wall and all the gates and crucified 3,000 leading citizens. To prevent the Babylonians from becoming extinct, Darius collected about 50,000 women from bordering nations to replace those strangled.

After the revolts were checked, Darius campaigned in Egypt, India, Scythia, and Greece. In Greece, his army was defeated in the battle of Marathon (490 B.C.). He died in 486 B.C.

During the succeeding reign of Xerxes (485-465 B.C.), Babylon again revolted and much of the city was destroyed. The three-ton gold statue of Marduk was melted down, wealth was confiscated, and what was left was heavily taxed. His campaign against the

Greeks cost him 20,000 men by the courageous stand of Leonidas with 300 Spartans and 700 Thespians at Thermopylae. He went on to burn Athens, but his navy was badly defeated at Salamis, and the following year, 479 B.C., his army was defeated at Plataea and the remains of his navy were defeated at Mycale. He was assassinated in 465 B.C.

Then followed a number of unsavory reigns, with assassinations and poisonings, ending up with Darius III, the last of the Persian rulers (335-331 B.C.).

Seleucid Era

In 336 B.C., Philip II of Macedonia was stabbed to death, reportedly at the instigation of his divorced wife, Olympias. His son Alexander, then 20 years old, took up where his father left off. In 334 B.C. he crossed over into Asia Minor, routed the Persian army at Granicus, consolidated his hold on Asia Minor, conquered Egypt (332 B.C.), visited the desert shrine of Amon at Siwa, and founded Alexandria. He then returned north, defeated the Persian army a second time at Issus, just north of Antioch, and again at Arbela, 25 miles east of Mosul. Babylonia and Mesopotamia were won without resistance. From Susa he went to Persepolis, which he burned, and then on to India. He envisioned twin capitals of his empire — Babylon and Alexanrdria — but death overtook him in 323 B.C. in Babylon at the age of 33. Then followed a struggle for empires among Alexander's generals, with Seleucus I Nicator ruling an empire which, at its height, included Persia, Mesopotamia, Syria, most of Asia Minor, and part of Thrace. Because of the expense involved in cleaning up the vast piles of rubble in Babylon, Seleucus built a new capital in 312 B.C. on the west bank of the Tigris about 40 miles north of Babylon. He named the city Seleucia. The exact location is disputed but is supposed to have been just north of the Royal Canal and opposite the mouth of the Delas River, possibly the Tell Omar site. The city commanded navigation on both the Tigris and Euphrates rivers and eclipsed Babylon in wealth and splendor. Its population was reported to be 600,000. It was burned by Trajan (c 116 A.D.) and again in 164 A.D. by Gaius Avideus Cassius. Now nothing remains. As for Babylon, only the priests of Marduk and the other temples remained in the depopulated ruins.

The Parthian king Mithradates I of the Arsacid dynasty conquered Mesopotamia about 140 B.C. The Parthians ruled from Ctesiphon, with intermittent duels with the Romans, until 228 A.D., when they were replaced by the Persian Sassanian dynasty (228-634 A.D.). They in turn were replaced by the Moslems. The Turks ruled from 1534 A.D. with oppressive stagnant regimes and constant strife between pretenders to power, until World War I. A monarchy was supported under the protectorate of the British until 1958, when it became a republic.

Babylon, in its 2,000-year history, survived many a staggering blow and one marvels at the recoveries that were made. About the beginning of the Christian era, it finally succumbed to old age. It left a heritage which contributed materially to neighboring civilizations, including that of Greece and, through them, to our own.

CYLINDER SEAL FROM UR
(University of Pennsylvania Museum, Philadelphia)

SCIENCE AND THE ARTS

Written Language

An archaeologist might say that the earliest language records consist of the tools of the hunt and the kitchen. Pottery is probably the most useful item in classifying early cultures. Somewhere along the line, man began to draw pictures to portray objects; hence these are called *pictograms*. Later the use of the pictogram might be extended to connote another object or an abstract idea. For example, an open book might indicate a "library" or it might mean "education." When so used, the symbol is called an *ideogram*. Pictograms and ideograms need have no connection with the sounds made by the oral reader but nevertheless are intelligible regardless of the spoken language. Thousands of symbols are required, such as the 3,000 to 40,000 of the Chinese language. Such a script has the advantage that it is understood in each of the many Chinese dialects, even though a pot of tea would be pronounced something like "te" in one section and "cha" in another. The symbol *4* is understood in many languages; "four" is not.

The next step in the development of a written language is to have the picture denote a sound, in either a monosyllabic or a polysyllabic word, as in a rebus. When so used, the symbols are called *phonograms*. By this time, the written language has become a mixture of ideograms and phonograms with some symbols serving dual roles and sometimes with several versions of each. Where the context didn't indicate the meaning intended, the ancient scribes resorted to a class of unpronounced signs called *determinants* usually placed before the word to indicate the category to which the word belonged and thus eliminate the ambiguity. In the meantime, the symbols may have been simplified and modified for ease in writing until they had little resemblance to the original.

The dissection of a word into syllables is not difficult, but it still leaves a large number of symbols if one is assigned to each possible syllable. The final step of breaking the syllable down into consonants and vowels was a very difficult one. Neither the Mesopotamian nor the Egyptian language made it.

There seems to be general agreement that the earliest written language is that which developed in the southern part of Mesopotamia, then called Sumer, and that it antedated the Egyptian by possibly a century or two. During the so-called Uruk period (3600-3000 B.C.), pictograph writing was introduced, the earliest example being a small limestone tablet found at Kish which is believed to be dated about 3500 B.C. Over a thousand fragments with crude pictograph inscriptions were found in the Uruk IV stratum. About 900 different symbols were pictured, but no ideogram was found. Originally, the characters were written in a verticle line from top to bottom with the columns starting at the right. A clay tablet with pictographic inscriptions from the Jemdat Nasr period (c 3000 B.C.) shows the early numbering system was with a base of 10. A stylus with a circular cross section, when pressed into the clay at an angle, produced half-moon symbols representing units and when pressed head on, produced full moons for tens. By 3000 B.C. there was a transition to an ideographic and phonetic script and a change in the character of the symbols.

Sketching detailed pictures on moist clay is not very satisfactory and this prompted a change to the triangular head-and-tail type of symbol as the cuneiform element. The term *cuneiform* stems from the Latin word *cuneos,* signifying a wedge. The records are principally on clay tablets, about the size of the hand, on which symbols were engraved with a reed or wooden stylus while the clay was still moist. The wedge-like impression is made by pressing the square or triangular head into the clay and pressing the sharp edge of the stylus in the desired direction to produce the line. The tablets are baked, either in the sun or in kilns, thus leaving a reasonably permanent record. Sometimes correspondence tablets are provided with clay envelopes. The system was not particularly suitable for insuring continuity of multi-tablet books even though the scribes would sometimes identify each tablet with a notation such as "tab-

CLAY TABLETS WITH PICTOGRAPH SYMBOLS
and the use of "half-moons" to denote units and full moons to denote
tens in an early decimal system (c 3000 B.C.) (British Museum)

let X of series Y" with the closing line of a tablet repeated as the
opening line of the next. Storage must have been a problem because of size and weight. Another disadvantage was that the entire
tablet had to be written at one time while the clay was still moist
and care had to be exercised when continuing the text on the ob-
verse side. However, the method did have the advantage of plentiful clay and the record was permanent. When less durable papyrus
and parchment became available, as in the last stages of the Babylonian culture, records of entire periods have been lost. In Egypt,
the dry climate prevented deterioration of the papyrus records.

Most of the records relate to commercial transactions, legal,
and administrative matters but practically nothing of a historical
nature. There are literary tablets with omens, fables, proverbs, and
epics of Gilgamesh, Creation, and the Flood. Other tablets record
astronomical events, mathematical tables and problems, medical
texts, bilingual dictionaries, practice tablets by students, and cata-
logues of tablets. The historical records, such as those of kings and
victories, were generally not on tablets but on bricks buried in the

MAP OF REGIONS OF THE WORLD
relating to the conquests of Sargon of Agade. From Babylonia (c 600
B.C.) (British Museum)

foundations of temples and palaces. They were not for publicity —
only the priests and scribes could read them anyway — but were a
sort of report of the king to the deity.

By 2500 B.C. the system had become highly conventionalized.
When the Semitic Akkadians under Sargon I (2334 B.C.) subdued
the Sumerians, they adopted not only the script but many of the
words as well. In other cases, the symbol and the concept were
kept, but they applied their own oral word. Thus, the identical word
sign for heaven was pronounced *an* in Sumerian, *shamu* in Akkadian, and *nepish* in Hittite. The same word sign was used for the
concept of god, but words in the respective languages were *dingr,
ilu,* and *shiuni*. The determinants were identical in all the languages
using cuneiform script: Sumerian, Babylonian, Assyrian, Elamite, Hittite, Hurrian, Ugarit, and others.

𐎫 TH, THA	𐎡 F, FA	𐎹 Y, YA	𐎷 MI	𐎹 Z, ZA	𐎣 K, KA	𐎿 S, SA		
𐎭 D, DA	𐎨 C (CH), CA	𐎰 T (THR), TA	𐎱 P, PA	𐎡 I	𐎺 WI	𐎠 A	𐎬 TU	
𐎤 KU	𐎥 G, GA	𐎢 U	𐎲 H, HA	𐎭 DU	𐎦 GU	𐏁 S (SH), SA	𐎛 H (KH), HA	𐎵 NU
𐎶 M, MA	𐎩 J, JA	𐎺 W, WA	𐎽 RU	𐎪 JI	𐎾 L, LA			
𐎲 B, BA	𐎫 T, TA	𐎴 N, NA						
𐎼 R, RA	𐎮 DI	𐎢 MU		𐏐 WORD DIVIDER	𐏋 KING	𐏃 COUNTRY	𐏈 EARTH	𐏊 AHURA-MAZDA

EARLY PERSIAN ALPHABET

By the end of the 3rd millennium, there began a gradual conversion to phonetic writing and the number of symbols was reduced from about 2,000 to about 600: six vowel sounds, about 300 syllables and about 300 ideograms. Many were ambiguous. Although the Sumerians had lost their identity by that time, their language was replaced by Akkadian and the many cuneiform tablets found at Tell el-Amarna in Egypt (of the 14th century B.C. era) indicate that the Akkadian was used for international diplomatic correspondence throughout the Near East area.

By the 4th century B.C., Aramaic with an alphabetic script had essentially replaced Akkadian, although cuneiform tablets were still used during the Seleucid era, particularly for science. By the time of the Christian era, its use had dwindled to extinction.

In the meantime, cuneiform characters were adapted to the Persian language about 600 B.C., using 41 symbols. There were 23 consonants, 10 consonant-vowel combinations, 3 vowels (a, i, u), 4 ideograms (king, province, country, and "Ahura Mazda," Lord of Light), and a word divider. The script seems to have been used primarily for monumental purposes. Its unusual importance, however, was in providing the clue for deciphering the cuneiform scripts.

TOMB OF CYRUS THE GREAT (529 B.C.)
The tomb is at Pasargadae, the original capital of the Persian Empire.

The outstanding Persian inscriptions one might consider monumental are those in Iran at Persepolis and Behistun. These extol the prowess of Darius I, who ruled over the Persian Empire from 521 to 486 B.C. At the beginning of his reign, the capital of the Persian Empire was at Pasargadae, about 85 miles north of Shiraz. With the expansion of the empire, Susa, the Elam capital, was occupied in winter; Ecbatana (modern Hamadan), the capital of Media was the summer capital; and present day Persepolis was occupied during the spring months. The old capital of Pasargadae was abandoned and now the sole occupant is a stork nesting on top of a tall column. The only item of interest is the stepped tomb of Cyrus (Kurush) the Great. Originally there was an inscription:

> "Stranger, I am Cyrus, the founder of the Persian Empire, the sovereign of Asia. Envy me not, therefore this sepulchre."

The ancient name of the site the Greeks called Persepolis, the City of the Persians, is not known but has been called Takt-i-Jamshid, the Throne of Jamshid, a celebrated hero-king of Persia. It is situated about 40 miles northeast of Shiraz, publicised as the city of gardens, nightingales, and poets. A 30-acre platform, 1200 feet north to south and 900 feet east to west, was constructed at the foot of Kuh-i-Rahmat, the Mountain of Mercy, using retaining walls varying from 4 to 41 feet in height depending upon the terrain. On top of this platform were spacious halls for official receptions and entertaining representatives of various countries, for festivals, for palaces of the king, queen and other members of the court, a treasury, and quarters for the military guards.

Most outstanding is Darius' palace of audience known as the Apadana. The central hall had thirty-six 60-foot columns and each of the three porches had twelve columns, all with capitals of immense two-headed lions and bulls. Of the seventy-two, only thirteen partial columns are still standing. Magnificent double stairways of gray marble on the north and east sides are beautifully carved with scenes showing representatives of sections of the empire bringing gifts of gold and produce to the emperor. One section shows Persian and Median soldiers.

Courtesy of the Oriental Institute, University of Chicago

STAIRWAY PROCESSION OF MEDE NOBLES

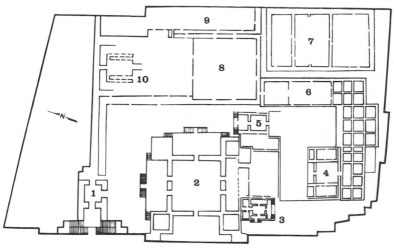

PLAN OF PERSEPOLIS

1. Entrance Hall
2. Apadana, Audience Hall to palace of Darius
3. Private palace of Darius
4. Private palace of Xerxes
5. Council Hall called Tripylon
6. Queen's apartments
7. Three halls of Royal Treasury
8. Audience Hall of Xerxes, Hall of 100 Columns
9. Military area
10. Unfinished entrance hall

The largest reception palace in the area was the Hundred Column Hall of Xerxes. Only the bases of these columns remain. The walls of the gates show Xerxes, in bas relief, seated on top supported by representatives of his empire or, in one case, by Persian and Median spearmen.

The oldest, greatest and most important inscription at Persepolis is on the retaining wall of the southern terrace. There are three versions, Persian, Elamite and Akkadian.

The tombs of the last Achaemenian kings, Artaxerxes II and III and Darius III* (unfinished) are in the mountainside overlooking the Persepolis palaces. The tombs of Darius I, Xerxes I, Artaxerxes I and Darius II are at Naqsh-i-Rustan, about four miles north of Persepolis.

*Kings with the same name were distinguished by giving the names of their fathers and grandfathers and not by number.

Persepolis was not a political capital but sort of a dynastic shrine where kings met with representatives from various parts of the empire, received their tribute, and celebrated the spring festival. It was to this Persian capital that Alexander the Great came after the defeat of Darius III in the battle of Arbela in 331 B.C. and in a drunken fit set fire to the royal palace and destroyed one of the great monuments of Asiatic civilization. The amount of treasure was so great that one historian claimed it took 5,000 camels and 10,000 mules to carry it away.

In 1761 the Danish government sent a scientific expedition to Egypt, the Near East and India. A member, Karsten Niebuhr, found himself the sole survivor in 1765 and on his way home he stopped off in Persia. Travelers in the 1700's reported seeing inscriptions on some ruins and Niebuhr spent three weeks at Persepolis. He made careful copies of nearly all the inscriptions at Persepolis and concluded that three different languages were involved, as the symbols were not the same on the three groups of panels. From copies of the inscriptions, he made a list of 42 signs of the simplest panel and noted that the script read from left to right.* This turned out to be the Old Persian. The other two have been named Elamitic (Susian) and Babylonian. (Akkadian).

Many people tried their hand at decipherment without much success. It was noted that a group of three characters occurred very frequently and a group of seven occurred often. These might signify "King" or "King of Kings," in which case the word immediately preceding might be the monarch's name. G. F. Grotefend, a 27-year-old schoolmaster of Göttingen, Germany, assumed that each character represented a letter or sound, and found one group he assumed to be:

A Great King, King of Kings   Son of B
C Great King, King of Kings   Son of A, King

*A right-to-left text was for the convenience of the right-handed stonemasons who chiseled inscriptions on stone. For a writer, this sequence results in the text being covered up by the hand and so a writer prefers the left-to-right sequence. In the transitional period when man tried to make up his mind which was the better, inscriptions sometimes involved both sequences—left to right, right to left on the next line, then left to right, and so on. The Greeks called this sequence *boustrophedon*, signifying "as the ox plow." The 6th century B.C. civil code at Gortyn in Crete is an example.

He noticed that B had not been king. In searching for a group of grandfather, son, and grandson in which the grandfather had not been king, he decided to try Darius and Xerxes for A and C, and Hystapes for B, since the father of Darius had not been a king. He substituted one of several possible phonetic Persian names for the Greek Hystapes and substituted KHSH and SH for the Greek X in Xerxes (Khshayarsha). With some maneuvering he obtained 13 characters, of which 4 turned out to be wrong. Inscriptions on the tomb of Cyrus gave 5 more, so that by 1815, 14 characters were known. Grotefend's work was criticized as worthless and his papers were refused publication. Recognition did not come until 1893, 40 years after his death. Eugene Burnouf, Professor of Sanskrit in Collège de France, claimed priority for 12; however 8 were wrong and 2 had already been determined. Christian Lassen, a Norwegian professor at Bonn, remembered that Herodotus had noted that Darius had set up pillars with the names of all the nations represented in his army. From a list of proper names at Persepolis, he identified 20 and added 6 more characters. By 1845 only a few characters remained unidentified and rough translations could be made.

Behistun is a small caravanserai town of mud-brick buildings located about 250 airline miles southwest of Tehran on the old silk route from China through the old Persian caital of Ecbatana (modern Hamadan) and Kermanshah to Babylon. The town is about 80 miles west of Hamadan and 24 miles east of Kermanshah.

Since Hamadan is built over Ecbatana, there is no trace of the latter and there is little chance that the ancient city will ever be excavated. About 8 miles west of the city, however, are two similar, except for names, trilingual inscriptions cut in the rock face, each panel about 5 by 7 feet. One is of Darius and the other of Xerxes.

The translation of the Xerxes panel is as follows:

A great god is Ahuramazda, who created the earth, who created yonder sky, who created man, who created happiness for man, who made Khshayarsha king, king of many, king of countries containing many men, king of this great earth far and wide, son of Darayavash, an Achaemenian, a Persian, son of a Persian with an Aryan lineage.

INSCRIPTIONS OF DARIUS AND XERXES AT HAMADAN

THE TRILINGUAL INSCRIPTION

Hamadan boasts of two tourist attractions. One is a modern mausoleum of Avicenna (Abu Ali ibn Sina), (980-1037 A.D.) a famous philosopher, physician and premier who died in Hamadan. The other is the tomb of Mordecai and Esther. The biblical story speaks only of Susa and the whole story cannot be authenticated.

The Behistun inscriptions (516 B.C.) are on the face of a 1700-foot Gibralter-like mountain, about 200-300 feet above the road. They are very inconspicuous and the casual driver-by would never see them. The monument tells how Darius killed Gaumata, defeated the numerous rebels, and restored the Persian Empire. The overall length is about 75 feet and the height about 50 feet. The lower tier consists of three panels in Elamite, or Old Persian, and five panels in later Persian. Above is a sculptured relief of Darius with his foot on the prostrate form of Gaumata. Darius is followed by two ministers and he faces nine rebel leaders with ropes around their necks. The group is topped by a figure of the winged god Ahuramazda. (A copy of this sculptured group is on a monument in a small traffic circle in Kermanshah.) The sculptured group is flanked on the left with two panels of Akkadian text and on the right with four panels of supplementary texts. Part of one panel was defaced to provide room for another figure. The stone steps were destroyed after the sculptor finished, so that the inscriptions are very inaccessible, their bottom being a hundred feet above the highest point to which a man can climb.

Henry C. Rawlinson, a student of Greek, Hindustani, Arabic, and Persian, and a lieutenant in the British army, was assigned in 1835 to Kermanshah as military adviser to the Shah. After many months of leisure work and by dangling on the face of the cliff, he copied the inscriptions with great accuracy. By 1837 he had succeeded in transcribing about half of the Persian text and by 1846 all the characters had been identified and the Persian text transcribed. In 1844 he succeeded in coying the Elamite version and turned it over to Edwin Norris, who deciphered most of it by 1852.

Rawlinson, with the aid of a Kurdish boy, took paper casts of the entire Babylonian text in 1847. Compared with the Old Persian, this turned out to be very complex with over 400 different characters. Not only were there no separation marks but some

BEHISTUN MOUNTAIN BEARING DARIUS' INSCRIPTION

THE FACE OF THE BEHISTUN MOUNTAIN
The inscriptions are slightly above and to the right of the trees.

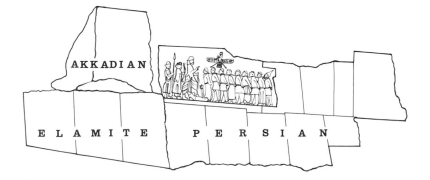

KEY TO THE BEHISTUN INSCRIPTIONS

REPRESENTATION OF INSCRIPTION
SCULPTURE IN KERMANSHAH

words were indicated at times by several phonetic symbols and
sometimes by an ideographic word sign. Pronunciation had to start
with proper names. Edward Hincks, an Irish clergyman, stated in
1850 that all signs represented a consonant preceded or followed by
a vowel. He also noted that a given sign could be used as a word
sign, a syllable, or a determinative. By 1850 Rawlinson had identified 150 characters and deciphered 500 words.

As the Babylonian script was the same as the Sumerian, the
interpretation of the latter amounted essentially to a translation.
Fortunately the Babylonians had provided the priests with linguistic
aids, such as rare phonetic values, grammatical dictionaries, and
line-by-line translations of hymns and incantations. By the end of
the century, tens of thousands of tablets became available through
excavations—by now the total may approach half a million—and
their translation kept the Sumerologists busy. A Sumerian grammar
by Arno Poebel in 1923 put such translation on a scientific basis.

Astronomy

Although Mesopotamia led the world in the field of astronomy for nearly three millenniums, the chronology of progress is very indefinite. This is due in part to the situation in which a primitive people are endeavoring to explain a world of bewildering phenomena. Progress must necessarily be slow and it is difficult to say what the status was at any particular time. Furthermore, the records are in a strange language with an even stranger script, which defied deciphering and it was only by chance that this was finally accomplished. The records, fortunately, were durable, but they were buried in the rubble of forgotten cities, many intact, many only fragmentary, and countless lost. Many of the thousands of tablets in museum collections remain to be studied and many have yet to yield to the excavating archaeologist. The wonder is not that the record is incomplete but rather that we know as much as we do.

By the end of the 3rd millennium, 12-month lunar calendars were in use and many of the stellar configurations had been outlined and named. One claim is that the Akkadian called the stars of the ecliptic Innum, and Pidnu-sha-Shame, the "Furrow of Heaven." At the time of Hammurabi, intercalary months were inserted to bring the lunar calendar in step with the sun. In the late 17th century B.C., observations of the risings and settings of Venus were recorded. By the end of the 2nd millennium, the synodic periods of the planets were known. Subsequent to 747 B.C., eclipses were systematically recorded and it is believed that they realized that solar eclipses occurred only at new moon and lunar eclipses at full moon. By 670 B.C. eclipses were being predicted. Tables were improved around 500 B.C. and were further improved around 400 B.C. By 300 B.C. the ephemerides were well developed. They must have been disappointed with their predictions of solar eclipses, as relatively few were visible in Babylon. Lunar eclipses are observable over a much larger area and their successes should have been high.

There is little evidence of formal Sumerian astronomy except what can be inferred from their calendar based on the moon's 29½-

day period.* The city-states all seemed to have a year of 12 lunar months with an occasional intercalary month to bring the lunar calendar in accord with the solar year. The city-states each had control of their own calendar and the names were seldom the same. A comparison of the Ur, Nippur, and Babylonian calendars is given below. The Babylonian calendar is the basis for the Jewish calendar of today.

	UR	*NIPPUR*	*BABYLONIAN*
March-April	Se-Gur-Kud	Bar-Zag-Ga	Nisan
April-May	Mas-Ku-Ku	Gud-Si-Di	Ayaru
May-June	Ses-Da-Ku	Sag-Ga	Simanu
June-July	U-Ne-Ku	Su-Numun-Na	Tammuz
July-Aug.	Ki-Sig-Nin-A-Zu	Ne-Ne-Gar	Abu
Aug.-Sept.	Ezen-Nin-A-Zu	Kin-Innin-Na	Ululu
Sept.-Oct.	A-Ki-Ti	Di-Ku	Tashritu
Oct.-Nov.	Ezen-Sul-Gi	Apin-Du-A	Arakhsamma
Nov.-Dec.	Su-Es-Sa	Gan-Gan-Na	Kislimu
Dec.-Jan.	Ezen-Makh	Ab-Ba-E	Tebetu
Jan.-Feb.	Ezen-An-Na	As-An	Shabatu
Feb.-March	Ezen-Me-Ki-Gal	Se-Gur-Kud	Adar

The names tended to be descriptive of the duties to be performed and were respectively: *Month of Sacrifice, Directing the Oxen, The Making of Bricks, Gathering of Seed, Firemaking, Festival of Ishtar, Holy Altar, Opening Irrigation Canals, The Very Cloudy Month, Month for Plowing, The Curse of Rain,* and the month for *Sowing of Seed.*

By the beginning of the 2nd millennium B.C., stellar groupings were well advanced as indicated by cylinder seals. Boundary stones in the late Kassite period were embellished by figures of familiar constellations. The Creation Epic states that Marduk organized the heavens and assigned three stars for each month of the year, similar to the decans of the Egyptians. The 12 lunar months were the equivalent of 354 days and intercalary months had to be inserted to bring their lunar calendar in step with the solar year. There is a record of Hammurabi's ordering: "This year has a deficiency. The coming month shall therefore be entered as a 'second Ululu.' " At first the intercalary months were inserted at

*For their synodic lunar month they used 29 + 31/60 + 50/3600 + 8/216,000 or 29.5306 days. The current accepted value is 29.5336 days.

irregular intervals and it was not until the 5th century B.C. that a total of seven months was added at fixed intervals through each 19-year period. For several years during the reign of Ammisaduqa (1646-1626 B.C.), observation of the risings and settings of Venus were recorded, the earliest documented observations in Mesopotamia. By this time, Venus was recognized as both a morning and an evening star. By the end of the millennium, the synodic periods of the planets had been determined. This may have influenced the formalization of celestial omens, for if the fate of men was affected by the positions of the planets, it was important that their positions and movements be accurately plotted. Associations of some of their gods with the sun, moon, and planets are as follows: Shamash the sun-god, Sin the moon-god, Nabu associated with Mercury, Ishtar with Venus, Nergal with Mars, Marduk with Jupiter, and Ninib with Saturn. A series of 70 tablets lists a total of 7,000 omens. However, celestial omens did not rank with observation of the entrails of animals, particularly the livers of sacrificial sheep. Recorded horoscopes seem to be rare, as the earliest are dated 410 and 263 B.C., and did not enter into the lives of the ordinary people before the Seleucid era.

The observational instruments of the ancient astronomers were a water clock (clepsydra), a simple gnomon sundial, and a *polos* consisting of a hollow hemisphere with the shadow of a bead indicating not only the time of day but also the date during the half year. The 24-hour day was divided into 12 *beru* of 30 *gesh* each. Subsequent to 747 B.C., eclipses were being recorded systematically and observational reports were made to the court. By this time they recognized that solar eclipses were possible only at new moon and lunar eclipses occurred only at full moon. A note during the reign of Essarhaddon (681-669 B.C.) states that an eclipse had been calculated but was not observed because of clouds. This indicates that the prediction of eclipses was definitely a part of the program of Mesopotamian astronomers at this time. By 568 B.C. the courses of the planets were definitely fixed in degrees and minutes with references to constellations and stars. Prior to about 500 B.C., the intercalary months were introduced without any specific regularity.

From then on, a total of seven lunar months was introduced at regular intervals (every third year) during each 19-year period. This may have been concurrent with the detailed lunar tables devised by Nabu-Rimanni. The Metonic cycle (19 solar years = 6,939 days 14.4 hours; 235 lunations = 6,939 days 16.5 hours), attributed to Meton (465-385 B.C.), is one in which the phases of the moon occur on the same days of the year. Although it is said that Meton used the data of Nabu-rimannu, he may have borrowed more than just the data. The fact that a new program of intercalary months had been inaugurated in Mesopotamia before Meton was born would indicate that the Metonic cycle was already known. It should be pointed out that this is not the same as the so-called Saros cycle. Because of the attraction of the sun for the moon, the new moon would be above or below the direct line of the sun and the earth at 19 years. Conditions are more favorable at 18 years 11.32 days, which is the Saros cycle. Since very few solar eclipses of a Saros cycle would be visible in Mesopotamia, it is extremely unlikely that the Mesopotamian astronomers recognized the Saros cycle in solar eclipses. However, in the Seleucid era they were grouping lunar eclipses with 18-year intervals. The term *Saros* was first applied about 1000 A.D.

Nearly all the information on Babylonian astronomy has been obtained from fragmentary texts in the Babylonian Archives of the British Museum, which was copied by T. G. Pinches and J. N. Strassmaier in the period 1880 to 1900. These are published in the volume *Late Babylonian Astronomical and Related Texts* edited by A. J. Sachs (Brown University Press, 1955). Included in the above are 159 texts on mathematical astronomy which were published with translations and commentaries by O. Neugebauer, *Astronomical Cuneiform Texts* (London, 1955). The 1,648 texts included in the above publications probably represent only a small proportion of others in unsorted collections in various museums. Over half are dated and these are from the Seleucid era, that is, after 312 B.C. The texts are classified as follows: mathematical astronomy (159), astronomical diaries (835), normal star almanacs (122), almanacs (96), Goal-Year texts (155), planetary observations (45), mathematics (18), astrology and miscellaneous (173).

Of interest are the ones relating to the moon which list lunar eclipses in 18-year groups. The texts are of the Seleucid period, but the eclipses date back to 747 B.C. This is the "Saros" period as applied to the moon. In the 700 years of observations, starting with a lunar eclipse in 747 B.C.,* solar eclipses are mentioned only twice. This might be interpreted as inability to determine any regularity in solar eclipses because of their being observed less frequently. Only about 10 percent of the solar eclipses would be visible in Babylon (one in every four or five years), whereas usually one and sometimes two lunar eclipses might be observed each year.

The Babylonian day began in the evening and the lunar month began the evening when the new crescent moon first appeared. To a primitive people, the moon must have been an awe-inspiring object, full of mystery, emerging from the sun like the horns of a bull, watching over them with increasing light, and then reverting to the horns and disappearing again into the sun. Observations of the moon must have started at the dawn of their civilization—at first casually and then with ever increasing exactitude. The attitude of the astronomer-priest, as he saw the data accumulate, was to try to find an empirical solution. His ephemerides told him when the crescent first appeared and when it was last visible. He had his difficulties. First of all, visibility was affected by the 30° to 80° variation in the angle of the moon's path with the horizon. The relative velocities of the sun and the moon varied throughout the year. It was for recording these data that they divided the equator and the ecliptic into 360 parts. Another difficulty is the variation of the moon on either side of the ecliptic. This may amount to as much as 5° and is particularly disturbing near the solstices in determining the appearances and disappearances of the moon. With detailed tables of the relative motion of the sun and the moon, it should be possible to determine when the moon could be close to conjunction, or opposition. Then, with data on the relative latitude of the moon

*Oppolzer's *Canon de Finsternisse* does not list any lunar eclipses in 747 B.C. There are two solar eclipses listed, but the path of totality of one was from the vicinity of Australia to the North Pacific Ocean; and of the other, in the Atlantic Ocean and southern Africa. Neither of these would have been visible in Mesopotamia.

with respect to the ecliptic, formation of eclipse tables was the next easy step.

Determination of the Babylonian lunar theory is due primarily to Jesuits J. N. Strassmaier, J. Epping (*Astronomisches aus Babylon,* 1889), and F. X. Kugler (*Sternkunde und Sterndienst,* 1907-1924).

The names of only five Mesopotamian astronomers are known, and they are of the late period:

NABU-RIMANNI (fl 490 B.C.) devised lunar tables which were the results of the most elaborate computation. Positions of new and full moons were given by degrees along the sun's path with an accuracy in the combined motions of the sun and the moon of 10 seconds in one year. The length of the year was calculated as 365 days 6 hours 15 minutes 41 seconds. Meton used Nabu-rimanni's figures for his calculation of the Metonic cycle.

KIDINNU (fl 375 B.C.) determined the solar year with an error of only 4 minutes 32 seconds. Some say that he may have discovered precession. In any case, it is believed Hipparchos made use of star plots of Kidinnu and Nabu-rimanni in his calculation of precession. Kidinnu is considered the author of improved lunar tables.

BEROSSOS (b c 340, fl 280 B.C.) was a priest from the temple of Marduk in Babylon. Antiochos I, king of Syria, engaged Berossos to write a history of Mesopotamia to prove that civilization there was at least as old as the civilization of Egypt. His history in three books covered: Book I Creation to the Flood, II The Flood to Nabonassar, and III Nabonassar to Cyrus. Later he opened a school of astrology in Cos.

SUDINES of Pergamon (fl 240 B.C.) may have been an *émigré* from Babylonia. His lunar tables, believed to be of Babylonian origin, were used for centuries.

SELEUCUS of Seleucia (fl 180 B.C.). Little is known of him except that he was a firm supporter of the heliocentric model of the solar system as proposed by Aristarchos, and also that he attributed the rise and fall of the tides to the moon.

The following are some unauthenticated notes regarding Mesopotamian constellations. It will be apparent that many of the figures

associated with the constellations as we know them today were
assigned several millennia ago by the Mesopotamians.

Andromeda.—The story of Marduk and the dragon Tiamat
may have been the basis for the story of Perseus and Andromeda.
The stars of Andromeda and some of the Northern Fish had the
Sumerian name of *Ama* and the Akkadian name of *Eritu,* signifying
The Pregnant Woman.

Aquarius.—The constellation was associated with the 11th
month, Shabatu, the Curse of Rain, in January and February. The
water urn was known in Sumerian as *Gula* or *Guisa,* a jar with
overflowing water. The Akkadians knew it as *Ka* or *Ku-ur-ku,* the
Seat of Flowing Water. It was also called *Ramman* or *Rammanu,*
the God of the Storm. Earlier, it may have been the god *Imma*
pouring water from an urn.

Aquila.—The Sumerian name for the constellation was *Idkhu*
or *Idkhu Zamam*a signifying The Eagle or The Living Eye. The
Akkadian name was *Nasru.*

Aries.— The Sumerian name for The Ram was *Lulim* and the
Akkadian equivalent was *Agaru.* At about the time Aries marked
the time of the vernal equinox, the constellation and the brightest
star seem to have been called *Ku, I-ku,* or *I-ku-u,* equivalent to the
Assyrian *Rubu,* The Leader or The Prince. Cuneiform inscriptions
attributed to Hamal have been variously interpreted as *Dil-kar,*
The Proclaimer of the Dawn, and *Dil-gan,* the Messenger of Light.
Other names are *Lu-nit,* the Ram's Eye, and *Si-mal,* or *Si-mul,* the
Horn Star.

Auriga.—The Sumerian and Akkadian names ascribed to this
constellation are respectively *Gar* and *Nar-Kab-Tu,* possibly meaning a Chariot. The constellation is depicted almost exactly on a
sculpture found at Nimrud, with the shepherd carrying a goat,
Capella, on the left arm. The name Dil-gan has also been ascribed
to Capella by some authorities as *Dil-gan-I-ku,* the Messenger of
Light, or *Dil-gan-Babili,* the Patron Star of Babylon. These names
may have applied when Taurus marked the vernal equinox and
transferred later to Hamal.

Boötes.—The Sumerian name for the Shepherd of Heaven was

Sib-Zi-Anna. The Akkadian equivalent was *Riu-But-Same.* The name *Papsukal* or *Papsukala,* the Guardian Messenger has been ascribed to the Arcturus.

Cancer.—The constellation was known as the Northern Gate of the Sun at the time the constellation marked the summer solstice. Other names which have been claimed for it are *Nan-garu, Puluk-ku,* and *Nagar-assagga.*

Canis Major.—The Sumerian *Lik* and the Akkadian *Kalbu* have been ascribed to Canis Major. The constellation was often pictured much as today, a dog standing on its hind legs watching Lepus, the hare. Many names have been ascribed to Sirius, but identification is uncertain. Some of these names are *Kak-shisha,* the Dog That Leads, *Kak-shidi,* the Creator of Prosperity, *Du-shisha,* the Director, *Tis-khu, Mul-lik-ud,* the Star Dog of the Sun. In addition to the above Akkadian names, *Kak-ban, Kal-bu,* the Dog, and *Kakkab lik-ku,* the Star of the Dog, have been attributed to the Chaldeans and *Kalbu Sa-mas,* the Dog of the Sun, to the Assyrians.

Canis Minor.—The Sumerian and Akkadian names for Canis Minor were respectively *Pallika* and *Kalab-Me.* Procyon may have been called *Kakkab Paldara,* Star of the Crossing of the Water Dog.

Capricornus.—The Akkadian *Su-tul,* the Yoke, and the Sumerian *Munakha,* the Goat-fish, *Shah,* or *Shahu,* the Ibex, and *Niru,* the Yoke, have been ascribed to the constellation.

Cassiopeia.—The names *Kasseba* and *Tsalamu* have been ascribed to this constellation.

Cetus.—Cetus was known as The Great Dragon with the Sumerian names of *Bis-Gal* and *Kumar* and the Akkadian name of *Mamluv.*

Corvus.—Corvus was The Great Bird called *In-Dugud-Khu* by the Sumerians and *Ramanu-Ikabbid-zu* by the Akkadians.

Draco.—During the period Thuban was the polar star, it received considerable attention and the following names have been ascribed to it: *Tir-An-na,* the Life of Heaven, *Dayan Same,* the Judge of Heaven, *Dayan Sidi,* the Favorable Judge. These represented the god Caga Gilgati. The names *Dayan Esiru,* the Prospering Judge, and *Dayan Shisha,* the Directing Judge, have also been cited.

Eridanus.—The Sumerian name for The River of God, or The River of Heaven, was *Pur-Edin.* The Akkadian name was *Eru-Edinu.*

Gemini.—Castor and Pollux were The Great Twins called *Mastabba-Galgal* by the Sumerians. The Akkadian name was *Tuame-Rabuti.*

Hercules.—The tales of the Greek hero may have been borrowed from the adventures of Gilgamesh associated with the 12 signs of the zodiac. The constellation was referred to as *Lugal,* The King, by the Sumerians and as *Sarru* by the Akkadians.

Hydra.—The Great Snake was known as *Tsir-Gal* and *Tsiru-Gallu.*

Leo.—The Great Dog (or Lion) was known as *Lik-Gula* to the Sumerians and *Aru-Rabu* to the Akkadians. Regulus was called *Gus-ba-ra,* the Flame of the House of the East. Denebola has been associated with the names *Lamash,* the Colossus, *Sa,* Blue, the Assyrian *Samu,* and *Mikidisati,* the Burning of Fire.

Libra.—The symbol associated with this constellation is believed to represent an altar and a flame, such as the Tower of Babel. As the Life Maker of Heaven, the constellation was called *Ziba-Anna* in Sumerian and *Zibanitu* in Akkadian.

Lupus.—The Beast of Death was the Sumerian *Ligbat* and the Akkadian *Kalab-Mutani.* *Zibu* and *Urbat* have also been ascribed to the constellation.

Lyra.—The constellation had the formidable Sumerian and Akkadian names of *Ra-Di-Tar-Ta-Khu* and *Karib-Barkhati* signifying a large bird of prey such as a vulture.

Orion.—It has been suggested that the name is derived from the Sumerian *Uru-anna,* Light of Heaven. The constellation was also known as *Sib-Zi-Anna-Ningirsu,* Lord of the Heavenly River.

Pegasus.—The constellation had the Sumerian name of *Ansu-Kurra* and the Akkadian *Si-Su,* both referring to a horse. The current name is Phoenician.

Pisces.—Some of the stars of the Northern Fish were associated with the stars of Andromeda, possibly as an umbilical cord. Some of the stars represented the Cord Place and were called the Sumerian *Durki* and the Akkadian *Riksu*. The stars of the Southern Fish were the Fish of the Canal and were called the Sumerian *Sila-Da-Kha-Bi* and the Akkadian *Non-Nagbi*. *Nuni* or *Nunu*, The Fishes, has also been ascribed to the constellation.

Sagittarius.—The constellation seems to have been The Winged Fire Head with the Sumerian name Pa-Pil-Sak and the Akkadian Kakkab Kastu, The Stars of the Bow. The constellation is pictured on boundary stones of Sippar. Several stars are believed to have been identified with certain names: Alpha with *Nibat Anu*, Beta with *Ur-ner-gub*, Sole of the Left Foot, and Sigma with *Nunki*, Star of the Proclamation of the Sea. Nunki was the name of the capital of the first kings of Sumer.

Scorpius.—The constellation is portrayed on many boundary stones. The Sumerians called it *Girtab*, The Stinger. The Akkadian equivalent was *Aqrabu*. Antares was known by several names, among them *Dar-An-Khu*, The Evil One, *Bilu-sha-ziri*, the Lord of Seed, *Dar Lugal*, the King of Lightning, and *Kakkab Bir*, the Vermilion Star. Theta was the Euphratean *Sargas* and Lambda, *Sarur*.

Serpens.—Serpens and part of Ophiuchus comprised the Prince of the Serpent with the Sumerian name of *Nu-Tsirda* and the Akkadian *Namassu*.

Taurus.—Taurus was known as The Bull of Heaven and was called *Gut-Anna* by the Sumerians and *Alap-Same* by the Akkadians. Its double title *Te Te* referred to the Hyades and the Pleiades. The figure appears on a seal (about 2150 B.C.) as a demi-bull representing the crescent moon. A cylinder seal mentions *Gut-an-na*, the Heavenly Bull, in connection with rain. Aldebaran was the Leading Star, *Ku, I-ku*, or *I-ku-u*, before Aries came to denote the vernal equinox. The same fate befell the name *Dil-gan*, the Messenger of Light. El Nath (Beta) was *Shur-narkabti-sha-iltanu*, the Star in the Bull to the North, and Zeta was *Shur-narkabti-sha-shutu*, the Star in the Bull to the South. The Hyades and the Pleiades seem to have been *Mas-tab-ba-gal-gal-la*, the Great Twins.

Ursa Major.—Ursa Major was The Long Chariot called the Sumerian *Margidda* and the Akkadian *Rukubu-Rabu*.

Virgo.—Virgo was also known as The Proclaimer of Rain with the Sumerian name *Ab-Nan.* Its Akkadian name, *Siru,* denoted an Ear of Corn. In Babylonia, the constellation was known as the wife of Bel and as *Sa-Sha-Shiru,* the Virgin's Girdle. It was also *Emuku Tin-tir-Ki,* the Might of the Abode of Life, a common title also for Babylon.

Mathematics

The big contribution of the Sumerians to mathematics was a place-value system with a base of 60, that is, a sexagesimal system. They had no symbol for zero; that did not come for nearly two millenniums later, about 300 B.C. But they left a space and when a zero came at the end of a number, its omission wasn't too serious, as the base was so large that it was evident what value was intended. There is no record of any of the problem texts which are so numerous in later Babylonian mathematics, but the framework and the methods for performing arithmetical operations were developed and that is an exceedingly important step. The 360-day year and the 30-day month may have influenced the adoption of the sexagesimal system in place of the earlier decimal system. But there were other advantages, such as large numbers requiring fewer symbols, and the provision for a large number of fractions. The system is still with us in our time system and in our units of latitude and longitude.

Basically, their numerical symbols utilized two sizes of the cuneiform wedge for units below 10 and a V-shaped symbol on its side, formed by two wedges, for 10's. It will be noted that the single wedge could represent 1, 60, 3600, or any other power of 60 and the V-shaped symbols could represent ten times these values. In a space-value system this presents no difficulty. In a decimal system, we are accustomed to a numeral representing any power of 10. When it is used alone, however, judgment is involved and the value intended must be determined from the context. The system provided for a large number of fractions, the reciprocals of 2, 3, 4, 5, 6, 10, 12, 15, 30, and 60. Table texts, many of them

0	1	2	3	4	5	6	7
8	9	10	11	12	20	21	30
40	60	70	90	100	180	120	200

DENOTED 1, 60, 3600, 216,000, ETC.

DENOTED 10, 600, 36,000, 2,160,000, ETC.

MESOPOTAMIAN NUMERAL SYSTEM
The "zero" symbol may have been invented as early as 500 B.C. but at least was in general use after 300 B.C.

DENOTED UNITS IN EARLY DECIMAL SYSTEM

DENOTED TENS IN EARLY DECIMAL SYSTEM

from Nippur, consist of multiplication and reciprocal tables, squares and cube tables, the corresponding tables of roots, and tables of compound interest. The multiplication tables give the products of 1 to 60 multiplied by numbers 1 to 20 and by 30, 40, and 50, from which other products are obtained by addition. Division was performed by multiplying the reciprocal of the divisor.

In the pictographic era, a decimal system used a circular symbol for tens and an elliptical or half-moon symbol for units.

Most of the mathematical texts are from the time of the 1st Babylonian dynasty (1894-1595 B.C.) and represent the highest level ever attained in Babylonia. The only real contribution of the later periods is the introduction of the zero symbol. The date of its introduction is uncertain. It was in general use by 300 B.C., but a table of squares found at Kish shows that its invention may have come as early as 500 B.C. Among the table texts is a list of triads of Pythagorean numbers for 15 right angles from a 45° triangle to one of 30° and 60°. They were interested in a general formula for giving the diagonal of all squares. A tablet showing a square with figures for the side and diagonal gives the $\sqrt{2} = 1 + 24/60 + 51/3600 + 10/216,000$ or 1.414213. This figure was the one used by Ptolemy more than 1,500 years later. The relations of the sides of a right triangle and the hypotenuse were known a thousand years before Pythagoras. They knew how to determine the areas of rectangles, and of right and isosceles triangles. For π they used $3\frac{1}{8}$, although a method of computing the area of a circle as being $1/12$ of the circumference squared gives $\pi = 3$. They knew the angle inscribed in a semi-circle is a right angle.

Problem texts were for the purpose of teaching mathematical procedures and often gave the answers and ended with "such is the procedure." A few illustrations follow:

> Find the area of an isosceles triangle knowing the lengths of the sides. The solution involves the Pythagorean theorem.
> Six times the area of a square field added to $3\frac{1}{2}$ times the side gives 906. What is the side of the field?
> What is the sum of the first ten terms of a geometric progression with a ratio of 2? The answer is:
> Double the last term and subtract 1.

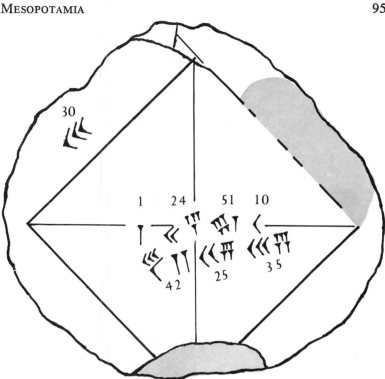

SKETCH OF YALE BAB. COLL. 7289 shows the ratio of the diagonal to the side of a square. Ratio $= 1 + 24/60 + 51/3600 + 10/216,000 = 1.4142129$. Diagonal of square with side $30 = 42 + 25/60 + 35/3600 = 42.426388$. (Multiplication by 30 is easily performed by dividing by 2, its reciprocal, and shifting to a higher order similar to multiplying by 5 in the decimal system.)

Find a number which when added to its reciprocal gives a certain number. The solution takes the form $x^2 - ax + 1 = 0$.

How long will it take for a sum of money to double itself at compound interest of 20%? The equation takes the form $(1 + 0.2)^x = 2$.

The result of adding the excess of the length over the width of a rectangle to the area is 183; the sum of the width and the length is 27. Find the length, width, and area. The solution involves simultaneous equations.

In general, mathematicians of Mesopotamia sought to reduce
their problems to arithmetic and algebra, whereas the Greeks
sought to solve theirs by geometry. There is nothing to indicate
that Egyptian mathematicians of the pre-Greek era were involved
in any abstract mathematics; rather, they limited their activity to
practical problems encountered in surveying and construction.
Although Babylonian mathematics is elementary compared to that
of today, during a 1,000-year period (1600-600 B.C.) they stood
alone. Their system of numeration contained three outstanding
potential contributions which the world was slow to accept. It took
over a thousand years for the space-value system and a symbol for
zero to be incorporated in a Hindu-Arabic system in the 9th century A.D. and to reach Europe via Spain in the 10th century A.D.
They applied the same base to coinage and weights and measures
(360 grains = 1 shekel; 60 shekels = 1 mina; 60 minae = 1
talent). Even today, English-speaking nations subscribe to the
metric system only as a secondary system. The sexagesimal base
is still with us in the 60 minutes and 60 seconds of our time scale
and in latitude and longitude.

Medicine

Only a few medical texts have been published, but they show,
as expected, that early Mesopotamian medicine was very crude. A
person's illness was assumed to be due to an evil spirit invading
the body and the cure often involved the incantation of the temple
priest. Medicine was sometimes administered to drive the demons
out. The concoctions were made up of native herbs of many kinds;
animal products, such as blood, fat, milk, bones and some minerals. They were sometimes swallowed along with beer or honey.
Surgery is not mentioned. Wounds and broken bones lent themselves more to the care of the physician. The sanctions for mal-
practice, as prescribed by the Code of Hammurabi, were so severe
that unless a cure was more or less assured, a physician was not
likely to attempt treatment. This tended to discourage experimenta-
tion, and knowledge of anatomy was slight. The heart was the most
important organ, as the pulse indicated connection with all parts

of the body. The liver was also considered to be very important and figured particularly in omens. When a carcass is opened, the liver is not only the most conspicuous organ but also the bloodiest, as it holds one-sixth of the body's blood supply. It is the only major organ without arterial blood supply, and death from shock is due primarily to a deficiency of blood supply to the liver.

CLAY TABLET WITH CUNEIFORM INSCRIPTION
FROM THE TEMPLE LIBRARY AT NIPPUR

The medical text is the only one known from the third millenium B.C. It contains more than a dozen remedies of salves, fiiltrates and liquids to be taken internally. Neither the quantity of each ingredient, nor the frequency of application, nor the specific disease is mentioned. One prescription reads: "Pulverize the seed of the carpenter plant, the gum resin of the markasi plant, and thyme, dissolve it in beer; let the man drink it." (Photo and caption courtesy of the University of Pennsylvania Museum, Philadelphia)

Literature

Of the several hundred thousand Sumerian tablets, only about one percent are of a literary nature, the rest being commercial records, practice tablets and the like. Although there are some literary tablets from the last half of the 3rd millennium, the bulk of them were written about 1750 B.C., several centuries after Sumerian had become a dead language. These are largely from the Nippur excavations of the University of Pennsylvania. A clay tablet, 2½ by 1½ inches and dated about 2000 B.C., is a catalogue of 62 titles of hymns, lamentations, myths, and epic tales. Though the tablets date from late Sumer or post-Sumer periods, the literature is no doubt much earlier and further excavations may result in tablets contemporary with their authorship.

Many of the tales involve their gods and goddesses, who were legion. In a primitive world with so many strange and unexplained phenomena, it was evident that there were forces which exceeded those of man. They had, however, no other basis for portraying those powers than to project their own world and experience to divine personages and provide them with immortality and superhuman powers. If a king could have his wishes carried out by some official or servant, the gods should be able to achieve more by their commands. The gods were immortal, but they had to have a house in which to live, they had to eat, and they were not moral beings but experienced the same emotions as man, with lust, cruelty, greed, violence, and fondness for sacrifices. The philosophy of the people was that they were created from clay to perform manual labor so as to relieve the gods of that necessity.

> Blood, I will mass and cause bones to be.
> He shall be charged with the service of the Gods
>   That they might be at ease.

If his life was hard, it was the will of the gods. Man had no philosophy of rewards in the afterlife to comfort him; if there was a life in the hereafter, there was no reason to believe that it would be different from the present. All the land belonged to the gods and the individual had only a proprietary interest. Each state was the domain of a particular god: Uruk belonged to An, Nippur to Enlil, Ur to Nannar, Lagash to Ninurta, and so on. However, the entire pantheon was revered throughout Sumer and each city-state was likely to have temples to all the gods. The major gods were unapproachable to the layman and homage could be performed only through the medium of the priests, and even they were rarely seen.

Among the Sumerian tales are the story of Creation from the primeval sea, Paradise (Dilmun), a story of the goddess Ninti being created from Enki's rib, the Flood, Inanna's descent to the nether world and her resurrection, and an incomplete version of the story of Gilgamesh, which, in a more complete form, is Babylonia's outstanding literary epic.

Most of the literature of Babylonia is believed to be a product of the 1st dynasty, but the myths are for the most part similar to the Sumerian with Semitic names. One outstanding epic, called *Enuma Anu Enlil* from its opening sentence, was recorded on seven clay tablets (the fifth is missing) with over 1,000 lines. There are a number of similarities to events in the first two chapters of Genesis, including the story of the Flood. Uta-Napishtin of Shuruppak (modern Fara) was told, "Destroy thy house and build a vessel; leave thy riches and store in the vessel the seeds of all of life." He built a vessel 120 cubits (180 feet) high, and the storm raged for six days and six nights. The seventh day was peaceful, but all the earth had been changed to mud. The vessel came to rest on Mount Nisr, near the lower Zab River in Kurdistan. A dove and a swallow were freed, but they returned when they found no place to light. Later a raven was freed and when it did not return, they left the vessel.

The Creation myth opens with nothing but the sweet-water ocean, Apsu, and the salt-water ocean, Tiamat. From this union there resulted a brother-sister pair, Anshar and Kishar, who had a son, Anu, a sky-god. He, in turn, created Ea (also called Nudimmud), god of wisdom and underground waters. Ea slew Apsu, the father of all the gods, and assumed his power. His son, Marduk, became the head of the Babylonian pantheon. It was Marduk who divided the colossal body of Tiamat, the salt-water ocean, into the sky and earth. "Anu, Enlis, and Ea, he made occupy their places." He organized the constellations and the calendar, built gates in the east and the west for the sun to enter and depart, and caused the moon to shine forth at night. He is often represented as armed with a scimitar slaying a dragon. Man was created by Ea's slaying a god and mixing his flesh and blood with clay.

The Babylonian Epic of Gilgamesh is an elaboration of various tales about Gilgamesh, a legendary king of Uruk. He endeavors to achieve immortality and toward the end of his adventures, he comes to Uta-Napishtin, the only mortal to have achieved eternal life. Gilgamesh is told of a thorny seaweed, but it is snapped by a serpent before it can be eaten and death becomes inevitable. The serpent, however, gets everlasting life. Might this have some bearing on the use of the serpent as the symbol for the medical profession?

Below are some of the more important members of the Sumerian heavenly hierarchy:

Nammu, Mother-goddess, gave birth to heaven (An) and earth (Ki)

An, Heaven-god, was considered the supreme ruler of the pantheon at one time

Ki, Earth-goddess, at times identified with Ninmah, the great queen, Ninhursag, queen of the mountain, and Nintu, the queen who gives birth

Enlil, Air-god, son of An and Ki; separated heaven from the earth; replaced An as head of the Sumerian pantheon

Ninlil, Air-goddess, Enlil's queen

Ninurta, war god, son of Enlil

Nanna, or *Nannar,* Moon-god, usually represented by an old man with a long beard and wearing a turban; because of the mystery of the moon changing from crescent to full, he was called "He whose deep heart no god can penetrate."

Ningal, The great lady, Nanna's queen

Utu, Sun-god, son of Nanna and Ningal

Enki, Water-god, also the god of wisdom who organized the earth in accordance with the general plans of Enlil

Inanna, Goddess of love, daughter of Nanna and sister of Utu, the sun-god; also goddess of war and as such associated with Venus as a morning star; as goddess of love, associated with Venus as the evening star

Ereshkigal, Underworld goddess, Inanna's sister

Dumuzi, Shepherd-god, wed to Inanna; banished by Inanna to the underworld for his contemptuous attitude; Semitic name is Tammuz

The chief deities of Babylonian mythology were:

Apsu, Primordial god, personification of fresh water

Tiamat, Primordial goddess, personification of salt water

Anu, Sky-god, father of Ea

Ninnah, Mother-goddess

Ea, God of earth and water. represented as a goat with fish's tail; also called Nudimmud; earthly residence at Eridu

Marduk, Chief god of Babylon, son of Ea; had 50 titles; assumed the titles and powers of Sumerian Enlil; emblem was a metal implement witn a triangular head, a weapon or a spade; associated with the planet Jupiter

Nabu, Son of Marduk, secretary to the assembled gods; invented writing; symbol sometimes a serpent-headed dragon, or a stylus, or a chisel

Enlil, God of the air, master of men's fates; at Nippur he was the god of hurricanes but lost that character when he was changed to Bel, or Baal (lord)

Sin, Moon-god, symbol was the crescent moon

Ishtar, Goddess of love and fertility, queen of the heaven; daughter of the moon-god Sin; associated with the planet Venus; also goddess of war

Shamash, Sun-god, god of justice and judge of heaven and earth; represented as seated on a throne holding a scepter and a ring in his right hand; son of the moon-god Sin

Nergal, God of the underworld, he had been god of destruction and war but became overlord of the dead; symbol was a sword or a lion's head

Ereshkigal, Queen of the underworld

Tammuz, Vegetation-god, the Sumerian Dumuzi; loved by Ishtar; forced to descend to the underworld; death bewailed by funeral chants every summer

Ninurta, War-god, consort was an earth-mother, Gula; represented by a club and two S-shaped snakes

CARL A. RUDISILL LIBRARY
LENOIR RHYNE COLLEGE
HICKORY, N. C. 28601

Arts

In general, the art objects from Mesopotamia do not compare in quantity with those from Egypt, nor in quality, as there are only a few items which show comparable artistry. Stone sculptures are rare, as is to be expected in a land where all rock had to be imported. No material was available for the artisans to develop their skills. Building material consisted of mud bricks and it is difficult to make such structures decorative. In the later periods, colored glazed bricks were used and in some cases mosaics were assembled with colored cones inserted in the moist clay. The designs of painted pottery prior to the 3rd millennium were cruder than in Persia during the same period. The outstanding sculptured art object during the period is the Warka alabaster vase now in the Archaeological Museum in Baghdad.

The 3rd millennium produced some lovely things, primarily from Ur. The Standard of Ur, now in the British Museum, is a hollow box about 20 inches long and 8 inches wide ornamented with scenes in mosaic of shell, red limestone and lapis lazuli inlaid in bitumen. Battle scenes are shown on one side and banquet scenes on the other. In the Museum of the University of Pennsylvania is a harp with a gold and lapis lazuli head of a bull. Here also is the "Ram-in-the-Thicket," a goat with its forefeet resting on a simulated tree. The head and legs are covered with gold and the fleece and base are covered with lapis lazuli. Copies of the above are in the Baghdad Museum, as well as such originals as the golden wig-helmet of Prince Mes-kalam-shar, a woman's golden headdress, a gold ceremonial knife with a gold filigree sheath, necklaces, gold and blue ornaments, and gold cups and vases. One of the outstanding sculptures of this period is the seated figure of Gudea, the governor of Lagash (c 2150 B.C.).

The beginning of the 2nd millenium was a period of great building activity with ziggurats. The Hammurabi Stela is from this period. Cylinder seals contain an amazing wealth of fine detail, but sculptures in the round are still poor. The Assyrian period is characterized by large beautiful reliefs of lions, and winged bulls with human heads. Palace-wall reliefs show battle and hunting scenes. In the late Babylonian period, because of the architectural magnificence of the lion-flanked Processional Street, and the Ishtar Gate with glazed mud bricks with bulls and dragons, Babylon was called the wonder city of the world.

PART TWO

GREECE

"SUCH a small place and so much glory!"

Thus spoke Charles V as he viewed the crypt in the cathedral in Granada where rested the remains of Ferdinand and Isabella and his parents, Juana and Philip.

How appropriate that statement seems as one views the Agora in Athens from the steps of the Temple of Hephaestus! Here, at one time or another, trod every well-known personage of the ancient world.

But also, how appropriate for the entire city of Athens!

How appropriate for all of Greece!

Small it is—the land area of today's Greece is about the same as that of Florida. Together with the ancient Greek settlements in present-day Turkey, southern Italy, and Sicily, the total area would no more than double. As for glory, one hardly knows where to start. Let us not include what the military man would consider glory. The country's political history is one of wars between the city-states and with other nations with the accompanying bloodshed, pillage, and destruction of property. Greece in all her history hardly ever had more than a few years of continuous peace. There is no glory in that. Internal strife weakened her and made her vulnerable to invasion by foreign armies.

But in the arts and sciences, the story is different. It must be kept in mind that the Greeks started out near the bottom. They had so little to build on that it is almost inconceivable to us today. Their early idea of the world was a disk comprised of lands around the Mediterranean; by the 3rd century B.C. they knew that the earth was round and that its circumference was within a few hundred miles of today's accepted value (Eratosthenes). A heliocentric system of the sun and planets was also proposed (Aristarchos), but that was too imaginative for that period—nearly 2,000 years before Copernicus. The rudiments of atomic theory were proposed (Leucippus and Democritos) and Archimedes is a familiar name in physics and mathematics. Essentially no progress was made beyond the mathematics of the Greeks until the 16th century. Even today's geometry texts are but versions of that of Euclid. The medical profession had its early steppingstones laid by Erasistratos, Herophilos, Hippocrates, and Galen. The Greeks introduced vowels into the Phoenician alphabet and literature appeared fully developed in Homer's classic *Iliad* and *Odyssey*. Hesiod and Pindar are well-known names in poetry. The physical theater was developed, as at Epidaurus, and the drama developed from simple dances to the chorus and to the tragedies of Aeschylus, Sophocles and Euripides, and the comedies of Aristophanes. Historians Herodotus, Thucydides, and Xenophon are still quoted. Socrates, Plato, and Aristotle exemplify those who endeavored to find the reason for our being and how to live. Aristotle's works on science were considered the absolute authority for nearly 2,000 years. That they did not succeed in getting an ideally satisfactory government for Greece is not surprising; the civilized world still does not have one. Science has progressed far in the last 25 centuries but government hardly at all.

Pericles crowned Athens' golden age with the Parthenon and other edifices and fostered such sculptors as Phidias, Myron, and Polycleitos; Praxiteles and Lysippus came later. Greek sculpture has never been surpassed and such works as "Nike of Samothrace," "Aphrodite of Melos," "Discus Thrower," "Dying Gaul," and the Laocoon group are familiar to all.

In religion, the Greek masses found greater solace in their mythological deities than in the abstract tenets of virtue and ethics of the philosophers. However, the Christian religion might not have developed, or even survived, if it had not been for the Greeks. The Old Testament, as we know it, was written by the 72 Hebrew rabbis who were called to Alexandria to translate it into Greek. No complete text before that era exists. The New Testament was written by Greek, or Greek-educated, apostles, and in the Greek language.

Finally, the greatest assemblage of physicists, mathematicians, philologists and philosophers in Alexandria developed and crystallized scientific knowledge to a point beyond which little progress was made until the 16th century A.D.

Therein lies the glory of ancient Greece!

Greece of today is a small country of 51,000 square miles, about one-third of it in rocky, denuded islands. This is about the size of the state of Florida. More than 80 percent is mountainous, with the only extensive plains being in Macedonia and Thessaly. It doesn't seem possible that this land could ever develop a culture which was destined to become the basis of Western civilization. It is even more incredible when one realizes this took place while the Greeks were almost continually engaged in warfare. Yet if ever a people changed the way of life for the world, it was the Greeks in the period 500 to 200 B.C.

Before the start of the Bronze Age, about 2600 B.C., there were only sporadic agricultural settlements in the Aegean area. In Asia Minor, this was the era of Troy I. Activity increased in the next 500 years (2600-2100 B.C.) with bronze plows, weapons, new pottery, some cities, the start of maritime trade, and the religious worship of the Earth-Mother, mistress of fertility and motherhood. These people may have had their origin in, or at least had close association with, Anatolia, as is evidenced by place names ending in *nthos* and *ssos*. This was the Early Minoan period in Crete, with colonization from Asia Minor. It was also the period of Troy II, the period of Schliemann's golden treasure.

During the next 500 years (2100-1600 B.C.), there were invaders from the north. These were the first Greek-speaking people, Ionians, a part of the general expansion of Indo-Europeans that took place about that time. They were extremely primitive and it is evident that they introduced no particular innovations but rather assimilated the culture of their predecessors. Mycenae became the important center. Before the end of the period, there was a second invasion from the north, the Achaeans. Culture in Crete was more advanced, being influenced greatly by Egypt, with palaces at Knossos, Phaestos and Malli. It was the period of Linear A script, which is Egyptian in character but apparently an independent system of Cretan glyphs. It has still not been deciphered.

The succeeding 500 years (1600-1100 B.C.) was the age of Mycenae, with other citadels at Tiryns, Pylos, Athens, and other city-states. It was the age of the beautiful golden treasures now in the National Museum in Athens. These were strongly influenced by Minoan art. The language was an archaic Greek which was shared with Crete and which utilized the Linear B script, derived in part from Linear A. Crete flourished with renewed building activity and works of art. Around 1400 B.C. the island was invaded by Achaeans from Greece and Knossos was destroyed. This signaled the decline of the Cretan civilization as the glory departed to Mycenae where it survived for another two centuries. The ill-fated Trojan expedition took place about 1200 B.C.

THE PHAESTOS DISK
is a terra cotta tablet about 6 inches in diameter with 45 characters. There are 118 signs in 30 sections on one face and 123 in 31 sections on the other. It is believed to be contemporary with Linear A but possibly not even Cretan. An Anatolian origin has been suggested. Decipherment has not been possible.
(Archaelogical Museum, Heracleion, Crete)

THE LION SCULPTURE ABOVE THE
ENTRANCE GATE TO MYCENAE

THE GRAVE CIRCLE AT MYCENAE
where Schliemann found beautiful golden treasures.

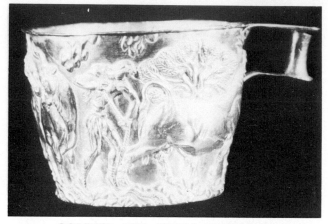

GOLDEN CUP FROM MYCENAE
(National Museum, Athens)

The Iron Age was ushered in about 1100 B.C. concurrently with the invasion of Dorian Greeks from the north, possibly from the basin of the Danube. They had been taught by the Hittites to smelt and fashion iron. They occupied much of central Greece and all of the Peloponnesus, except Arcadia, and laid waste all of the Mycenaean cities. With their destruction the art of writing was lost for three centuries. Each new invader was less civilized than the inhabitants and the latter moved on. Gresham's law in economics states that "bad money drives out good" and the same statement seems to hold for people. It was about this time that massive migrations to Asia Minor took place: Ionians to the region between the Hermus and Meander rivers, with the city of Phocaea at the north and Miletus at the south, the Aeolians to the north of the Ionians and the Dorians to the south (Cos to Rhodes). Then followed several centuries of consolidation with the development of the city-state. The Greek alphabet was formed by adding vowels to the Phoenician alphabet; it was the age of Homer and Hesiod (800-700 B.C.). The first Olympiad took place in 776 B.C. The period from 750 to 600 B.C. was an era of large-scale colonization westward to Sicily, Italy and the western Mediterranean, and eastward to the Dardanelles, the Sea of Marmara, and the Black Sea. Money was invented, stimulating trade and giving rise to an economy based not only on agriculture but also on movable goods.

By the end of the 7th century B.C., Greece entered what might be called the Hellenic period, in that the people called themselves Hellenes, after Hellen, the son of mythical Deucalion and Pyrrha, the only human beings who escaped the great flood. There was a sense of uniformity in the way the city-states developed and a feeling of similarity, and yet no national spirit. Each city-state was a unit unto itself with frequent disastrous conflicts with its neighbors. They averaged only about 50 square miles, many with only 5,000 citizens. Athens, with an area of about 1,000 square miles, had a population at its peak of 43,000 adult male citizens with a total, including women, children, and slaves, of not more than 250,000. By this time, the early monarchial government had first been replaced by one of autocratic landowners, who in turn gave way to a non-hereditary ruler called a tyrant. He was dependent upon popular support by the small peasant and middle-class merchants. He fostered agriculture, stimulated commerce, inaugurated building of public works and temples, and encouraged artists and poets. But tyrants generally want to perpetuate themselves in power and the system was replaced by a wiser autocratic government or by a democracy. Peisistratus and his sons Hippias and Hipparchos thus ruled Athens from 560 to 510 B.C., when they were expelled under the leadership of Cleisthenes, the true founder of Athenian democracy.

The 6th century also saw the rise of philosophers, such as Thales and Pythagoras; the *Iliad* and the *Odyssey* were selected from the Homeric poems, formalized and recited in connection with the Panathenaean festival in Athens; lyric poetry developed; and various mystery cults flourished. Cyrus, king of Persia, defeated Croesus of Lydia, assumed sovereignty over the Greek cities of Asia Minor, and prepared to invade Greece.

The 5th century opened with invasion by Persia. First, there was the defeat of the forces of Darius at the battle of Marathon (490 B.C.), with Greek casualties 192 and Persian 6,000. Then the second invasion, by Xerxes this time, in 480 B.C., with the heroic stand of Leonidas with 300 Spartans and 700 Thespians at Thermopylae, the Persian destruction of Athens, and the Persian defeat at Salamis. The following year (479 B.C.) the remnant of the Persian army was defeated at Plataea and the Persian navy was destroyed at Mycale. In the ensuing years there were a number of sporadic encounters, but peace was finally signed in 449 B.C.

In the meantime (477 B.C.), a confederation of Athens and Greek cities on the islands and in Asia Minor was formed. The communal treasure was stored at Delos, but in a few years, with the danger of Persia past, the Delian Confederacy degenerated into an Athenian empire. In 461 B.C., Pericles became the sole leader of Athenian democracy and was repeatedly voted the leader for 30 years. It was to be a Periclean age. Pericles reformed the magistrate courts and set about beautifying Athens, the cost to be defrayed by transferring the treasury from Delos to Athens (454 B.C.). Although involved militarily almost continually, Athens finally enjoyed 14 years of almost unbroken peace from 445 to 431 B.C. But it was an uneasy peace. Athenian prosperity aroused the envy and distrust of the Spartans and needed only a little to trigger what turned out to be the Peloponnesian War. It started with trouble in a small, isolated community called Epidamnus (Durres, Albania), between factions originally from Corcyra (Corfu) and Corinth. At first the controversy involved only those two cities, but Corcyra appealed to Athens for aid. For Athens, there were two aspects which affected her decision: would the alliance give her the opportunity to develop trade in the west and, secondly, could she afford to have Corcyra's navy fall into the hands of Corinth? In the end she decided to make a defensive alliance with Corcyra and come to her aid. This brought Sparta into the fray, although efforts were made to avoid an armed conflict. However, according to Thucydides, "the youths of the Peloponnesus and Athens were numerous; they had never seen war and were, therefore, willing to take up arms." The war dragged on from 431 to 404 B.C. Attica was ravaged and a plague killed off 20 percent of the population of Athens, including Pericles. In the midst of the hostilities, Athens sent an expedition in 415 B.C. to help out Segesta in that city's war with Syracuse. That armada and a second relief expedition were squandered, as few of the Athenians ever returned. The end of the war came in 404 B.C. For Athens, who once thought she was invincible, it ended in a humiliating defeat. A body of 30 Athenians was chosen to organize the government, codify the laws and rule until the laws could be put into effect. However, they were no sooner appointed than they set about to ensure that they would remain in power by wholesale persecution, banishment, confiscations, and executions. It was the reign of the Thirty Tyrants. It lasted about a year before they were dislodged by an exile group and the democrats were again in control of the city.

The century was also one of great activity in the arts. The theater produced the incomparable Aeschylus, Sophocles, Euripides, and Aristophanes. In philosophy there were the Sophists, Socrates and Anaxagoras; Pindar, the great lyric poet flourished in Thebes; Herodotus and Thucydides were eminent historians; Hippocrates of Chios was the mathematician of the century; Hippocrates of Cos was the physician of all time. Under Pericles the city was adorned with temples, public buildings, and works of art culminating in the structures on the Acropolis. Phidias, Myron, and Polygnotes were among the many painters and sculptors.

Athens had contributed most to the defeat of the formidable Persian Empire, risen to the heights of culture and prestige, and ended the century in the depths of inglorious defeat.

What a century!

During the first half of the 4th century B.C., Greece was involved in war among the various states. Sparta's allies were disgruntled because they received "no land, wealth nor honor" from the Peloponnesian War and Corinth and Thebes entered into an alliance with Athens, their former enemy. Athens, with Persian gold, again fought Sparta. Both were still weakened from the previous hostilities and everything went wrong with Sparta. She induced the Persian king to arbitrate, which he did to his own advantage by keeping Asia Minor for himself. Sparta maintained her own supremacy in Greece, but a crash was impending. In 371 B.C. the

Theban army under Epaminondas defeated the Spartans. In 600 years of Dorian rule, no enemy had been seen within their territory. A few years before, every Greek city had bowed to her will; now she was scarcely mistress of land ten miles from the outskirts of the city. For ten years, Thebes was supreme, but with the death of her two brilliant generals, Epaminondas and Pelopidas, Theban power collapsed. Greece was once more left a prey to strife and dissension.

The scene now shifts to Macedonia, where Philip II ascended the throne in 359 B.C. It took him 22 years to become master of Greece. In a council in Corinth in 337 B.C., he proposed a Hellenic League in which each member would be free to govern and promote commerce and trade as of old. The only obligation to Macedonia was to support his expedition to Persia. The Greek cities had no choice. Philip was a brilliant organizer but was destined to be overshadowed by his son. He was assassinated in 336 B.C. and was succeeded by Alexander, who was then 20. The history of Greece for the rest of the century revolves around Alexander and the aftermath of his death.* He launched his campaign in 334 B.C. and fought and defeated the Persians in battles at Granicus, Issus, and Gaugamela (Arbela). In the 11 years before his death at 33 in Babylon, he conquered Egypt, Phoenicia, Asia Minor, Syria, Babylonia, Persia, and part of India. He was a lucky man—he died at the peak of his power. After his death there was a series of assassinations among the relatives of Alexander in their struggle for succession, and a struggle among Alexander's generals for a division of the empire. It is not pleasant reading.

It was a momentous century for learning as well. Socrates died in 399 B.C. It was a period of development of philosophical schools: Antisthenes and the Cynics, Plato and the Akademia, Aristotle and the Lyceum, Epicuros and the Garden, Zenon and the Stoa. Scopas, Praxiteles, and Lysippus represent the sculptors; Apelles and Polygnotos, the painters. The Epidaurus theater was designed by Polycleitus the Younger.

The 3rd century B.C. began with Alexander's empire divided

*This is discussed elsewhere in connection with the story of Pella, the Macedonian capital.

among four of his generals: Cassander was to become the king of Macedonia and Greece; Lysimachus held Thrace and western Asia Minor; Seleucus was allotted eastern Asia Minor, Syria, Babylonia and Persia; and Ptolemy was confirmed in Egypt and Phoenicia. The realm of Lysimachus disintegrated as Thrace relapsed into a state of semi-barbarism and Asia Minor came to be dominated by Pergamon. Pontus and Bythinia remained independent, as they had never been part of the empire. The great cities of classical Greece were involved primarily in ceaseless internal struggles, too worn out by previous wars to do much else. However, the spreading of Greek culture continued from Alexandria, Antioch, Rhodes, Pergamon, and Seleucia. The schools of philosophy in Athens continued but were overshadowed by the men who gravitated to other centers, primarily Alexandria. It was the era of Euclid, Eratosthenes, Aristarchos, Erasistratos, Herophilos, Archimedes, Apollonios of Perga, and a host of others. The Altar to Zeus and other sculptures decorated the acropolis in Pergamon, and Rhodes had its school of sculpture and architecture which produced the Colossos. It was indeed a glorious century for advancing man's knowledge.

Aggravated by the tyrannical behavior of Philip V of Macedon about the beginning of the 2nd century B.C. and his declaring war against states of Asia Minor, Pergamon and Rhodes called upon Rome for aid. Philip had also agreed with Hannibal to wage war against Rome and that afforded Rome another reason for entering Greece. Philip was defeated, but the Roman general, Flaminus, was lenient in his terms, letting Philip retain his kingdom on condition that he abstain from hostile acts against Rome and not interfere in any way with the rest of Greece. It was a chance for Greece to restore her dignity, but apparently she had fallen too low and was decadent beyond hope of recovery. With Greece left to herself, Antiochos, spurred on by Hannibal, invaded Greece and Rome was again involved. Antiochos was defeated and signed the Peace of Apameia in 188 B.C. Twenty years later, a third war instigated by Macedonia resulted in Rome's setting up puppet governments throughout Greece. A Macedonian revolt and a decla-

ration of war against Rome in 147 B.C. by the Grecian Achaean
League resulted in Rome's taking extreme measures. Corinth was
entirely destroyed, thousands of men were killed and, except for
hundreds of works of art carried off to Rome, the rest perished
in flames. Pergamon was bequeathed in 133 B.C. to Rome, who
then became the absolute mistress of the Mediterranean. In the
end it was Rome that was Hellenized and it was through her that
Greek culture was passed on to the rest of Europe.

Progress in science continued during the 2nd century B.C. represented by Hipparchos of Nicaea and Poseidonios of Apamea at
Rhodes, and Aristarchos of Samothrace and Hypsicles at Alexandria. But it was tapering off. In the Christian era the outstanding
men were Ptolemy (150 A.D.), Galen (175 A.D.), and Diophantus
(275 A.D.). War and Christian fanaticism destroyed the Alexandrian libraries; the lamp flickered and after a few years went out.

Athens

Throughout the long tumultuous history of Greece, Athens,
though conquered, sacked and razed, somehow managed to survive and regain her leadership in the nation. In addition to a strategic commercial location, sometime, somehow, the seeds of culture
were sown, flourished and eventually attracted more and more adherents. It was not a large city, a little over a mile in diameter inside the city walls, and the focal point of its community life was the
Agora, the market place, civic center and scene of much of the
social and intellectual activity. It was the Agora which brought to
mind the remark of Charles V: "Such a small place and so much
glory!"

Today there isn't much to remind one of that glory. True, the
Temple of Hephaestus is fairly well preserved and across from it,
strangely out of place, is the 1956 version of the Stoa of Attalos.
For the rest of the Agora, there are but the remnants of some of
the foundations. From the vantage point of the steps of the Temple
of Hephaestus one sees, a half a mile to the right, the hill called the
Pnyx, the legislative assembly place of Athenian citizens after they
moved from the Agora in 508 B.C. To the left of the Pnyx is the

Areopagus (Hill of Mars), the site of the High Court of Justice. It became a powerful oligarchic body like the Senate in Rome but it was deprived of real political power in 462 B.C. St. Paul is supposed to have spoken here to the Athenians in 52 A.D. Overlooking the Agora is the Acropolis with the Propylaea, the Erechteum, and the Parthenon, the most imposing monument in all Greece. In the distance, to the left, is Mount Lycabettus, where Meton and Euctemon made their astronomical observations. A cable railway now makes the ascent relatively easy.

The Agora was only 700 feet across. In the Mycenaean era, before 1100 B.C., the site was used as a cemetery but by the 5th century B.C. it was a well-established place of assembly with administrative buildings, shed-like buildings with deep porches called stoa, and the Temple of Hephaestus. The administrative buildings were near the southwest corner of the square and included a round building, the Tholos, which served as an office and dining place for the presiding officers of the Council, and a large building called the Bouleuterion where the Council held its regular meetings. Prominent on the west side is the Temple of Hephaestus, a well-preserved Doric structure situated on a small hill called Kolonos Agoraios. It was formerly called the Theseum in honor of the legendary king who defeated the besieging Amazons. However, excavation of bronze-casting pits indicate it was probably associated with the smith-god Hephaestus. It was the first building erected (449 B.C.) in the beautification program of Pericles after the defeat of the Persians. The stylobate measures 104 by 45½ feet and supports 6 columns on the ends and 13 columns on the sides. The ratio of the length to the breadth is 9:4, which is the same as in the Parthenon.

Below and to the left of the Temple of Hephaestus was the Stoa of Zeus, a favorite haunt of Socrates, and along the north side of the Agora, now beyond the railroad tracks, were the Stoa of the Herms and the Painted Stoa (Stoa Poikile). The latter was so called because it had been decorated about the middle of the 5th century by paintings of mythical and historical battles. These were mainly by Polygnotos of Thasos, a realistic painter who introduced

THE AGORA VIEWED FROM THE ACROPOLIS
"Such a small place and so much glory."

new effects, such as the rendering of transparent draperies. It
served as a meeting place for adherents to the philosophy of Zenon,
who were consequently called Stoics. Diagonally across the Agora
from the southeast corner near the Acropolis to the northwest corner at the Dipylon Gate, was the processional street, the Panathenaic Way. Every four years a primitive wooden statue of Athena
in a small temple on the Acropolis was draped in a new robe, the
pellos. This was the occasion of the great Panathenaean festival, in
which the robe was carried along the Panathenaic Way up to the
Acropolis escorted by a procession of great size and splendor. The
procession assembled at early dawn near the Dipylon Gate with
the robe displayed on the mast and yardarm of a ship on wheels.
Priests, magistrates and other dignitaries, maidens carrying sacrificial vessels, sacrificial animals, and a splendidly mounted cavalry
made up the procession. Scenes from this procession are portrayed

THE ATHENS AGORA
The Acropolis in the background.

in the Parthenon frieze. It was in connection with this festival that
the *Iliad* and *Odyssey* were first formalized from Homeric poems
and recited (c 535 B.C.).

Over the years, changes and additions were made. The Temple
of Ares was erected between the Panathenaic Way and the Heph-
aesteum. Late in the 2nd century B.C., the original stoa on the
south side was replaced and the Middle Stoa added. In this same
period, King Attalos II of Pergamon, who had been a student in
Athens, built a stoa on the east side. In 15 B.C. the Romans added
Agrippa's Odeon near the center of the Agora. Most of the buildings of the Agora were destroyed in 267 A.D. when a marauding
Teutonic tribe called Herulians sacked Athens. The American
School of Classical Studies reconstructed the Stoa of Attalos in
1953-1956 and it now serves as a museum and workshop in connection with the excavations.

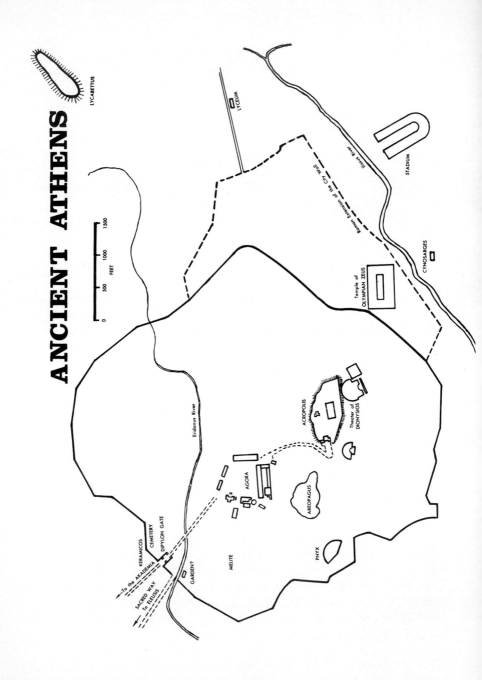

ANCIENT ATHENS

LYCABETTUS

LYCEUM

STADIUM

Ilissus River

Roman Extension of the City Wall

CYNOSARGES

Temple of OLYMPIAN ZEUS

1500

1000

500

FEET

0

Eridanus River

ACROPOLIS

Theater of DIONYSIOS

AGORA

AREOPAGUS

To the AKADEMIA

CEMETERY

DIPYLON GATE

SACRED WAY
To ELEUSIS

GARDEN?

MELITE

PNYX

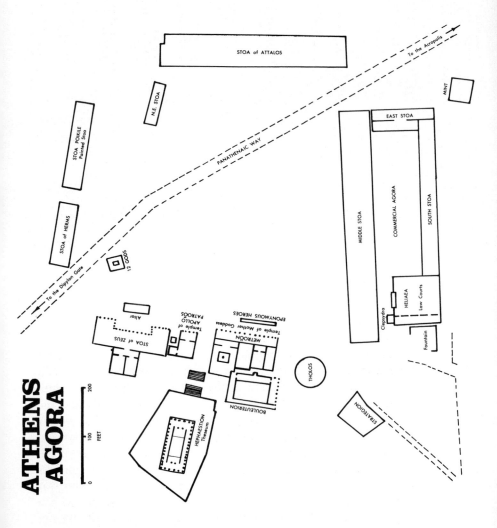

ATHENS AGORA

STOA of ATTALOS

To the Acropolis

N.E. STOA

STOA POIKILE
Painted Stoa

PANATHENAIC WAY

MINT

EAST STOA

STOA of HERMS

To the Dipylon Gate

12 GODS

MIDDLE STOA

COMMERCIAL AGORA

SOUTH STOA

Clepsydra

HELIAEA

Law Courts

Fountain

Altar

STOA of ZEUS

Temple of
APOLLO
PATROOS

EPONYMOUS HEROES

Temple of Mother
Goddess

METROÖN

THOLOS

BOULEUTERION

HEPHAESTION
Theseum

STRATEGION

200

100

FEET

0

THE PARTHENON
The most important monument in all Greece. It was constructed in the period 447-433 B.C. and housed a large statue of Athena, the patron goddess of Athens.

No other structure symbolizes the glory of Athens and of all Greece as does the Parthenon, atop the Acropolis. It was constructed in the period 447 to 433 B.C. with architects Ictinus and Callicrates under the direction of the sculptor Phidias. Apart from the overall artistic result, the careful attention to details and the application of devices to counteract optical illusions is of particular interest to the architect and the engineer. The structure consisted of two distinct halls, back to back, one to house the statue of the goddess and the other, the treasury. It was dedicated to the goddess Athena, the city's divine guardian (Athena Parthenos), who was represented by a 40-foot helmeted gold and ivory statue with a winged victory in her right hand and a spear in her left. By her feet at her right side was a round shield and near the spear was a serpent. The face, arms, and feet were of ivory and her long chiton garment and helmet were made of 44 talents, or 2,530 pounds, of detachable gold plates. The transfer of the Delian treasury to Athens made this possible.

The length of the base of the Parthenon is 228 feet and the breadth 101 feet, a ratio of 9:4. Seventeen columns are viewed from the side and eight from the front and back. The structure was embellished with sculpture. Ninety two metopes carved in high relief depicted battles of gods and giants on the east side, between the Greeks and the Amazons on the west, scenes of the Trojan war on the north, and fights between the Lapiths and centaurs on the south. The two pediments, with over 50 figures in the round, portrayed the birth of Athena on the east and the contest between Athena and Poseidon on the west. The frieze along both sides and continued over the two end porches showed scenes of the Panathenaic procession. It was carved as carefully as though it were to be viewed at eye level instead of from 35 feet below. The average relief is only one and a half inches, but the extraordinary modeling makes the figures appear to project much farther when viewed from below by light reflected up from the white pavement. The back of the pedimental structure was carefully finished, though it was never intended to be seen.

Aspects that make for perfection are usually not noticed by the casual viewer, or are taken for granted; it is the lack of them that is noticed. Some of the considerations which went into the design of the Parthenon and other temples may be of interest. Temples were generally oriented east to west. There was an even number of columns in front to avoid obstructing the centrally placed entrance. Viewed from the side, there was one more than twice the number of columns on the end. In the Parthenon, the ratio 9:4 of the length to the breadth is also the ratio of the breadth to the height above the frieze, and also in the ratio of the width of a column and space to the width of the column. The column height is equal to the width of three columns and the two intervening spaces. A row of columns on a flat base with alternating light and dark bands produces an optical effect of a sag in the middle. To offset this effect, the four sides of the stylobate (upper step of the base) are curved slightly upward (two inches in 100 feet), similar to a pillow with the corners slightly depressed. The axes of the columns lean inward about half a foot, since they would appear to tip outward if erected perpendicularly. The columns, though tapered, are slightly bulged near the middle with a maximum of three quarters of an inch about two-fifths of the way up. Otherwise they would show a pinched effect. This correction is called entasis. The corner columns are a little thicker than the others.

Columns are fluted to avoid reflections of the sun and a fine shadow effect is produced by keeping the groove depth constant as the width of the grooves diminishes toward the top. Doric columns have 20 shallow flutes which meet in a sharp edge; Ionic columns have 24 deep flutes which do not quite meet. The Ionic colunms are somewhat slenderer than the Doric columns and are provided with a base which serves to distribute the load somewhat. The capitals are the most distinctive feature of the columns. The Doric is the simplest with a simple inverted truncated cone. The oldest of the ornamental capitals is the Aeolic found on two temples in the district of Aeolis. It consists of a pair of volutes rising from a central stem like a lily with an upward and outward movement symmetrical with the axis. The Ionic is somewhat similar, but the volutes stem from a horizontal section. One adverse feature of the Ionic capital is encountered in corner columns because of its unsymmetry. This is avoided in the Corinthian capital designed by Callimachos, who flourished in the second half of the 5th century B.C. A Corinthian girl died and her nurse put some of her things in a basket with a tile on top and placed it on the girl's tomb. An acanthus plant grew up all around the basket and gave Callimachos the idea for the design. Callimachos was the first to drill holes in marble and his sculptures were noted for their flawless precision, often overelaborating the details.

The Propylaea is more or less overshadowed by the more imposing Parthenon, but the same meticulous care went into its construction. It was begun in 437 B.C. with Mnesicles as the architect and was finished in five years at a cost of $1,600,000. To the right of the gateway after the entrance is the Temple of the Wingless

Victory. This is the presumed site where King Aegeus threw himself to death when the ship bearing Theseus back from Crete still carried the black sails. The temple is really not a part of the Propylaea, but because of it the wing on the side is smaller than the one on the left, which was a picture gallery with scenes from Homer's *Iliad* and *Odyssey*.

The Parthenon was closed by Emperor Theodosius in 393 A.D. along with other pagan temples. Emperor Justinian converted it into a Catholic church in 535 A.D. and in 1466 A.D. it was converted into a mosque by the Turks. In a war with the Venetians, the Parthenon was used as a powder magazine and was partly destroyed in 1687 as the result of a Venetian cannon ball. During the occupation by the Venetians they endeavored to remove some of the pedimental statues but only succeeded in having them crash and break. For over a century the ruined temple was neglected. In 1749 twelve figures were left; in 1800, only four. Pleased with the British defeat of Napoleon in Egypt in 1801, the Turkish Sultan gave Lord Elgin, the British ambassador, permission to remove "miscellaneous marbles," which the ambassador extended to collecting everything he could dismantle, including one of the Caryatids of the Erechtheum porch. These were intended for his home in Scotland, but he ran into financial difficulties and the marbles were sold to the British government in 1816 for inclusion in the British Museum. The establishment of Greek sovereignty in 1831 reduced further damage to a minimum and in the 1920's, repair of the structure was authorized.

On the south slope of the Acropolis are two theaters, the Theater of Dionysos and the Odeon of Herodes Atticus. The auditorium of the former is almost semi-circular in form and seated 14,000 people in 78 rows of seats. A modern road now cuts across the upper part. The site was associated with the festival of Dionysos as early as 500 B.C., although the semi-permanent form in stone dates from 330 B.C. Changes and improvements continued until the end of the 2nd century A.D. During the Dionysos festivals, drama competitions were held in which the audiences each day sat through three tragedies, a satyr play, and a comedy. Here were produced the plays of Aeschylus, Euripides, Sophocles, and Aris-tophanes.

The Odeon of Herodes Atticus, a wealthy rhetorician, was built in 161 A.D. and served as a concert theater. The 32 rows of seats could hold an audience of 5,000.

The nearby Olympian Zeus temple was one of the largest of the Grecian temples, 135 by 354 feet, being surpassed only by the temple of Zeus in Agrigento and the Artemision in Ephesus. It was begun in a modest way in the 6th century B.C. under the rule of Peisistratus but was abandoned for four centuries because of in-sufficient funds. Work was resumed again in the 2nd century B.C., again abandoned and finally completed in 132 A.D. under Emperor Hadrian, who added his own statue to that of Zeus. There were 20 columns as viewed from the side and 8 in front, of which 15 stand-ing and one prostrate remain. They are 56.5 feet high and 8 feet in diameter.

It was stated earlier in connection with the Agora that here, at one time or another, trod every well-known person of the ancient world. Let us see who were the more prominent men in Athens associated with the arts and sciences.

SIMONIDES of Kea (556-469 B.C.) was the earliest of the famous lyric poets. Early in life he went to Athens and lived under the patronage of the tyrant Hipparchos. He is said to have intro-duced the distinction between the short and long vowels (epsilon and eta, omicron and omega) which was afterward adopted in the Ionic alphabet. He won 56 prizes in competition. His popularity was so great that he had considerable influence in the political world and his poems could command almost any price. He is the author of the inscription to Leonidas and the Spartans at Ther-mopylae:

> Go tell at Sparta, thou that passenth by,
> that here, obedient to her word, we lie.

With a change in government in Athens, Simonides traveled to Thessaly and then to Sicily, where he died.

AESCHYLUS of Eleusis (525-456 B.C.) was the first of the three playwrights of tragedy of whose work entire plays survive. His plays reflect his own association with the events involved, as he was a soldier in the battles of Marathon and Plataea. He participated in 20 competitions and as each entry consisted of four plays, he must have written at least 80 dramas. He won the first prize 13 times. He was invited to the court of Hieron I in Syracuse in 476 B.C., the occasion being the founding of a new town called Aetna on the site of present-day Catania. Here he composed *The Women of Aetna*. During his visit in 472 B.C., his play *The Persians* was produced in Syracuse. Other plays are *The Suppliants,* about 490 B.C., the oldest Greek drama extant; *Seven Against Thebes,* the third play of a tetralogy produced in 467 B.C.; *Prometheus Bound,* a trilogy, about 460 B.C.; and *Agamemnon,* a trilogy, about 458 B.C.

The word *tragedy* literally means "goat-song," *tragos* being the Greek word for goat, and *oide* the word for song. It was sung by the chorus dressed as satyrs or clad in goatskins in the ritual of goat sacrifice at the altar of Dionysos. As drama, tragedies were based on the religious ritual and exhibited at the festival of Dionysos. The subject was always some traditional story of gods and heroes with the representation of some religious rite. Neither the form nor the subject matter could be changed. At first there was a spoken interlude by the chorus leader which developed into the leader being a specific actor with the chorus providing the background and action. This was the situation at the beginning of the 5th century. The predecessors of Aeschylus used only one actor. Aeschylus added a second, an *answerer*. He liked gorgeous and spectacular effects and developed drama along the lines which became traditional. He is considered the father of Greek drama and the first tragedian.

Aeschylus went back to Sicily in 458 B.C. and died two years later in Gela.

PINDAR (522-443 B.C.) is considered the greatest of the lyric poets of Greece. A native of Thebes, he was educated in Athens and wrote many poems in her praise. He traveled extensively throughout Greece, to Sicily, and to Cyrene. He expressed his preference for poetry rather than sculpture by "No sculptor I, to fashion images that shall stand idly on one pedestal for aye; no, go thou forth from Aegina, sweet song of mine, on every freighted ship, on each light bark." He composed hymns to the deities, choral dance songs, songs of praise, dirges, odes of victory. His period of activity was from 502 to 452 B.C. He died in Argos in 443 B.C. It is said that when Alexander the Great razed Thebes in 335 B.C., the home of Pindar was spared.

ANAXAGORAS (499-427 B.C.) was born in the Ionian town of Clazomenae (now called Urla), 24 miles west of Smyrna (Izmir). He was the first teacher of natural philosophy in Athens, having moved there in 463 B.C. soon after the Persian Wars. His theory of the universe assumed a chaos of infinitesimally small particles which *nous* transformed into order. *Nous* was a vague force which might have been physical or spiritual but with some insinuation that it was intelligence. All matter was homogenous no matter how small and it had existed from all eternity. It was a doctrine of dualism with mind and matter existing as two distinct entities. His scientific knowledge was meager and much of it was wrong, but he was inquisitive and he brushed aside superstitions in order to find rational answers. The moon was a body like the earth and both were flat disks resting on nothing. The sun was molten metal "as large as the Peloponnesus." The great meteorite of 467 B.C. came from the sun. He was the first to list the Moon, Sun, Venus, Mercury, Mars, Jupiter, and Saturn in that order. Although it had been stated by others, he knew that the moon was iluminated by the sun and that eclipses were caused by the intervention of the earth for lunar eclipses and intervention of the moon for solar eclipses. He was the first to offer a rational explanation for the Nile flooding, stating that it was due to melting snow in the upper waters of the Nile, although it is due to rain and not snow. He attempted to "square the circle" and is traditionally the first to have presented that problem. He was interested in anatomy and medicine and experimented on animals. From his dissection of the brain, he recognized the lateral ventricles.

Among his friends and those he taught were Pericles and Euripides. Pericles became highly unpopular at the beginning of the Peloponnesian War. Ill treatment of his friends was one of the measures taken against him and this may have been contributory to the charging of impiety and Persian leanings against Anaxagoras. In 432 B.C. he was sentenced to exile. He went to Lampsacus (Lapseki) on the southern coast of the Dardanelles and died there in 427 B.C.

SOPHOCLES (495-406 B.C.) was born in Colonus, in the neighborhood of Athens. He served with Pericles in the Samian War (440 B.C.) as a general. He had an amiable disposition and was generally on good terms with everyone. Attributed to Sophocles are the good-natured remarks about his fellow tragedians Aeschylus and Euripides. Of Aeschylus he said he was often right without knowing it, and of Euripides, that he represented people as they are, and not as they ought to be. Of over 100 dramas, seven remain: *Ajax, Electra, Oedipus, Antigone, Trachinian Maidens, Philoctetes,* and *Supplices.* He used painted scenery in the background and was the first to introduce three actors on the stage. Concentration is a distinguishing characteristic of tragedy; it was even more so with Sophocles. To allow more time for dialogue, the time allotted to the chorus was reduced to one fifth or slightly more. The destinies of his characters were not entirely dependent on fate but subject also to their own actions.

HIPPOCRATES of Chios (fl c 460 B.C.) was a teacher of mathematics in Athens and the greatest mathematician of the century. He was the author of the first systematic treatise on geometry. He originated the method of reduction followed in Euclid's *Elements* whereby each step in solving the problem has to be substantiated by a previously proven theorem or postulate. He was the first to use letters to designate points and lines in geometric figures. In his efforts to square the circle, he determined the areas of certain crescent-shaped lunes formed by constructing semi-circles on the three sides of an isosceles right triangle. The sum of the areas of the two lunes thus produced is equal to the area of the triangle. The statement holds true for any right triangle whether or not it

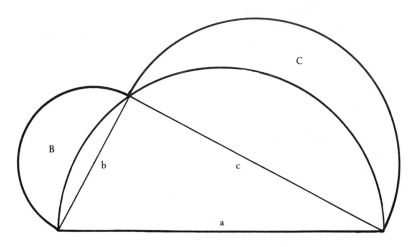

AREA OF LUNES FORMED BY THE SEMICIRCLES
DRAWN ON THE SIDES OF A RIGHT TRIANGLE

The sum of the areas of lunes B and C is equal to the sum of the areas
of the two semicircles on "b" and "c" less the areas of the segments
adjacent to "b" and "c." The area of the segments is equal to the area
of the semicircle on "a" less the area of the triangle. We have then:

AREA LUNE B + AREA LUNE C
$$= \pi \, b^2/8 + \pi \, c^2/8 - (\pi \, a^2/8 - \text{AREA OF TRIANGLE})$$
$$= \pi \, /8 \, (b^2 + c^2 - a^2) + \text{AREA TRIANGLE}$$
$$= \text{AREA TRIANGLE since } a^2 = b^2 + c^2$$

is isosceles, but Hippocrates knew it only for an isosceles triangle.

One of the problems which concerned mathematicians of the
time was the duplication of the cube. To duplicate a square, one
needed only to construct another square on the diagonal of the
first. Was there not some similar means for duplicating the cube?
It got to be known as the Delian problem. One story was that the
Athenians appealed in 430 B.C. to the oracle at Delos to learn
what they should do to stay the plague in their city. The oracle
replied that the altar of Apollo should be doubled in size. Euripides expressed it this way in one of his tragedies:

> Too small has thou designed the royal tomb.
> Double it; but preserve the cubic form.

Hippocrates showed that a solution involved finding two mean proportionals between two given lines.* Menaechmos (c 350 B.C.)
found such mean proportionals by the intersection of two parabolas
and also by the intersection of a parabola and a hyperbola. Diocles
(c 180 B.C.) found a solution using a cissoid curve. Eratosthenes
had a method which involved the intersections of the sides of three
identical right triangles. Archytas had a solution which involved a
cylinder, a torus, and a cone.

EURIPIDES of Salamis (c 484-407 B.C.) was the third of the
great playwrights of tragedy in ancient Greece. He was a pupil of
Anaxagoras and a friend of Protagoras, Herodotus, Sophocles, and
Pericles. It was said that Socrates never went to the theater unless
there was a play by Euripides. He lived in Salamis, 15 miles west
of Athens, overlooking the site of the famous sea battle in which
the Grecian fleet defeated that of Xerxes. He lived much alone and
hated society, living, it is said, in a cave with a beautiful sea view.
His wife's name was Melite.

He wrote 75 plays, of which 18 have come down to us and
some are still occasionally produced. Four of his plays won first
prize in competition. He chose situations of violent stress with men
and women in the grip of passion, or torn by conflicting impulses.
He sought dramatic effects by ingenious devices, *deus ex machina,*
and leaving it to the gods to come up with the solution. For this,
he has been criticized. His characters approached closer to ordinary
life than those of Aeschylus or Sophocles. He liked formality and
adhered to the ancient Dionysiac ritual even more closely than
Aeschylus. Each play opens with a solitary figure giving a prologue
which makes for atmosphere and starts the play off with dignity
and quiet. The play builds up climax after climax with the last
scene much like the first, with a peaceful end. The chorus in the
early days of Aeschylus occupied half of the performance; with
Sophocles, it was reduced to one fifth. Euripides increased both its
length and importance, thereby contributing both beauty and dramatic power. This the chorus does by expressing in music the

*$a : x = x : y$, or $x^2 = ay$; and $x : y = y : b$, or $y^2 = bx$

$x^2 = ay$; $x^4 = a^2 y^2 = a^2 bx$; $x^3 = a^2 b$

If $b = 2a$, then $x^3 = 2a^3$ and a cube with a dimension x would have
a volume twice the original cube with a dimension of a.

yearning of the body and emotions common to the world. Some of the Athenian war prisoners in the stone quarries in Syracuse won their freedom by teaching their captors the choruses of Euripides.

Euripides was very much discouraged by the corruption and savagery of the war party in Athens. In one of his plays he expresses his bitterness in the words of one character who says he would rather die a slave in Delphi, where one is not jostled off the pavement by the scum of the earth, than be a free man in Athens, a city full of terror where good men dare not to speak. His popularity waned; they tried to prosecute him for impiety. So, at 76, he went into voluntary exile to the court of Archelaos in Pella.

POLYGNOTOS of Thasos (fl c 455 B.C.) was a famous painter who worked chiefly in Athens and was admitted to citizenship there. He decorated the walls of the Stoa Poikile with scenes of the Trojan War, scenes of the Greeks and the Amazons in the Temple of Hephaestus, and frescos in the treasury at Delphi erected by the people of Chios. He showed only tinted outlines on a colored background without shading and without perspective. He introduced the rendering of transparent draperies and was praised for his headdresses of various colors and his speaking expressions.

PROTAGORAS of Abdera (481-411 B.C.) taught for a while in his home town of Abdera, which was a coastal town in Thrace northeast of the island of Thassos and near the present town of Porto Lago. He also taught in Sicily, but most of his teaching was in Athens. Teachers in Athens taught grammar, rhetoric, eloquence, ethics, and to be wise. These traveling teachers were called Sophists, some of whom were good and some unscrupulous. They were very much in demand, as they were thought to have the latest ideas, although the doctrine of the teacher was his own. Protagoras was the first of the Sophists.

His knowledge was extensive and he criticized mathematicians for their abstract thinking, making them realize that their arguments pertained only to ideal figures. He taught that "an able talker can strengthen a weak argument" and that "man is a measure of all things." Another statement attributed to him is, "What appears to be true to you is true for you and what appears to be true to me is true for me." He was the first to formalize the Greek language and work out rules of grammar. In 443 B.C. he was chosen by Pericles to draw up a constitution for the colony of Thurii. He became very wealthy and it was said that in his 40 years of teaching he accumulated ten times as much money as the sculptor Phidias. In his book *On the Gods,* he stated, "Concerning the gods, I am unable to say whether they exist or not—nor, if they do, what they are like." In 411 B.C. he was condemned for impiety and perished in the wreck of the ship carrying him to Sicily and freedom.

SOCRATES (470-399 B.C.) was one of the few philosophers born in Athens. He was an eccentric personality, dressed very plainly, always walked barefooted, and ate frugally. He lived a simple life by choice. His teachings were in the Agora, or wherever people would gather. In a broad sense of the word, he could be called a Sophist, but he did not give formal lectures and did not expect payment. His cross-examination method was to pretend not to know anything and to ask questions tending to trap the conversationalist or lead him to the desired conclusion. His teachings were slanted toward practical and human problems, disapproving geometry as an exercise and discouraging pure science and abstract philosophical thought. His maxim was "Know thyself." In spite of his antagonism toward science, his attitude of skepticism and freedom from prejudice was beneficial. He insisted that discussion without knowing as many facts as possible was unproductive. Many young men who attached themselves to Socrates were to be the great thinkers of Greece, among them Plato. He was so irritated by incessant wars and political intrigue that there was some tendency in his teachings to destroy moral faith and patriotism without leaving anything in its place. Youths, before they had developed self-discipline, used his teachings to justify their lack of restraint. He was regular in prayer, but since only the gods "know what is good for us, our prayer should be 'grant me what is good' without dictating what the blessing should be." Men miss happiness because they don't really know what it is and education should teach men not to use wealth or power wrongly. His criticism of those in power was that too often they measured national greatness by wealth and empire rather than by character.

Aristophanes ridiculed him in his *Clouds;* his enemies could not bear his self-righteousness; a contemporary man in the market place would probably have tolerated him as an incessant talker and a bore; but posterity has judged him to be a very remarkable man. He was charged with rejecting the gods acknowledged by the state and with corrupting the youth. Two youths in particular, Alcibiades and a leader of the extremists named Critias, were obnoxious to the democrats. The prosecutor asked the death penalty and the court had the choice of imposing the sentence demanded by the prosecutor or one proposed by the accused. He could have saved himself by cautious words and a reasonable defense, but unwilling to curry favor, he was arrogant and antagonized the judges. He had been condemned by a legally constituted court which could not be disregarded without disloyalty to the law. He was condemned to die by drinking a poisonous concocotion of hemlock. Among his disciples present at his death was Eucleides of Megara (450-380 B.C.), who took refuge and founded a school at Megara. Plato had already sought refuge there.

ANTIPHON (fl c 430 B.C.) was a Sophist who suggested squaring the circle by inscribing a regular polygon, such as a hexagon, and then doubling the number of sides until the polygon seemed to coincide with the circle. The area of the polygon could be computed in terms of the radius of the circle and provide a close approximation of the area of the circle, π r², and hence, the value of π . He is not to be confused with Antiphon the Orator, who flourished about the same time.

THUCYDIDES (c 471-400 B.C.) is known as the historian of the Peloponnesian War up until 411 B.C. In 424 B.C. he was named one of two generals to defend the Athenian outposts in Thrace. These were essential to the protection of the Thracian gold mines and the Dardanelles grain route from the Black Sea. In 423 B.C. the Spartans captured the main Thracian settlement and Thucydides was exiled. It is believed that the history of the war was written mainly in Thrace (423-404 B.C.), where his family had property. However, he also traveled extensively in Peloponnessus and Sicily. The circumstances of his death are not known.

METON (465-385 B.C.) and EUCTEMON seem to have been associated together in astronomical observations, some of which were made on top of Mount Lycabettus. They were the first to discover the unequal lengths of the seasons, with an approximate length of 95 days for spring, and 92, 89, and 90 days for summer, autumn, and winter respectively. It was to correct for this that Callippus (370-300 B.C.) had to add extra spheres to the plan of Eudoxos.

Meton is best known for the Metonic cycle, 235 lunations corresponding to 19 solar years. This is quite accurate using modern values:

$$235 \times 29.530588 \quad \text{days} = 6,939.688180 \quad \text{days}$$
$$= 6,939 \text{ days } 16.5 \text{ hours;}$$
$$19 \times 365.24219878 \text{ days} = 6,930,60177682 \text{ days}$$
$$= 6,939 \text{ days } 14.4 \text{ hours.}$$

Since the completion of the 235th lunation occurs about two hours later than the completion of 19 solar years, it will be a day late after 228 years. The Metonic cycle is the ecclesiastical basis for fixing Easter. His plan for the 235 lunations was 12 lunar years of 12 lunar months and 7 years of 13 months. Of the total number, 125 were 30-day months and 110 were 29-day months, making a total of 6,940 days. He is reported to have used the Mesopotamian figure of 365 days 6 hours 15 minutes for the solar year and on that basis, 19 solar years also equal 6,940 days. Both figures are slightly in error and by 100 years after Meton, a discrepancy was apparent, which Callippus proposed to correct by substituting a 29-day month for a 30-day month in a 76-year period. Assuming a revised figure of 365.25 days in the solar year, there are 27,759 days in 76 years and 27,760 days in the lunar months according to the old Metonic plan. The one-day correction by Callippus again brought the solar and lunar calendars into step. However, the length assumed for the solar year was still in error by 0.008 day. Hipparchos of Nicaea (190-125 B.C.) made an additional correction of one day in four Callippian periods which reduced the discrepancy to about one and one-half days in 304 years.

In front of the Pnyx *cavea,* southwest of the Agora, is the foundation of a sundial put up by Meton about 432 B.C.

ARISTOPHANES (c 448-385 B.C.) was the outstanding playwright of comedies in ancient Greece. The term *comedy* comes from the Greek *komos* meaning a "revel" and all extant comedies ended with a revel scene. They consisted of the performances of a ritual of the fertility spirit Dionysos which involved a union of the sexes and was grossly indecent. They were performed at the festival of Dionysos, who was the god of wine, ecstasy, and forces of nature. The form of the play was not restricted as in the case of tragedy and only one play was submitted in competition. Neither was there any restriction on the material presented until 414 B.C. near the end of the Peloponnesian War, when a law was passed banning political attacks. The politicians were apparently sensitive regarding their conduct of the war.

Aristophanes was fortunate in that during his fruitful years there was no satirical censorship and he spared no one. Of his 44 or more comedies, 11 survive: *Acharnians* (425 B.C.), *Knights* (424), *Clouds* (423), *Wasps* (422), *The Peace* (421), *The Birds* (414), *Lysistrata* (411), *Thesmophoriazusae* (410), *The Frogs* (405), *Ecclesiazusae* (395), and *Plutus* (revised 388). He won four first prizes, three second and one third, surpassing all other writers of comedy. In *Clouds* he satirizes Socrates: A youth (Alcibiades) is sent to Socrates to be cured of his dissoluteness. The youth becomes accomplished in dishonesty and impiety and the conclusion shows the father preparing to burn up Socrates and his hall of contemplation.

ANTISTHENES (c 441-371 B.C.) is generally considered the founder and the only philosopher of the Cynic school. He was educated at a gymnasium called Cynosarges, which was open only to half-citizens of Athens. It was located on the left bank of the Ilissus River south of the Temple of Olympian Zeus. The term *Cynic* stems from the name of the school, which means "white dog." The name was derived from a white dog which snatched part of the victim Diomus was sacrificing to Heracles. One of the parents of Heracles was a mortal, hence the school was for those with only one Athenian parent. Cynicism was not a formal school but rather an attitude toward life with the tenuous doctrine that happiness is based on virtue, which includes justice, abstinence, forbearance and moderation. The adherents lived in the austerest fashion and did not accept statements or conventions at their face value. As critics of established authority, they had a following among the common folk and asceticism led some to a hermit life. Later, his followers degraded his doctrine by depreciating all knowledge and despising morality, a mark of intellectual bankruptcy. The most publicized follower, though not a philosopher, was Diogenes.

ISOCRATES (436-338 B.C.) was the son of a wealthy flute manufacturer who lost his wealth during the rule of the Thirty Tyrants. During this period, he taught rhetoric in Chios and upon his return to Athens (c 392 B.C.) he opened a school near the Lyceum. The school had an enrollment of about a hundred and included orators and historians, each of whom paid 1,000 drachmas. The names of 41 of his pupils are still known, and in a contest sponsored by Queen Artemisia II of Halicarnassus at the inauguration of the monument to King Mausolos, there was not an orator who had not been a pupil of Isocrates.

His weak voice and shyness kept him from being an orator himself, but he had great political influence. His speeches written for others, particularly against the Persians, brought him considerable wealth. He was an intense patriot and through much of his life he endeavored to have Greece united as a nation. He continued teaching up to the end of his 98 years.

XENOPHON (430-354 B.C.), an aristocratic Athenian, joined an army of Greek mercenaries to fight on the side of the younger Cyrus against his brother Artxerxes II of Persia. The insurrection failed and the mercenaries were left stranded. Xenophon was elected their leader and he brought 10,000 men 1,200 miles to Trebizond in the southeast corner of the Black Sea and turned them over to a Spartan general. The long trek through enemy territory pointed out the weakness of Persian defenses and encouraged plans for Greek invasion of Persia. Xenophon was not in sympathy with the policies and institutions of Athens and on his return went to live in Sparta and, later, Olympia and Corinth. His history of Greece began where Thucydides left off (411 B.C.) and continued to the death of Epaminondas of Thebes in 362 B.C. He also wrote a defense of Socrates, his former teacher, which was considered more reliable than Plato's later writings.

PLATO (428-347 B.C.) was born in Athens of aristocratic parents. His name was really Aristocles, but he was nicknamed Plato by his wrestling master because of his strong build. When he was about 20, he became a pupil of Socrates for about eight years. After the execution of Socrates and a temporary refuge in Megara, he traveled extensively for 12 years in Greece, Egypt, and Italy, was enslaved by pirates, ransomed, and finally returned home at the age of 40 to found the Akademia. The ransom was paid by a certain Anniceris of Cyrene. Friends of Plato reimbursed Anniceris, but, though he took the money, he purchased a small garden and presented it to Plato. The site was about half a mile beyond the Dipylon Gate, the northwestern gate of ancient Athens. The land originally belonged to a hero called Akademos who disclosed to Castor and Pollux where Theseus had hidden their sister Helen. Akademos had left the grove to the citizens and it was adorned with statues and planted with olive and plane trees. The olive trees were reared from cuttings taken from the sacred olive tree by the Erechteum and produced the oil given as a prize to victors at the Panathenean festival. The grove was walled in and Plato's garden was within the enclosure. The site at present is a vacant field in a semi-industrial and low-priced housing district about a quarter of a mile west of the Hagios Tryphon church.*

---

*The Akademia site can be reached from Athens by going out Lenorman Street for two or three miles to Odos Eukleidou and turning left for a quarter of a mile to the end of the street. (Bus 145 from the Odos Keramikou terminal near Omonia Square).

On the road to Eleusis is a bus stop at an old olive tree, enclosed by an iron fence, called Ellia Platonos. Any association with Plato's Akademia is probably sentimental.

SITE OF PLATO'S AKADEMIA

The Akademia was a higher school of philosophy and ethics with the chief object of training men for the service of the state. In contrast to the Sophists and Socrates, natural philosophy and mathematics were considered important. The school was conducted on a seminar basis and attracted scholars from all over Greece in their search for knowledge. Plato's literary style was so beautiful that his audiences accepted his philosophy lest they themselves should be considered inadequate. His writings are in the form of dialogues, as he believed speech superior to writing and it enabled him to express his own opinions in the words of others without himself being committed. Socrates figures in most of the dialogues and, in writings during the latter part of Plato's career, is made to express opinions which are entirely contrary to the philosophy of Socrates when judged by Xenophon, his other biographer.

The Akademia considered mathematical discussions important, as evidenced by the traditional inscription over the portal of "Let

None But Geometers Enter.* Plato himself was not a mathematician and his contributions were insignificant. But he did stimulate others. Definitions were improved and reasoning was made more rigorous. He was profoundly impressed by the number series and music intervals of the Pythagoreans and endeavored to apply them to the cosmos. The universe was considered to be spherical and to rotate around the earth in 24 hours. The earth was also spherical and immovable, with the Sun, Moon, and planets carried along on an outer shell. These bodies, however, had motions of their own. Their distances from the earth were represented by the series 1, 2, 4, and 8 for the Moon, Sun, Mercury, and Mars and 1, 3, 9, and 12 for the Moon, Venus, Jupiter, and Saturn.

His whole philosophy can be divided into Logic, Ethics, and Metaphysics (theories of Reality and Knowledge). He integrated the Pythagorean philosophy of numbers, the concept of knowledge of Socrates, the Cynics' ideas of the difference between knowledge and opinion, and other philosophies with his own. Man's greatest happiness is found in a life of virtue which involves justice, temperance, courage, wisdom, and goodness and depends on the degree that man develops a rational and moral personality. The difficulty lies in being able to know what is absolute good. This stresses the importance of Knowledge. Plato held that Ideas were the only reality and that logical thought is alone true knowledge. There are two ways of developing thought: from the Idea downward to the particulars, and upward from the particulars to the Idea, the realm of absolute being. These methods typify the differences between the approaches followed by Plato and Aristotle. In the painting "The School of Athens" in the Stanze di Raffaello in the Vatican Museum in Rome, Plato is depicted with his hand pointed upward toward the Ideal, whereas Aristotle is pointing downward toward the more substantial particulars out of which the Ideal must be generalized.

Plato treated political science in three dialogues: *The Republic, The Statesman,* and *The Laws.* Plato had lived during a period of strife: the closing years of the Peloponnesian War, the ill-fated

* ΜΗΔΕΙΣ ΑΓΕΩΜΕΤΡΟΣ ΕΙΣΙΤΩ.

expeditions to Sicily, the Thirty Tyrants in which democracy utterly failed, and the revolts against Spartan domination. Persia had fallen because of tyranny, Athens because of excessive freedom. He was disillusioned with government in general and sought a solution in his plan for an idealistic State.

His Ideal State described in *The Republic* was exceedingly communistic. All land would belong to the state; 20 percent of the citizens would be warriors, counselors, and rulers of the state; the rest would be husbandmen. Women would participate on equal footing with the men as regards education and duties. There would be no marriages: mating of the good with the good and the bad with the bad would take place during certain holy hymeneal festivals, with the offspring of the good reared and the others destroyed. Children would be reared in nurseries with the women admitted to the fold but not knowing which child was theirs. All would live in common houses and meals would be in common. The true philosophers, lovers of truth, would rule.

There are obvious weaknesses with this State which Plato recognized and in *The Laws* he omits community of women and property. He relates how transgressions of the laws, inferior rulers, craving for wealth, desire for private property, and corruption of philosophy transform it into a military state. Arts of war prevail over arts of peace and the ruler is no longer a philosopher. The accumulation of wealth, to the extent that riches outweigh virtue and honor, leads to an oligarchical state in which wealth determines who shall rule. With unequal distribution of wealth and an indolent class of citizenry, the poor rise up and conquer by arms or fear, and thus form a democracy. But freedom, too, courts dangers. Emulating the desires and the spending habits of the well-to-do, the people live beyond their means. Youths do not listen to the counsel of their fathers; modesty, they call silliness; temperance they nickname unmanliness; moderation and orderly expenditure are vulgarity and meanness; insolence, they term good breeding; anarchy they say is liberty, waste is magnificence, and impudence is courage. Fathers and teachers fear their sons and pupils; the old imitate the young lest they be thought morose and authoritative; authority is resented, and at length laws are disregarded.

There are three classes of people in a democracy: those associated with government, an orderly class which in a nation of traders will generally represent the most wealth, and those who work with their hands. The latter, when assembled, are the largest and the most powerful class in a democracy. The wealth of the industrious is squeezed for distribution to the have-nots and those in power. A leader is nursed into greatnesss and, with the mob at his disposal, his acts become more vicious until he must either perish at the hands of his enemies or become a tyrant. In his early days of tyranny, he smiles and beams on all, puts an end to debt and monopoly of land, makes himself necessary to the State by going to war, thus enabling him to depress the poor with heavy taxes and keeping them at work. Then follows unpopularity, old associates oppose him, purges follow, and liberty passes into the worst form of servitude.

After Plato, Arcesilaos of Pitane headed the Second Akademia, and Carneades of Cyrene headed the Third. The Akademia of Plato's tradition lasted for about 150 years but continued in one form or another until A.D. 529—900 years after its founding, when it was closed by Emperor Justinian as a school of pagan and perverse learning.

THEAETETUS (415-369 B.C.) was a disciple of Socrates and of Theodoros of Cyrene. One of Plato's dialogues is a conversation between these three men. He was a contemporary of Plato and Archytas and is best known for his work on irrational numbers and polyhedrons. It was contrary to the ideas of the Pythagoreans that the diagonal of a square could not be represented by a finite number. Theodoros of Cyrene showed that the square roots of whole numbers, other than squares, up to 17 were irrational. Theaetetus treated incommensurables essentially as given in Book X of Euclid.

He was the first to write about regular convex polyhedrons and the proof that only five could exist* (tetrahedron, cube, octahedron, dodecahedron, and icosahedron), as given in Book XIII of Euclid, is ascribed to him.

DIOGENES of Sinope (c 412-323 B.C.), though not a philosopher, is the best known of the Cynic adherents. His father was in charge of the mint in Sinope, a town on the southern coast of the Black Sea, but because of some irregularity in the coinage, he was forced to leave. Diogenes attached himself to Antisthenes and was determined to distinguish himself by his contempt for luxury and honors. He wore a coarse coat, carried a staff, and depended on the bounty of the passer-by for sustenance. In his old age on a trip to Aegina, he was captured by pirates and sold on the slave market of Crete to a wealthy Corinthian who later freed him. He was nicknamed "The Dog" because he lived in a tub on top of which was a carved dog, the symbol of the Cynics. Stories tell of his searching for an honest man with a lighted lantern during daylight, and that he asked Alexander the Great to stand aside so as not to shade him from the sun. It may be that Diogenes had more to offer than incidents of this type to achieve immortality. Nevertheless, it would seem that he had little to offer and could only resort to such antics in order to attract attention to himself and to justify his abnormal way of life. Contempt is usually the characteristic of the have-nots, be it wealth or talent.

EUDOXOS of Cnidos (408-355 B.C.) was considered one of the greatest astronomers and mathematicians of his time and also achieved eminence in medicine and law. He studied with Plato in Athens for two months (385 B.C.) and later traveled to Egypt in company with Chrysippos, a physician. He observed for 16 months at an observatory near Heliopolis, where he was admitted to the

---

*A convex polyhedral angle must have at least three faces and the sum of its face angles must be less than 360°. Since each angle of an equilateral triangle is 60°, convex polyhedral angles can be formed by only three, four, or five triangles corresponding to a tetrahedron, an octahedron, and an icosahedron respectively. Since each angle of a square is 90°, only three squares can converge in a point and hence only a cube can be formed using squares. Each interior angle of a pentagon is 108° and hence only three such angles can converge in a point and only one polyhedron, a dodecahedron, is possible with regular pentagons. For other polygons, the interior angles are 120° or more, so that three such angles equal 360° or more and hence no regular convex polyhedrons are possible.

company of learned priests. In 378 B.C. he went to Cyzicus, at the neck of the Kapidagi peninsula on the southern coast of the Sea of Marmara. Here he founded a school which he transferred ten years later to Athens, in order to cooperate with the Akademia. Toward the end of his career he spent some time at the court of Mausolos at Halicarnassus and then returned home to Cnidos. His observatory at Cnidos still existed in Strabo's time (64 B.C.-21 A.D.).

From his stay in Egypt, he learned that their 365-day year gained a day every four years. He suggested a cycle of three 365-day years and one 366-day year, 300 years before its introduction during the reign of Julius Caesar. He introduced the celestial globe and published two books on astronomy, *Enoptron* ("Mirror") and *Phainomena,* and a book on geography, *Periodes ges*. In *Phainomena* (366 B.C.) he described in prose the general outlines of 44 constellations which were later versified by Aratos:

> *Northern:* Ursa Major, Ursa Minor Boötes Draco, Cepheus, Cassiopeia, Andromeda, Perseus, Triangulum, Pegasus, Dolphin, Auriga, Hercules, Lyra, Cygnus, Aquila, Sagitta, Corona Borealis, Ophiuchus
>
> *Zodiacal:* Aries, Taurus and the Pleiades, Gemini, Cancer, Leo, Virgo, Libra, Scorpius, Sagittarius, Capricornus, Aquarius, Pisces
>
> *Southern:* Orion, Canis Major, Lepus, Argo Navis, Cetus, Eridanus, Pisces Australis, Centaurus, Hydra, Crater, Corvus

Most of these configurations were evident to the inhabitants of the Fertile Crescent, each group ascribing their own mythical personalities. Some were mentioned by Homer. Thales suggested Ursa Minor in view of its use by Phoenician navigators.

Eudoxos interpreted the change in altitude of the stars with latitude as proof of the sphericity of the earth.

His model of the universe assumed each celestial body to be mounted on the equator of a sphere which rotated about an axis attached to another sphere with a different axis. By suitable choice of poles and velocities, one sphere was sufficient for the stars, three spheres each were necessary for the sun and the moon, and four spheres for each of the five planets. The 27 spheres formed an ingenious and, admittedly, elaborate system. However, the actual existence of the spheres did not enter into the plan; it was merely a means for representing the motions of the celestial bodies. He did not take into consideration the differences in the lengths of the seasons noted by Meton. To compensate for this, Callippus (370-300 B.C.) added two spheres each for the sun and the moon and one each for Venus, Mercury, and Mars. The model was replaced later by systems involving eccentrics by Apollonios of Perga or epicycles by Heracleides and Ptolemy.

When the Pythagoreans got involved with the diagonal of a square and found that there was no finite number expressing the square root of 2, they felt it was a serious conflict with their philosophy of numbers. Theodoros of Cyrene indicated that the square roots of 3, 5, 6, 7, 8, 10, 11, 12, 13, 14, 15, and 17 were also irrational. Eudoxos showed that they could be represented by the limits of a series of fractions* and covered it in his theory of proportion. The principles of this theory formed the basis for much of Book V of Euclid's *Elements*.

A related case was the five-pointed star, which was the emblem of the Pythagoreans. The five lines used in the construction of the star were intersected such that the ratio of a line to the large segment was equal to the ratio of the large segment to the smaller segment. Stated mathematically:

$a/x = x/ (a - x)$, which reduces to the quadratic equation
$x^2 + ax - a^2 = 0$, and
$x = (a\sqrt{5} - 1)/2 = 0.618a$

Since the value of x involves the $\sqrt{5}$, it is obviously irrational. This division of a line got to be known in the mid-19th century as the "golden section" and has been regarded by artists as a secret of beauty and the point of major interest in a picture.

*To approximate the square root of 2, a series was used as follows:

x	+	y	=	(x)		x	+	x	=	(y)		y/x		
0	+	1	=	1		0	+	1	=	1		1/1	=	1
1	+	1	=	2		1	+	2	=	3		3/2	=	1.5
2	+	3	=	5		2	+	5	=	7		7/5	=	1.4
5	+	7	=	12		5	+	12	=	17		17/12	=	1.417
12	+	17	=	29		12	+	29	=	41		41/29	=	1.413
29	+	41	=	70		29	+	70	=	99		99/70	=	1.4143

The values of x and y satisfy the equation $y^2 - 2x^2 = \pm 1$, whereas the relation between the hypotenuse and sides of a square is given by the equation $y^2 - 2x^2 = 0$.

HERACLEIDES of Pontus (388-310 B.C.) emigrated to Athens at an early age and studied at the Akademia. He was left in charge during Plato's visit to Syracuse in 361 B.C. In 339 B.C. there was an election for a new master and the votes were almost equally divided between Heracleides and Xenocrates of Chalcedon. Heracleides lost, however, and opened his own school. He is said to have written numerous brilliant works on many subjects but is best known for his ideas on astronomy. He believed in a geocentric universe but that the apparent daily motion of the stars, sun, and planets could be best explained by the rotation of the earth on its axis. This had also been suggested by Hicetas of Syracuse. Heracleides believed that Mercury and Venus revolved around the sun and suggested the idea of epicycles to account for irregularities in their motion.

XENOCRATES of Chalcedon (394-314 B.C.) left for Athens in his early youth and associated himself with the Akademia. When Plato was succeeded in 347 B.C. by his nephew Speusippos as head of the Akademia, Xenocrates and Aristotle left for Assus. In 339 B.C. he became the third head of the Akademia and remained there for 25 years. Although lacking in brilliance, he won universal respect by his earnestness, strength of character, and devotion to the Akademia. He adhered closely to the Platonic doctrine, with special attention to ethics. Philosophy was considered the best help in the attainment of virtue, as the philosopher does of his own accord what others do under compulsion.

ARISTOTLE (384-322 B.C.) was born in Stageira, a few miles from the northeastern coast of Chalcidice (Khalkidhiki). His father was an asclepiad who had been a court physician to the father of King Philip II of Macedon at Pella. At the age of 17, Aristotle was sent to Athens to complete his education and stayed there 20 years, part of the time at the Akademia. Shortly after the death of Plato, Aristotle and a friend, Xenocrates, joined a school at Assus, an Ionian city just north of the island of Lesbos. Here they were joined by his nephew, Callisthenes, and Theophrastos. Aristotle stayed there three years, two years in Lesbos, and then went on to Pella to be the tutor of Alexander the Great.

Aristotle returned to Athens in 335 B.C. and founded a new school in a gymnasium located outside the city walls in a grove sacred to Apollo Lyceios (wolf-god); hence the name Lyceum. The exact location of the Lyceum is not known but it was in the vicinity of Rigilis Square and the Byzantine Museum. The street is a busy thoroughfare with many embassies and an ultra-modern hotel. The school was burned in 200 B.C. by Philip V of Macedon and the trees were cut down by Sulla (87 B.C.) to make engines for besieging Athens.

Much of the teaching was done outside while walking around the gardens, so that the participants were called Peripatetics, "around the path." In the morning there would be discussions of abstruse questions with an inner circle and towards evening, Aristotle might deliver a polished lecture to a more diverse group. He remained with the Lyceum for 13 years, until the death of Alexander. Although his friendship for Alexander had ended with Alexander's execution of Callisthenes, his ties with Macedonia didn't endear him to the Athenians. Rather than get involved, as did Socrates, Aristotle moved to Chalcis, 40 miles north of Athens, where his people had originally migrated from. He died the following year.

All knowledge was Aristotle's field, the writings covering biology and other natural sciences, logic, rhetoric, ethics, metaphysics, economics, government, and literature. He was the biologist of the Lyceum and one-fourth of his writings are in this field, with an unusual amount of information on many subjects. He devised classifications for all kinds of plants and animals, studied anatomy and the function of parts of the body, embryology, habits of animals, ecology, and geographical distribution. In astronomy, Aristotle accepted the theory of four elements, namely, earth, water, air, and fire. Change was an accepted fact in the sub-lunar world. In the changeless world beyond the moon, a fifth element was necessary—aether. The universe was spherical because that was the most perfect shape. It was finite because it had a center—the earth; an infinite universe could not have a center. He invented the science of logic. The dialogues of Plato demonstrated the importance and method of logic, but Aristotle was the first to denote explicit principles.

In his *Politica,* Aristotle analyzed the different forms of government and started out with the premise that it was of course necessary to get the best people to govern. This, by definition, would be the aristocrats, as the Greek word *aristos* means "the best." Governments were classified into Democracies, Oligarchies, and Monarchies, with the danger that one would degenerate into another. An aristocratic government would degenerate into an oligarchy with a few ruling to their advantage; an oligarchy would degenerate into a monarchy and a monarchy into a tyranny. On the other hand, complete freedom of a democracy develops into the rule of the mob. Some of the chapter headings of his *Politica* are of interest: Structure of the State, Ideal Commonwealths, Forms of Governments, How to Proceed Framing a Constitution, Causes of Revolutions and How to Avoid Them, Organization of Democracies and Oligarchies, Criteria for Individuals and States, Picture of the Ideal State, and Educational System of the Ideal State.

Both Aristotle and Plato were interested in explaining a rational universe. Aristotle's earlier writings showed the influence of the Akademia, but in time his method of approach differed materially from that of Plato. Plato was an idealist and endeavored to make the particulars fit into the general ideal plan. Aristotle, on the other hand, was continuously accumulating information and believed it was necessary to have as complete an encyclopedia of information as possible in order to explain the universe. Raphael in his painting "The School of Athens" showed Plato pointing to the sky as if to signify that the ideal is the only real; Aristotle points to the earth to indicate where the answers are to be found.

The amount of information collected was indeed voluminous, so much so that up until the 16th century, new ideas were often not accepted unless they came within the framework of Aristotelian philosophy. This attitude Aristotle would be the first to discourage. From Córdoba, the Arabic seat of learning, and from Constantinople, where the Crusaders found some manuscripts, Aristotelian learning spread to Western Europe. By 1300 A.D., Aristotle was recognized as the master of knowledge. His treatises were studied century by century in cathedral schools and in monasteries. By the time of the Renaissance and the Reformation there was a rebirth of science as well and Aristotle was gradually bypassed. However, with increased interest in biology in the 19th century, it was again realized how extensive his contributions were. His analysis of governments should be "must" reading for legislators even today.

Aristotle bequeathed his library to Theophrastos, who in turn bequeathed it to Neleus, a disciple of Aristotle and Theophrastos, who took it to Scepsis near Mount Ida. Neleus bequeathed the books to his heirs, who had little regard for the books and locked them up. When searchers for the Pergamon Library came they hid the books underground in a trench. Much damaged, they were finally sold to Apellicon of Teos for a large sum of money. He endeavored to restore them and made new copies of the text, filling in the gaps often incorrectly. Sulla brought Apellicon's library to Rome, where fresh copies were made without any notes as to what corrections were made. Andronicos of Rhodes prepared the first edition (c 70 B.C.).

MENAECHMOS (fl c 350 B.C.) studied at the Akademia under Plato and Eudoxos. Not much is known about him except that he was interested in the Delian problem, namely, the duplication of the cube. Hippocrates of Chios had shown that a solution involved two mean proportionals between two given lines, namely: $a : x = x : y = y : b$, from which three equations can be derived: $x^2 = ay$ (parabola), $y^2 = bx$ (parabola), and $ab = xy$ (hyperbola). Menaechmos solved the problem by the intersection of two parabolas and also by the intersection of a parabola and a rectangular hyperbola. The two parabolas were drawn with a common vertex, their axes at right angles and the latus rectum of one being double that of the other. With $x^2 = ay$ and $y^2 = 2ax$, they will intersect at a point whose abscissa is given by $x^3 = 2a^3$.

This is the first time on record that conic curves had ever been mentioned, although not by the usual names of course, as they were applied by Apollonios of Perga a century later. Menaechmos obtained his curves by a plane perpendicular to the side of the cone and varying the apex angle. For an acute angle, the curve is an ellipse; a right angle gives a parabola; and with an obtuse angle, a hyperbola is obtained.

PRAXAGORAS of Cos (fl c 350 B.C.) followed Diocles of Carystos as head of the Dogmatic school of medicine in Athens. The basis of the school was the updating and systematizing the teachings of the Hippocratic school and served as a transition between that school and the new anatomy and physiology being developed in Alexandria. Praxagoras made a clear distinction between arteries and veins, believing that the arteries carried blood and the veins, air. His studies of the blood vessels led him to the study of the pulse and applying it to diagnosis. Herophilos of Chalcedon was one of his pupils.

THEOPHRASTOS of Eresos, Lesbos, (372-286 B.C.) headed the Lyceum after Aristotle left, and served 37 years. He first came to Athens to study at the Akademia. His meeting with Aristotle led to their being associated in Assus and later at the Lyceum. All told, over 2,000 students studied with Theophrastos in those years. One of his pupils was Demetrios of Phaleron, who went on to be the governor of Athens, and then the organizer of the Library and Museum at Alexandria. Theophrastos wrote 227 treatises on religion, politics, ethics, education, logic, astronomy, mathematics, meteorology, geology, and botany. He has been called "the father of botany" and dealt with 550 species. Plants were divided into foods, drugs, and poisons, so that botany had a very practical value. His books *History of Plants* and *Causes of Plants* treated of parts of plants and their classification, propagation,. horticulture, timber trees, herbaceous plants, cereals, medicinal properties, diseases, et cetera. He also wrote on minerals and gems. He was not only the first writer on botany but the greatest until the 16th century.

CALLIPPUS of Cyzicus (370-300 B.C.) taught at the Lyceum and tried to improve on Eudoxos' system of spheres by adding seven more spheres: two for the Sun, two for the Moon, and one each for Mercury, Venus, and Mars. This was to compensate for the difference in the lengths of the seasons discovered by Meton and Euctemon. He also improved the Metonic cycle by substituting a 29-day month for a 30-day month in a 76-year period.

EUDEMOS of Rhodes (fl 335 B.C.) was a pupil of Aristotle and he and his friend Theophrastos were the chief contenders for heading the Lyceum after the retirement of Aristotle. He was the first historian of science and his *Historia Geometrica* is the main source of pre-Euclidean mathematics. A work entitled *Eudemian Ethics,* outlining life as taught in the Lyceum, was either written by Eudemos or dedicated to him.

ARISTOXENES of Tarentum (fl c 335 B.C.) was a disciple of Xenophilos, a Pythagorean, and later of Aristotle. He was disappointed in not having been elected head of the Lyceum after the retirement of Aristotle. He is most famous for introducing semitones in the musical scale devised by the Pythagoreans. He also computed thirds and fourths of tones, but these were not used in the adopted chromatic scale.

The diatonic scale developed by the Pythagoreans about 500 B.C. was first suggested by their noting that certain combinations of tones, as produced by vibrating strings, were melodious. Since pitch, and vibrating frequency, were inversely proportional to the lengths of the strings, they arrived at the following relationships for three melodious chords:

Relative Frequencies	4	5	6	8	3	4	5	6	3	4	5	6
Frequency Ratios	1	5/4	3/2	2	1	4/3	5/3	2	9/8	3/2	15/8	9/4
Assigned Letters	C	E	G	C'	C	F	A	C'	D	G	B	D'

The entire scale was as follows:

Letters of the Scale	C	D	E	F	G	A	B	C
Frequency Ratios	1	9/8	5/4	4/3	3/2	5/3	15/8	2

Aristoxenes continued this plan. Starting with E and using the simple ratios of 3/3, 4/3, 5/3, and 6/3 with the 5/4 of E as a base, the following relationship is arrived at:

Relative Frequencies	3	4	5	6
Frequency Ratios	5/4	5/3	25/12	5/2
Scale Letters	E	A	C#	E'

It will be noted that the ratio 25/12 is greater than 24/12 corresponding to C′ and smaller than 27/12 corresponding to D′ and is therefore an intermediate tone, C#.

Starting with F as a base and using the same simple ratios as before, the following relationship is obtained:

Relative Frequencies	3	4	5	6
Frequency Ratios	4/3	16/9	20/9	2/3
Scale Letters	E	B flat	D′	F′

The ratio 16/9 is greater than 15/9 corresponding to A and smaller than 15/8 corresponding to B and is therefore an intermediate tone, B flat. The ratio 20/9 is very close to 9/4 previously computed for D′. Similarly, a whole set of semi-tones can be worked out. Since the whole tones may differ slightly, as in the case of 20/9 and 9/4 above, and the sharp of one note may differ slightly from the flat of the note above, a total of about 50 different notes would be required in each octave to take care of all the scales. The differences are generally so slight that compromise frequencies are satisfactory. Twelve evenly spaced notes in the range of one octave were selected with an interval of the 12th root of 2, or 1.059. This is called a scale of even temperament.

Aristoxenes wrote 453 books on music, philosophy, history, and education. In *Harmonica Stoicheia* he discussed the relation of pitch to vibration frequency, intervals, scales, combinations of intervals and tetrachords in scales, and melody. He wrongly believed that the speed of sound increased with pitch. Why is the voice higher when it echoes back? he asked. Largely through his efforts and the Pythagoreans', music was considered a science. Physics had not yet arrived. His other books on music covered rhythm, melody, musical instruments, and dancing in tragedy. Greek musical theory never surpassed that of Aristoxenes and he was considered the greatest musicologist of antiquity.

DICAEARCHOS of Messina (fl 320 d 285 B.C.) was a historian and geographer and wrote on a wide range of subjects, such as the history of culture, Homer, maps, a dialogue on the soul, and the height of mountains. He was the only Greek geographer between Hecataeus of Miletus and Eratosthenes and described the world from Gibraltar to the Ganges. His *Life in Greece* treats of geography, political conditions, theaters, games, and religions in Greece. He maintained that "man is man's worst enemy." Dicaearchos was a disciple of Aristotle and the latter's estimate of the size of the earth—circumference, 40,000 miles—may have come from him.

ARISTAEUS the Elder (fl 320 B.C.) was an early contributor to the study of conic sections, antedating Apollonios of Perga by a century. He also wrote on the five regular polyhedrons which served as a basis for Hypsicles' Book XIV of Euclid's *Elements*.

EPICUROS of Samos (341-270 B.C.) was the son of an Athenian family in Samos. He studied philosophy at the age of 14. While still in his teens, his family along with other Athenian colonists had to leave, settling in Colophon and other Ionian cities. At the age of 30, Epicuros taught in Mytilene on the island of Lesbos for a year. After four years in Lampsacus, he finally (306 B.C.) moved to Athens. He bought a house and garden near the Dipylon Gate in the section of the city called Melite, where he conducted the Garden school of philosophy.

Teaching was informal and life was simple. The presence of women made the school a subject of gossip and the success of the school caused envy among other factions. Epicuros adopted much of the philosophy of Democritos, including the atomic theory, which was extended to include spiritual (mind, soul, and gods) as well as material things. When a man dies, the atoms comprising his soul are redistributed.

Happiness, defined as a state of well-being and contentment, was a paramount goal. It was happiness derived from the full use of virtues, such as justice, abstinence, forbearance, and moderation. The disciples were advised not to marry nor have children and they tended to withdraw from life. They preferred to engage in philosophic discussions rather than search for scientific truths. They were not against science; just disinterested, not even acknowledging the sphericity of the earth. Science would develop with or without their good will. Superstition, myths, mysteries, astrology, and all forms of divination were rejected. Epicuros was not anti-religious, but he decried the kind of religion that Platonists and the aristocrats fostered for the "good" of the lower classes. The gods must be looked for, not in the stars, but in the hearts of men.

The struggle against superstition was not popular; the tide was running the other way. Fantastic ideas were borrowed from Egypt and the plain people were so deeply afflicted they preferred the solace of a mystical salvation in another world. The Stocis, soothsayers, demagogues, and religious communities were all against them. However, there was no change in principles of the school from the death of Epicuros to its final disappearance six centuries later.

The climax of the movement occurred in Rome with the enthusiasm of the poet Lucretius in the early part of the 1st century B.C., 200 years after the death of the founder. Such derogatory attributes as were charged against Epicureanism were due to its Roman converts. It is of interest to note that as late as 176 A.D., Marcus Aurelius created four chairs of philosophy in Athens— Stoic, Epicurean, Academic, and Peripatetic.

STRATON of Lampsacus (fl c 300 B.C.) was a pupil of Aristotle. He was called to Alexandria to be tutor to the crown prince who became Ptolemaios Philadelphus and at the same time assist with the establishment of the Library and Museum. The scientific tone of the Museum was due to him; otherwise it might have been a sort of philosophical academy. He succeeded Theophrastos as head of the Lyceum and held that position for 17 years (286-269 B.C.). Among his pupils was Aristarchos of Samos. He disbelieved the atomic hypothesis, as did Aristotle, as they both felt that matter was infinitely divisible. He wrote a book, *Meteorlogica,* in which he discussed weather, physics, astronomy, and chemistry. In the last field, the book treats of the constitution of matter, solids and solutions, and what happens when two different elements mix.

ZENON of Cition, Cyprus ((336-264 B.C.), the founder of Stoicism, was of Phoenician descent and arrived destitute in Athens as the result of a shipwreck. He associated with the Cynics and attended lectures at the Akademia and the school at Megara. In 310 B.C. he started teaching in the hall, or portico, on the north side of the Agora called the Stoa Poikile. The place was called the

Painted Stoa, as it had been decorated about the middle of the 5th century by Polygnotos of Thasos. It was from the Stoa that the philosophy of the school got the name Stoicism.

The Akademia and the Lyceum were too academic for most people, so that the potential audience was larger for schools of philosophy with less emphasis on science. Their ethical doctrines were high and stressed conscience, duty, self-sufficiency, justice, and fellowship of men. True goodness consisted in living in harmony with nature according to reason guided by physics and theology. The Cosmos must be regarded as a single whole, and Wisdom and Virtue constitute the true goal of man. Virtue is a law which governs the universe and is binding upon reason. Human law comes into existence when that obligation is recognized; justice is natural and not merely conventional. The individual should be allowed freedom, but with responsibility; and obedience to the law should be demanded. He must recognize that he is a member of a society of rational beings and that his own ends must be subordinate to the ends and needs of society.

Their science, which wasn't much, was derived from the Akademia and hence colored with mysticism. They did indicate that nothing passes unexplained—there is a reason for everything. Zenon sought out natural principles and moral ideals in the legends of the poetry of Homer and Hesiod. Their forms of worship were inconsequential. They believed in a Supreme Being but that divinity must also be ascribed to various manifestations and to the forces of Nature, and even deified men. What God is for the world, the soul is for men. They were indifferent to pleasure and accepted pain and death.

Stoicism was considered the highest ethical doctrine of the ancient world. Before Christianity, it became the ethical gospel of the more educated people, not only philosophers but statesmen and businessmen as well. For two centuries it was the creed and philosophy of the best Romans. Though Stoicism leaned toward astrology, mysticism, and divination, it could not compete with ritualistic religions which gave comfort and promised salvation to those in misery.

Following Zenon, teaching of Stoic philosophy was continued by Cleanthes of Assus, Chrysippos of Soli, Zenon of Tarsus, Diogenes of Seleucia, Antipatros of Tarsus, Panaitios of Rhodes, and others. Poseidonios of Apamea, the geographer (135-51 B.C.), headed the school in Rhodes. Note that these men were all from or near Asia Minor. Diogenes of Seleucia and Crates, the librarian at Pergamon, introduced the philosophy to Rome, where it attained its greatest popularity, including such adherents as Polybios, who was a hostage from Greece, Scipio, Cicero (who nevertheless condemned the Stoic acceptance of astrology), Seneca, and Marcus Aurelius.

CLEANTHES of Assus (301-232 B.C.) was a poet who succeeded Zenon as head of the Stoics. He combined Zenon's dualism of God and Matter into a pantheism and expressed his thoughts in a beautiful Greek religious hymn *"Hymnos eis Dia,"* a sort of Lord's prayer. Instead of "Deliver us from evil," the hymn states:

> Deliver men from all ignorance.
> Banish it, father, from their soul.
> Grant them to find wisdom, whereon relying.
> Thou rulest all things with justice.

CHRYSIPPOS of Soli (280-206 B.C.) was a logician and grammarian who assimilated, developed, and systematized Stoic doctrines and created their formal logic. He wrote 750 treatises and contributed so much to Stoic doctrine that it was said "without Chrysippos, there would be no Stoa."

CARNEADES of Cyrene (213-129 B.C.) was the founder of the Third, or New, Akademia. He was sent to Rome in 155 B.C. as an ambassador to justify certain acts of the Athenians and, incidentally, to give some lectures. They were very well received and developed much enthusiasm for Stoic philosophy. He held the view that the way things seem to a person are not necessarily the way things are. There is no criterion of truth. In regard to the Stoic theory of divine guidance, he stated that it could not be shown but that the world was the product of natural forces. He had such a high reputation in Greece that other philosophers came to listen to his lectures.

PANAITIOS of Lindos (185-109 B.C.) was a Stoic philosopher who taught in Rhodes and in Rome. He became head of the Stoic school in Athens in 129 B.C. He tried to reject astrology and divination, but was against the trend and had little success. However, Stoicism did become so attractive that it became the ethical gospel of the better-educated people.

PROCLUS of Byzantium (410-485 A.D.) studied at Xanthus, Lycia, in the extreme southwestern part of Asia Minor, and at Alexandria. In Athens he attended lectures at the Akademia and about 450 A.D. he became head of the Platonic school. Much of his literary activity was devoted to the writings of Plato. His works are of particular value as sources of historical information on the teachings of Euclid, Hipparchos, and Ptolemy. He wrote a commentary on Hesiod's *Work and Days*.

THE THEATRE AT EPIDAURUS
Built about 390 B.C. by Polycleitos the Younger and seats about 14,000. The acoustics are extraordinary.

Epidauros

ASKLEPIOS (13th century B.C.), so the story goes, was a chief
or prince of Thessaly who fought, or whose sons fought, in the
Trojan War. Homer's story of him is a plain tale of a mortal man
skilled in treating wounds. The myths and legends about him are
many and his symbol, a snake entwined on a staff, is that of today's
medical profession. The caduceus with two serpents on a staff signifies a herald, the symbol of Hermes (or Mercury), and has no
medical association. It is not known whether the temples of Asklepios, which began to make their appearance in the 8th or early 7th
century B.C., are an indication of a continuous line of healers or
whether the name was simply adopted by some healer at the much
later date. Over 300 temples were erected, the chief center apparently being at Epidauros, about 25 miles southeast of Corinth.

In the course of time, a number of imposing structures were
built at Epidauros. There were baths, a stadium, temples of Artemis, Aphrodite, and Asklepios, a 107-foot-diameter tholos with a
picture of Eros and slabs with the names of people healed, accommodations for the patients, and a theater. After possibly a
shock treatment of walking through a pit with yellowish-colored
snakes (in Libya, it was crocodiles), a bath, special purification
rites, sacrifices, and a tranquilizing treatment, the patient went to
sleep. He hoped he would wake up cured, or at least that the god
would reveal to him in a dream what treatment was necessary.
Everything was done to put the patient at ease with rest and entertainment in order to promote the psychotherapeutic treatment.

Each year thousands of patients bearing rich offerings made
pilgrimages to Epidauros. Human weaknesses were exploited, and
to live up to a godlike tradition, the priests brought in an element
of religious superstition with the material assistance of sacred serpents. The death rate was nil because as soon as death was imminent, the patient was hustled out of the sanitarium. In the course
of time, the priests devoted more and more of their time to the religious side, and lay assistants, called *asklepiadae,* took over the
medical and surgical treatment. These achieved more in a few years

than the superstitious priests had in centuries. It was from this cult that rational medicine and surgery in Greece grew.

The theater is not only the best-preserved of the ruins but after 2,300 years is still usable and every summer the National Theater presents an unexcelled series of performances of ancient drama. It was built about 390 B.C. by the Argive architect and sculptor, Polycleitos the Younger. The Greek theater presented drama and comedy and hence differs from the Roman theater, which presented spectacles of gladiatorial and animal fights with the spectators seated all around the arena. It evolved from the circular threshing floors of the type still seen in Crete. In Epidauros, the 55 rows of seats are arranged fan-shaped around the 65-foot orchestra (a Greek word meaning "dance"). The top row is 415 feet long and the seating capacity of the whole theater is over 14,000. The acoustics are fantastic. I don't know what they are with the theater filled, but when it is empty, a camera click or even a deep breath is readily heard in the top row. Such an excellently constructed structure deserves a place in a book on ancient science.

Pella

Pella was the ancient capital of Macedonia at the time of Alexander the Great. It is situated about 25 miles west of Thessaloniki on the main road to Edessa in what must be one of the largest areas of flat land in Greece. There was no trace of Pella until 1957 when a farmer, digging a storeroom under his house, found an Ionic column. Although test diggings indicate rather extensive occupation of the area, the excavations cover only a few acres. They show building foundations, some with mosaic floors. Six complete and several partial Ionic columns have been re-erected. Small black and white pebbles are used in the mosaics with lead strips to emphasize the outlines. The pictorial mosaics are housed in a small museum on the premises. Future excavations beyond the immediate area are uncertain. There are two mounds which appear promising, but one is covered with a modern city and the other is under cultivation by a private owner.

PELLA
The home of Alexander the Great.

Pella was an important seaport in the late 5th century B.C. when Archelaos moved the capital from Aegae, now known as Edessa. During the reign of Philip II it was in one sense the most important city in the Greek world. By the beginning of the Christian era, the encroaching marshes made it an unhealthy place to live on account of malaria, and by the end of the 1st century A.D., Pella had virtually disappeared. Nevertheless, Pella can be considered the fountainhead of a lot of history during the succeeding centuries—one of war, assassinations, treachery, pillage, cities razed, enslavement, deportation, and wholesale slaughter. It is not a pretty picture.

At the opening of the 4th century B.C., Macedonia was still almost uncivilized. Amyntas, the grandfather of Alexander the Great, was the first prince of the dynasty. His life was strongly embittered by intrigue and conspiracies carried on by his queen Eurydice. They had three sons: Alexander, Perdiccas, and Philip. In addition, there were three half-brothers. Amyntas was succeeded by Alexander, who found himslf engaged in a losing battle with

Boeotia and had to send Philip as hostage. Alexander was assassinated by Ptolemy of Alaros, who then ruled as regent for Perdiccas. When Philip returned (364 B.C.), Perdiccas had gotten rid of
Ptolemy, but a few years later he was killed in the onslaught of hill
tribes instigated by his mother. He left behind an infant son called
Amyntas. Philip, then 23 years old, seized the throne and killed
one half-brother, and the other two fled the country.

Philip married Olympias of Epiros (359 B.C.), who turned out
to be a rather bloodthirsty woman. They had two children, Alexander and Cleopatra. After he had divorced Olympias, Philip in
337 B.C. married Cleopatra, a niece of Attalos, one of his generals.
She bore him one son. It was at the wedding of Philip and Cleopatra that Attalos offered a toast in which he hoped there would be
a legitimate heir to the throne. Alexander, enraged, threw the contents of his cup in the face of Attalos and stalked from the room.
Philip tried to follow with a drawn sword but was too drunk and
fell. In addition to the three legitimate children of Philip, there
were at least two illegitimate children: mentally retarded Arrhidaeus, who later was known as Philip III, and Thessalonike, who
later married Cassander. It was generally assumed at the time that
he also fathered two of Alexander's generals, Antigonus Monophthalmos and Ptolemy.

Philip was murdered in Aegae in 336 B.C. by one of his guards
while walking to the theater in connection with the festivities celebrating the wedding of his daughter Cleopatra to her uncle, King
Alexander of Epiros. Suspicion was cast on Olympias, and even
Alexander, as the perpetrator of the crime. Alexander assumed the
throne. He was then 20 years old. To avoid any question of succession, Philip's wife Cleopatra and her infant son were put to
death, as was Alexander's cousin, Amyntas, son of Perdiccas.

To strengthen his Macedonian base before embarking on his
father's project of subduing Asia, Alexander quickly demonstrated
his military power to the northern tribes, and when Thebes revolted, he utterly destroyed the city, except the house of Pindar,
and the inhabitants were either slaughtered or sold into slavery.
Thus ended the city of Cadmus, which for 700 years had played

a prominent role in the history of Greece.

Entrusting his domestic concerns to Antipater, Alexander set forth in 334 B.C. on his Asian expedition with 5,000 horsemen and 30,000 foot soldiers. Before his death in Babylon 11 years later, his campaign had carried him south through Asia Minor, Phoenicia, and Palestine to Egypt, where he founded Alexandria, then back through Syria, Mesopotamia, and Persia to India. He left behind razed and pillaged cities, dispersed and enslaved populations, and untold people massacred.

The period following the death of Alexander was one of uncertain succession. Before Alexander left for Asia, Olympias had imprisoned Arrhidaeus and murdered Philip's second wife, Cleopatra, and her infant son. Of Alexander's family, there remained his mother, Olympias; his mentally retarded half-brother Arrhidaeus, later known as Philip III; his half-sister Thessalonike; his wife, Roxana (the daughter of King Oxyartes of Soghiana, a district north of Afghanistan now in the Soviet Union); her son, later known as Alexander IV; and Statira, the elder daughter of Darius, whom Alexander had married in 324 B.C. along with the mass weddings of his officers and men to Persian brides. Alexander was also reported as fathering a son, Heracles, by Barsine, daughter of Artabazus of Damascus and widow of one of Darius' generals. None of these could rule at the time and in a few years all would be dead except Thessalonike, who was married to Cassander. Olympias had her stepson Arrhidaeus murdered; his child was slain in the lap of his mother, Eurydice, who was sent a rope, a dagger, and poison; Barsine and Heracles were slain by Cassander when Heracles was 14, possibly about 318 B.C. Olympias was slain in 316 B.C. by relatives of men she had murdered; Roxana had Statira slain; Roxana and Alexander's son were imprisoned and were slain in 310 B.C. Although dead, Alexander IV remained as a fictional ruler until 307 B.C., when all pretense was abandoned.

The potential successors were Antipater, who was left behind in Macedonia; Perdiccas, who was Alexander's prime minister; Antigonus Monophthalmos ("one-eyed"); Lysimachus; Eumenes; and Ptolemy—all Alexander's generals. Antipater died in 319 B.C.

and was succeeded by his son Cassander. Antigonus defeated Eumenes in battle, had him executed and then called himself King of Asia Minor. Ptolemy appropriated Egypt. A lieutenant under Perdiccas, Seleucus, led a mutiny which ended with the murder of Perdiccas, and Seleucus aspired to Babylonia. Lysimachus headed up Thrace and part of Asia Minor. Antigonus was too ambitious for the others and in 301 B.C. he was beaten in battle and his holdings were turned over to Lysimachus. He in turn was defeated and killed in battle (281 B.C.) with Seleucus and a year later Seleucus was assassinated by Ptolemy Ceraunus, the oldest son of Ptolemaios I Soter. Except for Pontus and Bythinia, which had never been occupied by Alexander, Asia Minor came under the domination of Pergamon.

In Macedonia, Ceraunus, to fulfill his ambition of ruling, married Queen Arsinoë II, the widow of Lysimachus, and immediately murdered her two children and banished her to the island of Samothrace. He was killed in battle the following year (279 B.C.) and was followed by Antigonus Gonatas, a grandson of Antigonus Monophthalmos.

As for Alexander, it was two years before the splendid funeral carriage was finally completed, a large golden temple with bells hanging from the roof. The golden coffin was decorated with four paintings depicting scenes from his campaigns. Drawn by 64 mules, the cortege set off ostensibly for Macedonia. Ptolemy, who had seized Egypt as his share of the empire, felt that having the body in his domain would enhance his prestige. In Syria, therefore, he diverted the procession to Memphis. Later the body was removed to Alexandria, where it was entombed near the Museum.

When Alexander died, his empire was intact, but his image was beginning to tarnish. His troops revolted in India; Persepolis was burned in a fit of drunken excitement to satisfy, according to legend, the whim of lovely Thaïs, the mistress of one of his generals; he stabbed to death his best friend, Cleitos, who had saved his life at Granicus; he had Philotas executed, the commander of his calvary and the son of his best general Parmenio; Parmenio, who was left behind in command in Media, was put to death by secret orders; his character was gradually changing to that of an oriental despot, adopting Persian dress and requiring prostration in his presence; when criticized by Callisthenes, Aristotle's nephew was charged with conspiracy and executed.

Alexander was a fortunate man to have died at the height of his career.

EURIPIDES of Salamis (484-407 B.C.), one of the three outstanding Greek dramatists of all time, was critical of the war party in Athens during the Peloponnesian War. He was unsuccessfully tried for impiety and otherwise persecuted. In order to avoid further trouble, he accepted in 408 B.C. the invitation of King Archelaos of Macedonis to live at Pella.

ZEUXIS of Heraclea (464-398 B.C.) was one of the best-known Greek painters. He was the first to employ shading to achieve perspective. Up until that time, figures were merely outlines with flat masses of color. There is a story that his painting of a bunch of grapes was so realistic that it attracted birds. In Pella, he decorated the palace of King Archelaos. He may have resided in Ephesus. Seventeen of his works are known.

ARISTOTLE of Stageira (384-322 B.C.). There is a story that when Alexander the Great was born, his father, Philip II, sent a letter to Aristotle saying, "Know that a son is born to us. We thank the gods; not so much for the gift as for bestowing it at a time when Aristotle lives." When Alexander was 13 years old, Aristotle took over his tutoring (343-336 B.C.). After the death of Philip, Aristotle went to Athens and founded his school of philosophy, the Lyceum.

ARATUS of Soli (315-245 B.C.) was invited to Pella in 276 B.C. by King Antigonus Gonatas, whom Aratus had met in Athens. To celebrate the marriage of the king to Phila, daughter of Antiochos I, Aratus wrote the *Hymn to Pan*. At the request of Antigonus (c 275 B.C.), he versified Eudoxos' description of the heavens in a work called *Phainomena*. The first 18 verses were an invocation to Zeus referred to by St. Paul (Acts 17:28) in speaking of God.

> For in Him we live, and move, and are,
> As some also of your poets said,
> "For we are also his offspring."

Then followed 714 verses describing the constellations, circles of the celestial sphere, and the rising and setting of the stars. The following is a reference to the constellation Boötes:

> Behind and seeming to urge on the Bear,
> Arctophylax, on earth Boötes named,
> Sheds o'er the Arctic car his silver light.

The last 422 verses had to do with weather and were based largely on the works of Theophrastos of Eresos. It was also issued under a separate title, *Prognostica*.

When Macedonia was invaded by Pyrrhos, the king of Epiros, and Antigonus was dethroned, Aratus went to the court of Antiochos I of Syria, where he completed his edition of the *Odyssey*. When Antigonus was restored in 272 B.C., Aratus returned to Pella and remained there the rest of his life.

Stageira

Stageira is a small village of about 200 inhabitants situated about 5 miles from the sea on the northeastern coast of the Chalcidice peninsula. It is reached from the city of Thessaloniki by a 65-mile hard-top road which, for the most part is winding and mountainous. It serves to emphasize the importance of the sea for transportation in ancient days. The houses are neatly white-washed and the people seem proud that their village was the birth-place of Aristotle the Stageirite. Overlooking the village is a park with a statue of Aristotle bearing the inscription

ARISTOTELES

O

STAGERITES

ARISTOTLE (384-322 B.C.) was the son of an asclepiad who had been court physician to the father of King Philip of Macedon at Pella. At the age of 17, he left for Athens and studied at the Akademia under Plato for 20 years. Following the death of Plato, he spent some time in Assus, Lesbos, and in Pella as the tutor of Alexander the Great. Upon his return to Athens, he opened a school of philosophy called the Lyceum. In 323 B.C. he retired to Chalcis and died there the following year. He was the greatest philosopher of nature in antiquity and was considered the authority on natural science until well past the Renaissance.

ARISTILLUS (fl 280 B.C.) was an astronomer attached to the Museum in Alexandria. He and his associate Timocharis were the first to record the positions of stars by means of numerical distances from fixed positions in the sky instead of vague verbal descriptions.

Abdera

Abdera was an ancient city about 20 miles northeast of the island of Thasos. It is reached from the city of Xanti by a 20-mile road through a town called Abdira. The remains cover seven small hills and extend between two harbors. It was first settled by settlers from Clazomenae about 650 B.C. This settlement was destroyed by the Thracians and a new colony was formed in 544 B.C., when nearly the whole population of Teos migrated there in order to escape the oppression of the Persians. Among them was Anacreon, the composer of bacchanalian and love lyrics. Abdera became one of the richest of the Aegean cities, due to the good wheat lands and to the mountain pass which facilitated trade with the hinterland. From about 350 B.C., when Philip forced a semblance of unity in Greece, until Flaminius defeated Philip V in 197 B.C., Abdera was dominated by Macedonia. The ancient city is now entirely in ruins. There is a legend that the city got its name from a servant of Heracles called Abderos. He was killed by the man-eating mares of Diomedes that Heracles was sent to capture.

DEMOCRITOS (c 460-370 B.C.) came from a wealthy, noble family in Abdera, which enabled him to travel extensively in Greece, Asia Minor, Egypt (five years), Mesopotamia, and Persia. He laughed at the follies of mankind, and because of that, was sometimes referred to as "The Laughing Philosopher." Many of the aphorisms attributed to him are remindful of *Poor Richard's Al-*

manac. He was one of the great 5th-century philosophers and is best known for his development of the atomic theory first proposed by Leucippus. It is not known to what extent nor under what circumstances they joined in the development. The refinements are probably due to Democritos. The following statements give some of the broad features of the theory. The only things that exist in reality are the atoms and the void. Nothing can rise from nothing, and nothing can be reduced to nothing. The atoms are therefore eternal and non-created. So also is motion, as every motion results from a preceding motion. The atoms are indivisible and infiintely small and differ in shape, position, and arrangement. Some atoms are round and can roll over each other in liquids; others are rough, so that they cling together as in solids. They combine in accordance with fixed laws and not by chance, and this results in matter having different properties.

The soul was also considered by Democritos to be material, the atoms being fine, round, fiery, and constantly in motion. It was considered to be a manifestation of the body and perished with it. The popular belief in gods was attributed to incapacity to understand fully nature's phenomena and the need to resort to some superhuman agency. The moral system of Democritos called for the maximum of happiness stemming from good humor, just disposition, and equality of temperament.

His writings cover nearly every field: *Music, On Cheerfulness, Greater and Lesser World Systems, On the Mind, On Logic, On Senses.* Archimedes stated in his work *Method* that Democritos was the first to state correctly that the volume of a cone is one-third that of the cirmumscribing cylinder and, similarly, the relation of a pyramid to a prism. However, Eudoxos was the first to prove it.

PROTAGORAS (481-411 B.C.) taught for a while in Abdera and then went to Athens, where he was the first of the Sophists. He taught the usual repertoire of grammar, rhetoric, eloquence, and ethics. He became very wealthy, but because he cast some doubt on the existence of the gods, he was condemned for impiety. He perished in the wreck of a ship carrying him to freedom.

ANAXARCHOS (fl 330 B.C.) was a philosopher of the school of

Democritos and accompanied Alexander the Great to Asia. After
Alexander's death he was shipwrecked in Cyprus and executed by
the king of Salamis.

HECATAEUS (fl 300 B.C.) was a philosopher, historian, and
grammarian who accompanied Ptolemaios I Soter to Syria and up
the Nile to Thebes. It has been suggested that Soter wanted Hecataeus to prove to the Greeks that Egypt was the cradle of civilization and at least as old as the Mesopotamian civilization.

Samothrace

Samothrace is a small, barren, and rocky island with an area
of about 75 square miles located in the northern part of the Aegean
Sea about 30 miles south of Alexandroupolis. Mount Fengari domi-
nates the landscape. It is very inaccessible, with no harbor and poor
anchorage. There is, however, a weekly steamer service with Alexandroupolis. The village of Samothraki and the ruins are in the
northwest corner of the island.

Its inaccessibility granted it a certain amount of freedom from
involvement in the strife which beset Greece and her colonies in the
ancient past. It was settled by Greek colonists from Samos around
700 B.C., but there are many legends about the pre-Hellenic inhabitants. It was from Samothrace, the island of Electra, that Dardanus drifted to Troad, founded the Trojan dynasty, and taught the
Trojans the Samothracian Mysteries. There is also the story that
Cadmus, in searching for his sister Europa, came to Samothrace
and met and married Harmonia, who was being initiated into the
Mysteries.

The cult at first worshipped a great mother-goddess called
Axierus, probably the local equivalent of Cybele, the Phrygian
mother-goddess. There were also the twin divinities of fertility
called Kabeiri. The rites were secret, with elaborate initiation ceremonies. The Sanctuary of the Great Gods seems to have been very
popular in the Hellenistic period and most of the midsummer in-
stallation ceremonies were viewed by the kings of Macedonia and
the Ptolemies of Egypt. It was at such festivities that Philip II met

Olympias, the mother of Alexander the Great. The Sanctuary was closed in the 4th century A.D. by Theodosius I and the state of the whole island deteriorated.

The building nearest the sea is the Anaktoron, in which the initiation to the first degree took place, including some sacrificial rites. It dates from about 500 B.C. but replaced an earlier 8th- or 7th- century structure. The 60-foot circular rotunda called the Arsinoëion is believed to have contained sacrificial altars. It was the gift of Queen Arsinoë II in 281 B.C. It will be recalled that she married consecutively Lysimachus (298-281 B.C.), her step-brother Ptolemaios Ceraunos (280 B.C.), who immediately killed her two sons and banished her to Samothrace, and her brother Ptolemaios II Philadelphus (276 B.C.). The Central Terrace, or courtyard (304 B.C.), is believed to be where a rite was performed depicting Harmonia's quest in the underworld and her marriage to Cadmus. It was symbolic of the mourning in winter, and the sowing of the seed and renewal of the crops in spring and summer. It involved sacrifices to the underworld deities accompanied by a sacred banquet in which the libation vessel was deliberately smashed after the ceremony. The New Temple (320 B.C.), built on the site of older structures, was a place of worship and a baptism in bull's blood for those prepared to go all the way. Adjacent to the New Temple are a hall of votive offerings and an altar court. On the side of the hill are a few tiers of the 2nd-century theater and nearby is a structure with a fountain and an ornamental pool. This is the site of the famous "Winged Victory of Samothrace," also known as "Nike."

Nike exemplifies the winged type of victory—a draped female figure—which was designed and developed by Achermus of Chios (fl 550 B.C.). It was discovered in 1863 and is now in the Louvre. The donor is usually said to be Antigonus Gonatus in honor of the naval victory over Ptolemaios II off Cos in 258 B.C. However, the sculptor is believed to be Pythokritos, who flourished in Rhodes about 200 B.C. At that time, Rhodes was an ally of Rome and entered into the conflict against Antioch which ended in the defeat of Antiochus III and the signing of the Peace of Apamea in 188

B.C. Rhodes received for her services a part of Lycia and Caria. It is likely, therefore, that the Nike in Samothrace commemorates that victory.

ARISTARCHOS (217-145 B.C.) was the last librarian in Alexandria mentioned. He was one of the great philologists of Greece. He systematized the Greek grammar and produced editions of the *Iliad* and *Odyssey* which are the basis of present-day texts. He died in Cyprus.

Amaseia

Amaseia (Amasya) is located in the north-central part of Turkey, about 200 miles northeast of Ankara and 80 miles south of the Black Sea port of Samsun. It is picturesquely situated in a deep valley of the Iris River (Yeshil Irmak) with towering precipices on both sides which were fortified in ancient days. The peak on the north still has the ruins of a citadel. In the Hellenistic era it was the capital of the kings of Pontus with palaces and monuments. Even in Roman and medieval times, it was an important city and many of the Ottoman sultans acted directly as governors. The last king to reign there was the father of Mithradates the Great. In 1919, Mustafa Kemal issued his Manifesto Amasya condemning the pro-British government and announced a congress to propose

AMASEIA
The home of Strabo.

measures for saving Turkish national independence. There is a commemorative monument in the city square. Today, the city is a small provincial town with houses mainly of stuccoed mud bricks with red tile roofs. The shops are small with the wares out on the sidewalk—and few sidewalks.

About 40 miles south of Amasya is the ancient city of Zela, where Julius Caesar defeated the troops of King Pharnaces of Pontus, son of Mithradates the Great, in 47 B.C. Caesar announced the victory to the Roman Senate with the words *Veni, Vidi, Vici*— "I came, I saw, I conquered."

STRABO (c 64 B.C.-21 A.D.) was born of aristocratic parents, was well educated, and in 44 B.C. did graduate work in Rome. His philosophy was that of a Stoic, but he realized the need for myths and mysteries for the uneducated. He visited Armenia, Greece, Italy, the Nile as far as Ethiopia, and was well acquainted with Asia Minor. He spent five years in research at the Library in Alexandria. Shortly after 20 B.C. he revisited Rome before returning to Amaseia. From his studies, travels, and hearsay, he produced his *Geographikon* in 17 books divided about as follows: I and II Justification of Homer as the first geographer; criticism of Eratosthenes and Hipparchos; shape, size and mapping of the earth; III Spain; IV France and Britain; V and VI Italy; VII Central and Eastern Europe; VIII-X Greece; XI Black and Caspian Seas Area, Taurus, and Armenia; XII-XIV Asia Minor; XV India and Persia; XVI Mesopotamia, Syria, Arabia, Ethiopian Coast; XVII Egypt.

Geographikon is considered the most important work of antiquity in its field since it is the source of nearly all that is known of the geography of the Mediterranean world up to that time. It was completed during the period 11-7 B.C. but was revised as late as 18 A.D. Strabo also wrote a work on history and historical sketches in 47 books covering historical events from 146 B.C. This is now lost but was cited by Plutarch.

Amisus

Amisus is now a city of 63,000 called Samsun and is the biggest Turkish port on the Black Sea. The general region is mountainous with occasional valleys in which the principal crops are corn, sugar beets, and tobacco. The ancient town was about one and a half miles to the northwest on a plateau known as Kara Samsun and overlooking the modern town. It was founded in the 7th century B.C. by colonists from Miletus and was the second most flourishing Greek settlement on the Pontus Euxinus. After the conquest of Alexander the Great, it became part of the kindom of Pontus. In the war with the Romans, the inhabitants of the town set it on fire when forced to surrender. When the Seljuk Turks raided and captured the town in the 12th century A.D., its name was changed to Samsun. In May, 1919, Mustafa Kemal landed in Samsun and started the Turkish War of Independence.

DIONYSODOROS (fl c 50 B.C.) is believed to have lived in Amisus. He is known for the solution of cutting a sphere by a plane so that the volumes of the segments shall have a given ratio. This problem was proposed by Archimedes and Dionysodoros' solution involved the intersection of a parabola with a rectangular hyperbola. He also invented a type of conic sundial.

Sinope

Sinope (Sinop) is now a small port of 7,000 inhabitants on the seaward end of a peninsula near the middle of the southern coast of the Black Sea. It was settled about 630 B.C. by colonists from Miletus who built a naval station there. It was the terminus of the great caravan route from Mesopotamia and at one time was the most flourishing Greek colony on the Black Sea. At that time the Black Sea was called the Pontus Euxinus, *Pontus* signifying "the big sea" and *Euxine,* "hospitable." Earlier it had been called Pontus Axinus, "the inhospitable sea," but Heracles changed it, possibly for shaming the inhabitants into providing better treatment. On the west side of town is a citadel dating from Byzantine times, with walls and towers. There is no trace of the two ancient harbors on the sides of the peninsula and only the bay on the east side is now used. In November, 1853, the Russian fleet destroyed Sinop and a squadron of the Turkish navy. This signaled the start of the Crimean War.

DIOGENES (412-323 B.C.) was born in Sinope, where his father was the director of the mint. Because of an irregularity in the coinage, he and his family had to leave. In Athens, Diogenes attached himself to the Cynic school. On a trip to Aegina, he was captured by pirates and sold to a wealthy Corinthian who set him free. Diogenes spent the rest of his life in Corinth and lived in severe austerity. He was not so much a philosopher as an example of the teachings of Cynicism.

MITHRADATES VI EUPATOR, the Great (132-63 B.C.), was born in Sinope and succeeded to the throne at the age of 11. He nevertheless had to flee to the mountains because of the attempts on his life by his mother, who apparently favored a younger son. He returned in 111 B.C., threw his mother into prison and murdered his brother. His empire included the northern third of present-day eastern Turkey. The Romans had appropriated Phrygia during his minority and his aim in life seemed to be to drive the Romans out of Asia Minor. In a general massacre in 88 B.C., 130,000 Romans perished. He was finally defeated by Pompey, his troops revolted and he fled to Crimea, where he tried to commit suicide by poison. But he had developed such immunity that he had to order a Gallic mercenary to kill him. He was a courageous but ruthless ruler and concerned himself solely with maintaining and strengthening his own power. He killed all his concubines lest they fall into the hands of his enemies, and none of his followers felt safe.

He spoke 22 languages of the tribes of his empire, gathered Greek men of letters about him, and collected works of art. He was a botanist of a sort in that he investigated poisonous plants with a twofold purpose, namely, to get rid of troublesome individuals and to protect himself by suitable antidotes or immunity against poisons that might be directed against him. He was an avid collector of gems and it took the Romans 30 days to catalogue those in a single warehouse. The treasures were given by Pompey to the Temple of Jupiter Capitolines.

Heraclea (Pontica)

Heraclea is now the modern town of Eregli, a Black Sea port about 100 miles east of the Bosphorus. It was founded by the Megarians and Boeotians about 560 B.C. and was an important trading port, especially in the period 365 to 281 B.C. The city was sacked by the Romans in their war with Mithradates and never regained its prosperity. It is now a small lignite-mining port with no trace of the ancient city.

ZEUXIS (464-398 B.C.) was the first to introduce light and shadow to achieve roundness of form. Earlier artists employed only an outline and filled in with solid color. He may have resided in Ephesus.

BRYSON (fl 430 B.C.) went a step further than his contemporary Antiphon in trying to determine the area of a circle by considering circumscribed as well as inscribed polygons. By increasing the number of sides, the polygons approached the circle as a limit. He believed the area of the circle to be the arithmetic mean of the areas of the two polygons.

HERACLEIDES of Pontus (390-310 B.C.) migrated to Athens early in his life and was a pupil of Plato and Aristotle. He wrote on many subjects and was left in charge of the Akademia during Plato's visit to Sicily. Though not strictly a scientist, he taught that the earth rotated on its axis and that Mercury and Venus revolved around the sun. The first mention of epicycles is by Heracleides. They were proposed to explain the motions of Mercury and Venus. In 339 B.C. he left the Akademia to found his own school.

Byzantium

Byzantium, the modern Istanbul (from the Greek *eis ten polis,* meaning "to the city") was founded in 657 B.C. by the Megarians, who had previously founded Chalcedon. It was called Byzantium from their commander, Byzas. The general region was originally called Mysia, but its name was later changed to Bythinia, after a Thracian tribe called Bythinians. The advantages of the sheltered harbor of the Golden Horn, the gateway to Thrace, and avoiding involvement in the internal struggles in Greece proper, served to make Byzantium a great trading center. Fishing in the curved inner harbor was extremely profitable, hence the name Golden Horn. The city grew prosperous and strong—so strong, in fact, that it was able to resist the attacks of Gallic tribes and of Philip of Macedon. Thankful for a moon which disclosed Philip's preparation for a night attack on the city, they adopted a crescent moon as Byzantium's symbol.* It was not strong enough to resist the Romans, however, and it became a Roman province in the last century B.C. In an internal Roman quarrel, the city had picked the loser and Severus besieged Byzantium in 193 A.D., destroyed its fortifications, and put to death the magistrates and soldiers. Later, he decided to rebuild the city and erected a hippodrome, porticos, baths, and palaces.

The walls of the old Byzantium enclosed only the tip of the promontory on which the present Topkapi Palace is situated, out to the Museum of St. Sophia, a distance of slightly over half a mile. In 330 A.D. when Constantine moved the capital of the Roman Empire from Rome to Byzantium, the name was changed to New Rome, and later to Constantinople. Constantine built a palace, a forum, the first church of St. Sophia (Holy Wisdom), and enlarged the hippodrome. The city expanded rapidly, so that new walls were built two miles west of the old. Later, during the reign of Theodosius II (413 A.D.), the city had grown such that a third set of walls was built four miles further out.

Up to the time of Theodosius the Great (378-395 A.D.), there were not only Christian worshipers but also worshipers of Hecate, Hera, and Apollo. He decreed that Christianity was to be the only religion and that all traces of "paganism" were to be wiped out. It was during this period that temples and statues were destroyed throughout the Christian world, the Library at Alexandria was destroyed, and Hypatia was atrociously murdered by the Christian

*A further story on the crescent symbol may be of interest. When the Turks were besieging Vienna in 1683, they were undermining the city walls at a point where there was a bakery. The bakers notified the authorities, the Turkish attempt was thwarted, and the bakers were given the exclusive privilege of baking a special bread in the form of a crescent. Marie Antoinette, as the bride of Louis XVI, introduced the rolls to Paris and *croissants* have been a favorite item of Continental breakfasts ever since.

mobs. Up until the reign of Justinian (527-565 A.D.), the history of the empire is one of intrigues, treachery, crimes, depravity, hardships, destruction of property, defeats, and civil wars with one revolution following another.

Justinian restored order, instituted legal reforms, set up an authoratative government, and many new buildings were erected, among them the present St. Sophia Church, now a museum. His reign has been called the Golden Age of Constantinople. The architects of St. Sophia were Anthemius of Tralles and his nephew Isidorus of nearby Miletus. They were told to build the most magnificent church ever built. Marbles, columns, and sculptures were taken from other temples. Eight jasper columns were taken from the Temple of Artemis in Ephesus, eight red-porphyry columns came from the Temple of Jupiter in Baalbek, and 24 granite columns came from Egypt. Other materials came from Cyzicus, Athens, and Delos. Special light bricks were made in Rhodes for the dome, which is 100 feet in diameter and whose peak is 180 feet above the floor. It was said that 10,000 workmen and 100 master masons were involved. It was inaugurated in 548 A.D.

After Justinian, the power and glory of Constantinople faded. The land was overrun with invading barbarians, the greatest concern of the various emperors was to get rid of their rivals, the veneration of holy images was condemned, thousands of works of art and even jewels were destroyed, there were persecutions, and in 1204 A.D. the city was pillaged by the Crusaders. But Constantinople survived as capital of the Byzantine Empire until 1453, when it fell to the Ottoman Turks. Four ecumenical councils were held (381, 553, 680, and 869 A.D.) which dealt with the divinity of Christ and denied his subordination to God.

Today, Istanbul is a modern city of over a million inhabitants and with much of the old but with considerable new construction in progress. Each visitor to the city has his own sphere of interest, but it is likely that on the list of all will be found the Topkapi Palace with its collections and treasury of untold wealth, the Saint Sophia Museum, the Sultan Ahmet Mosque with its six minarets (1616 A.D.), and the adjacent hippodrome. For the historian and archaeologist, there are the Archaeological Museum and the Museum of Oriental Antiquities. The Archaeological Museum has, among other things, the alleged Sarcophagus of Alexander the Great with scenes of Alexander's life. It was, however, sculptured for a Sidonian prince, probably Abdalonymos who was appointed King of Sidon by Alexander. The Museum of Oriental Antiquities has extensive collections from the excavations at Nippur, Babylon, Nineveh, and Nimrud in Mesopotamia, Hittite excavations in Turkey and Syria, and Egyptian antiquities. Over 60,000 cuneiform inscriptions excavated in Mesopotamia are stored in the Museum's archives.

ARISTOPHANES (257-180 B.C.) was born in Byzantium but early in life moved to Alexandria, where he was associated with the Museum. He was primarily a grammarian and perhaps the greatest philologist of classical antiquity. He introduced punctuation, wrote many commentaries, and prepared better editions of various authors. He was the librarian during the period 195-180 B.C.

PHILON (fl c 130 B.C.) was a military engineer. He wrote a book, *Mechanike Syntaxis,* in which he discussed, among other things, water wheels and pumps. He invented the gimbal mounting used for magnetic compasses. He spent much of his time in Alexandria and some in Rhodes.

PROCLUS (410-485 A.D.) was born in Constantinople but was brought up in Xanthus in Lycia, in extreme southwestern Turkey. He studied in Alexandria and headed the Neo-Platonic school in Athens. He was a prolific writer, with much of his work pertaining to comments on Plato. He also wrote commentaries on Euclid and Ptolemy, and a short treatise on eclipses.

Chalcedon

Chalcedon, the modern Kadiköy, is located on the Asiatic side of the entrance to the Bosphorus. It was founded by the Megarians about 685 B.C. on a site previously settled by the Phoenicians. The Megarians were later criticized for not picking the more strategic site on the European side with the natural harbor of the Golden Horn, but that may have been the advantage of hindsight. The site picked was in Asia, which was, after all, their territory and the other side was considered unfriendly. Another consideration was that the currents from the Black Sea into the Sea of Marmara (called the Propontus, meaning "before the sea") was much stronger on the European side and inbound ships would naturally hug the Asiatic side. Furthermore, the site was an island, which made it easier to defend.

The term *Bosphorus* literally means "cattle crossing." In mythology it is associated with the nymph Io, one of Zeus' loves, whom he had changed into a heifer to avoid Hera's wrath. Hera discovered the deceit and sent a gadfly to torment the heifer in her wanderings.

Kadiköy, the Judge's Village, is reached by ferry from the Galata bridge in Istanbul. The ancient ports have sanded up and even the Byzantine buildings have disappeared. It is a charming residential city with resort hotels and wooden Turkish houses.

The 4th Ecumenical Council was called in 451 A.D. in response to protests against the highhanded procedure of the Ephesus "Robber Synod." The actions of the Synod were annulled and its leaders deposed. The Council reaffirmed the Nicene Creed that Christ had two natures and was both God and man at the same time.

XENOCRATES (394-314 B.C.) left Chalcedon in his early youth for Athens and associated himself with the Akademia. In 399 B.C. he became head of the school, a position he held for 25 years. He was not a great thinker, but his austere life and commanding personality made him an effective teacher.

HEROPHILOS (fl 280 B.C.) was the greatest physician of his day and was one of the founders of the school of anatomy at Alexandria. Being the first to dissect the human body, he made innumerable discoveries and many of the names he applied are still in use.

BOËTHOS (fl 180 B.C.) was associated with the school of sculpture in Lindos on the island of Rhodes. One of his works is the figure of a boy struggling with a goose.

Prusa

Prusa, the modern city of Bursa with 150,000 people, is located about 60 miles due south of Istanbul—across the Sea of Marmara and then inland about 15 miles. The city is situated about halfway up and along the side of a 1,500-foot mountain. It overlooks a wide cultivated plain to the north with clumps of cedars and slim aspens. Industrially, it is the center of the Turkish silk industry, the best Turkish towels are made in Bursa, and bee-keeping is important. The thermal springs were the source of Bursa's popularity in Byzantine times and still attract tourists. It was the first capital of the Ottoman Turks (1326-1413 A.D.), at which time the name was changed to Bursa. Its original name of Prusa stems from Prusa I, a king of Bythinia whose reign started about 250 B.C. The site was suggested to him by Hannibal, then a fugitive from the Romans. Circumstances later made Prusa dependent on the Romans and Hannibal committed suicide. Bursa was under consideration as the capital of the Turkish Republic in 1923, but, because of its proximity to the sea, it was felt that it was too vulnerable to attack.

Interest in Turkish history centers on a number of mosques and mausoleums, such as the Green Mausoleum and the Muradiye Mosque. Surrounding the latter is a group of mausoleums of the most important Ottoman sultans "forming perhaps the most peaceful and serene graveyard in the whole Turkish world."

ASCLEPIADES of Bythinia (124-40 B.C.) was born in Prusa and educated in Alexandria in the school of Erasistratos. He practiced in Mysia, a province of Troy and Mount Ida, and later in Athens. In 91 B.C. he went to Rome and became the first prominent Greek doctor to practice there. His attitude toward disease was that the equilibrium of the body elements was disturbed and that healing takes place when the equilibrium is restored. Change of diet, massage, exercise, bathing, and music (for the mentally ill) were included in his treatment. He had numerous pupils in Rome and the school they formed was called the Methodist School.

Nicaea

Nicaea (Iznik, i.e., *eis Nikea*) was founded in 316 B.C. by Antigonus, a general in the army of Alexander the Great and a potential successor. He called the city Antigonia and himself King of Bythinia. He was considered too ambitious by the other claimants for Alexander's empire and after his defeat by them in 301 B.C., his holdings were turned over to Lysimachus. Lysimachus renamed the city Nicaea, the name of his first wife. Under the Romans it was one of the most flourishing cities of the province of Asia. Justinian built a palace, a basilica, and baths, and when the Crusaders occupied Constantinople in 1204 A.D., Nicaea temporarily became the capital of the Byzantine Empire.

It is situated about 50 miles east of Bursa at the east end of Lake Iznik, formerly Lake Ascania. En route are olive groves and tobacco fields. In some villages, the houses are festooned with tobacco leaves hung out to dry. But the road is rough, and in view of the comparative inaccessibility even in this day and age, one wonders why the city should have attained such great importance. Today it is an ordinary small town which doesn't look very prosperous. There are remains of the double city walls with gates and towers, a theater near the lake which was constructed at the time of Emperor Trajan, and the St. Sophia Church.

Two ecumenical councils were held in Nicaea. The first was held in the Senatus (Byzantine Palace) May 20 to July 25, 325 A.D. The building is now covered by Lake Iznik. The Council was called by Emperor Constantine to clarify the attitude of the church in the relationship of Christ to God. One small group, headed by Arius and later by the Nestorians, maintained that Christ was human and subordinate to God. Another group held that he was not subordinate to God, that in fact he was God along with the Father and the Holy Ghost. The views of the bulk of the members were in between and they hesitated to adopt either philosophy. However, due in part to indifference and in part to pressure from the Emperor to decide on something, they adopted the stand that Christ and God were "identical in nature." This subterfuge didn't settle anything. Instead it made an issue out of a controversial question which only served to widen the breach, as it didn't state just *how* they were "identical."

Easter was another item on the agenda of the 325 A.D. Council. The Christian Easter is associated with the Crucifixion of Christ, which came at the Passover festival of the Jews. This started on the 14th day of the lunar month of Nisan without regard to the day of the week. The Gentile Christians associated Resurrection with the first day of the week, which is Sunday, and the previous Friday with the Crucifixion. With one group the observance was the first day of the week and with the other, the 14th day of the lunar month. The Western church generally kept Easter on Sunday and the Eastern church followed the Jewish observance. The Council decided that Easter should be observed on a Sunday and left the correct date to be decided at Alexandria, the foremost astronomical center. The present rule for determining Easter was decreed by Justinian in 547 A.D. It states that Easter should be the first Sunday 14 days after *new* moon after March 7, or, as generally figured, the first Sunday after *full* moon after March 21. If the full moon falls on a Sunday, Easter is the following Sunday.

The 7th Ecumenical Council was held in 787 A.D. It was called by Empress Irene Guardine to condemn the Iconoclasts, who were against the veneration of holy images in the church. Their policy had been agreed to in a Council in Constantinople in 754 A.D. The Nicaean Council was held in the St. Sophia Church, which is still fairly well preserved, it having served as a mosque. The interior seems small to house a large council.

HIPPARCHOS (190-125 B.C.) was one of the greatest astronomers of all time and an outstanding mathematician. Little is known of his life, although it is known that he apparently spent 15 years in Alexandria and 20 years in Rhodes. Among his accomplishments are the development of spherical trigonometry, the discovery of the precession of the equinoxes, the application of latitude and longitude to terrestrial map making, and the compilation of a catalogue of 850 stars.

Apamea (Bythinia)

Apamea in Bythinia, modern Mudanya, was originally a 7th century B.C. settlement by colonists from Colophon and called Myrlea. Destroyed in the latter part of the 3rd century B.C., it was rebuilt by Prusa I, king of Bythinia, and named Apamea after his wife. Mudanya was his daughter's name. It is a nondescript town which serves as the port of Bursa, 15 miles inland. An armistice signed here in 1922 ended the war between Turkey and Greece.

DEMETRIOS (fl late 2nd century B.C.) was a physician concerned primarily with gynecology and obstetrics. He wrote a 12-book treatise on pathology and another on symptoms and diagnosis. He differentiated between pneumonia and pleurisy and was the first to describe dropsy.

Cyzicus

Cyzicus (Kyzikos) is located on the triangular Kapidagi peninsula, which juts out into the Sea of Marmara about 6 miles northwest of Bandirma. The isthmus is quite low and narrow and the peninsula was once an island called Arctonnesus (Bear Island). Bandirma is visible across the water to the southeast. The entrance to the main portion of the peninsula has the remnants of the city wall and a couple of miles inland are the remains on two hilltops of an amphitheater. In its day, the temple of Hadrian (167 A.D.), which measured 110 by 300 feet, had columns 75 feet high, the highest of any classical temple. The marble came undoubtedly from the nearby island of Marmara, which gave marble its name, and ended up in the St. Sophia Church in Istanbul. The area itself is covered with brush, olive trees, and vineyards. Access to the ruins is along a narrow stony path.

An early settlement here about 1100 B.C. was named for Kyzikos, the king of the Dolmines. Jason and the Argonauts stopped here on their way to Colchis in search of the Golden Fleece. It became a Milesian colony in 756 B.C. and was refounded in 675 B.C. One part of the city was on level ground near the bridges to the mainland and part near a mountain called Arctonoros (Bear

Mountain). The acropolis was on a hill, a part of Mount Didymus. The city was well situated with two sheltered harbors and more than 200 ship sheds. The countryside was very fertile and the colony was so prosperous that their annual contribution of nine talents to the Delian League was the largest from the Hellespont area. The coinage was an alloy of gold and silver called electrum; the unit was the stater.* Strabo said the city rivaled the foremost cities of Asia in size and beauty and in the excellent administration of affairs.

Persians occupied the city from the middle of the 6th to the middle of the 4th century B.C. Its main period of prosperity was toward the end of the 5th century B.C. Alexander the Great invaded Asia Minor in 334 B.C. and it was on his advice that the two bridges were built between the island and the mainland. After Alexander's death, Bythinia managed to stay independent until 72 B.C., when it was taken over by the Romans. They made Cyzicus a military stronghold and a prosperous Roman trading center. It was during the 2nd century A.D. that many large structures were built, only to be severely damaged by a terrible earthquake.

EUDOXOS of Cnidos (408-355 B.C.) was considered one of the greatest astronomers and mathematicians of his time. In 378 B.C. he established a school in Cyzicus which he transferred to Athens ten years later. He is remembered principally for an ingenious system of concentric spheres as a means of representing the motions of the stars, sun, moon, and planets. His work on proportion formed the basis for much of Book V of Euclid's *Elements* and his description of 44 constellations was later versified by Aratus.

CALLIPPUS (370-300 B.C.) studied under Polemarchos in Cyzicus and followed him to Athens about 336 B.C. He taught at the Lyceum and endeavored to improve the system of homocentric spheres of Eudoxos by adding seven more spheres to compensate for the non-uniform motion of the earth around the sun. He im-

*The natural alloy of gold and silver as found in river beds was called *electron; electrum* was 20% silver and 80% gold. The pure gold stater weighed 124.5 grains and was equivalent to 20 silver pieces, each weighing 82 grains. The Cyzicus stater weighed 248 grains with 40-50% pure gold and the rest silver and some copper.

proved the Metonic cycle by substituting a 29-day month for a 30-day month in each 76-year period.

ATTALOS I of Pergamon (269-197 B.C.) built a temple at Cyzicus in remembrance of his wife, Apollonis, who was born there.

EUDOXOS of Cyzicus (fl c 130 A.D.) was a geographer who explored the Arabian Sea for Ptolemaios Euergetes in order to find a sea route to India. He found wreckage of a ship from Cadiz in the Indian Ocean which led him to believe that Africa could be circumnavigated. He made two or more voyages from Cadiz along the Atlantic coast of Africa.

Lampsacus

About halfway between Cyzicus and Lapseki, the modern name of Lampsacus, is a large level plain with fields of grain. Near the town of Biga is a small river identified as the Granicus of ancient times. It was along the banks of this river that Alexander the Great defeated the Persians in the first battle of his Asian campaign. This enabled him to conquer Asia Minor with the Persian naval bases, a necessary protective measure before he could proceed eastward.

Lampsacus is at the eastern end of the Hellespont and was settled by Ionian Greeks from Phocaea and Miletus about the 8th century B.C. There is a small, unimpressive town called Lapseki at or near the site of the ancient city. Lampsacus may, however, have been at the present village of Chardak, four miles farther east and opposite Gallipoli (Gelibou). The general region is one of those wide valleys often found as a river nears its outlet to the sea. Grapes seem to be the main product, other products being tomatoes, apples, and even lemons.

The name Hellespont is derived from the myth of Phryxus and Helle, who, to escape the cruel treatment of their stepmother, mounted a winged golden-fleeced ram sent by Poseidon to transport them to Colchis. The ram flew over land and sea, but Helle, frightened by the sight of the tossing waves beneath her, lost her hold and tumbled into the sea; hence the name Hellespont, the "sea of Helle." The strait is also known as the Dardanelles, which name also has a mythical ancestry. Dardanus and Iasius, sons of Zeus and the Pleiad Electra, had sinned against Demeter. Iasius was struck by lightning, but Dardanus fled Samothrace by crossing on a raft over to Troad. He married Batea, the daughter of the king, founded Dardania and the Trojan dynasty, and taught the Samothracian Mysteries to the Trojans. Dardania is the modern Chanakkale, near the western end of the strait. About four miles north of the city is the town of Abydos, where Xerxes built a bridge of boats for his army to cross in their ill-fated campaign to conquer Greece in 480 B.C. Here, too, Leander swam every evening across to the European side to meet Hero, a priestess in the temple of Aphrodite.

ANAXAGORAS of Clazomenae (499-427 B.C.) was the first Greek philosopher to settle in Athens. His endeavor to give scientific explanations of physical phenomena was contrary to the polytheism of the time. Because of his friendship for Pericles, the latter's enemies charged him with impiety and forced him into exile. He went to Lampsacus in 433 B.C., where he did some teaching until his death at 72.

ANAXIMENES (380-320 B.C.) was a rhetorican and historian who accompanied Alexander the Great on his Persian campaign.

STRATON (fl 300 B.C.) went to Athens and was a pupil of Aristotle. He was called to Alexandria to be the tutor of the crown prince and to assist with the establishment of the Museum. He succeeded Theophrastos as head of the Lyceum from 286 to 269 B.C.

EPICUROS of Samos (341-270 B.C.) was an independent philosopher who moved from Mytilene to Lampsacus and taught there for four years before going to Athens in 306 B.C. He founded a school of philosophy known as the Garden in which the paramount goal was happiness derived from the full use of virtues such as justice, abstinence, forbearance, and moderation.

THE TROY CITADEL

Troy

Homer's stories of the Trojan War, the *Illiad* and the *Odyssey*, have been household reading for centuries, not only in Greece but throughout the world. They were generally assumed to be only folk tales with no historical basis. However, a Heinrich Schliemann felt there was some truth in Homer's stories. He was born in 1822 near Hamburg, Germany. He served as a grocer's apprentice, as a bookkeeper in Amsterdam, started his own business in the indigo trade in Russia, and made a fortune as a military contractor during the Crimean War. He was in California looking for his brother when that state was admitted to the Union and everyone there, Schliemann included, automatically became a citizen of the United States. Visiting Homeric sites in Turkey, he became convinced that the Hissarlik (signifying "place of fortresses") mound, and not the Bunarbashi, was the site of Homer's Troy and his excavations in

LOOKING NORTH FROM THE TROY CITADEL

1878 proved that he was right. The effect upon written history, and upon archaeology in general, was tremendous. Because German archaeologists at first doubted Schliemann's claim that he had discovered Troy, he was reluctant to present the treasures to Germany. He finally agreed, however with certain stipulations: a special letter of commendation from the Kaiser, membership in the Prussian Academy of Sciences (which he didn't get), honorary citizenship of Berlin (only Bismarck and Von Moltke had been so honored), and the display in the Berlin Museum (Museum für Vor und Frühgeschicte) was to bear his name. During World War II, much of the pottery was stored in Lebus Castle on the Oder which was demolished by the Russians. The remainder of the treasure was stored in a bunker under the Zoo with its fate unknown.

The Hissarlik mound is situated about 5 miles from Kumkale, the western end of the Hellespont (or Dardanelles) and 20 miles south of Chanakkale, the largest city in the vicinity. The site is on the southern boundary of a flat plain 3 to 5 miles wide through which flow the Mederes (ancient Scamander) and Simois rivers. To the casual viewer, Troy itself is somewhat of a disappointment, but it cannot help being awe-inspiring to stand on the ruins and gaze at the plain where so much drama took place. It is the association, and not the ruins, that stimulates the emotions. Although archeologists have identified nine cities, this is not evident to the uninitiated. Identification requires detailed studies of building materials at different dates, orientation of buildings, pottery, coins, artifacts, implements, and sculpture inscriptions, and comparing these finds with the Greek mainland, Crete, and other islands where dating is more certain.

None of the nine historic Troys was as imposing as Homer's. His had broad avenues, temples to Athena and Apollo, royal palaces, and defense by "a thousand tribes." The excavated portion is barely 400 feet across, with buildings packed as if it were one large apartment house. This was undoubtedly the fortified citadel for the king and his court. The farmers, fishermen, artisans, and laborers must have lived outside the walls of this portion of the city. There just doesn't seem room for any "Trojan horse."

Troy I (3000-2500 B.C.)

Culture of this period was wide-spread over western Anatolia and northern Aegean area.

Weapons and tools were of bone and stone; a little copper but no silver or gold.

The monochrome pots are handmade and incised; sometimes filled with white; no similarities have been found elsewhere.

One house of comparatively large dimensions, with upper part reinforced with clay.

Towers on both sides of the south gate.

City was destroyed by fire.

Troy II (2500-2200 B.C.)

Seven phases in seven feet of excavation have been identified.

Schliemann's treasures belonged to this level, although he believed this to be Homer's Troy.

Jewelry showed contact with other cultures — gold, silver, lead, and ivory.

Treasure included four gold vessels, an electrum goblet, eight miscellaneous silver tankards and vessels, two diadems with chains of small gold leaves pendant from a horizontal chain, necklaces, bracelets, earrings, 75 coils (probably hair fasteners), and 8,700 gold beads of various shapes and sizes.

Daggers, spearheads, knives, three chisels, and a saw were of copper or bronze although real bronze was not in general use. Three green nephrite battle axes and one blue were found along with many rock crystal sections of spheres which may possibly have served as heads of scepters, swords, daggers, or battle axe handles.

Five hundred idols were mainly of stone.

Pottery was wheel-made and predominantly black, grey or red. Some pots were beak-spouted and some were in animal or in human shapes.

Palace consisted of several rectangular rooms with a hearth in the middle; the lower part of the walls was of stone, while the upper part consisted of mud bricks reinforced with wooden beams.

End of Troy II was a great disaster. All houses contained fire-scarred wreckage but what brought about the total destruction is not known — possibly an earthquake as articles were abandoned in haste.

Troy III, IV, and V (2200-1800 B.C.)

A marked decline in population and in prosperity.

Only novelty is the one-handled, long-necked, and wide-beaked jug.

Pottery is monochromic; bowls decorated inside with Latin crosses.

No frescos or inscriptions.

Troy VI (1800-1300 B.C.)

People were of different origin and traditions, possibly Greek-speaking people from the north similar to those that invaded the mainland of Greece about this same period.

New wave of prosperity, with a city wall 15 feet high on top of a 20-foot slope; 600 feet in diameter, twice the size of the older cities.

Small cubicles serving as housing were laid out on terraces. The new plan took no account of houses and streets that existed before.

Gray-ware pottery similar to that found on the Danube; painted potsherds which are definitely Mycenaean.

City perished by violence, possibly an earthquake.

Troy VIIa (1300-1200 B.C.)

Era of the Trojan War. Culture similar to Troy VI.
Characterized by the presence of Mycenaean pottery.
Walls are rebuilt but inferior to those of Troy VI.
Destroyed by fire.

Troy VIIb (1200-900 B.C.)

Invaded by Thrace.
Decorations on the pots and on the handles.
Destroyed by fire.

Troy VIII (900-350 B.C.)

Shining black pottery with branches and leaves in the form of a
   fishbone.
Invaded by the Persians (6th century).

Troy IX (350 B.C.-400A.D.)

Temple of Athena.
Alexander enlarged the town.
Sacked by the Romans (65 B.C.).
Rebuilt after Caesar's visit.
Theater and altar are from the Roman period.
Lost sight of after the 5th century A.D.

Assus

Assus is located 30 crow-flight miles south of Troy near the
hamlet of Behram. It is a magnificent site on the terraces at the foot
of an 800-foot hill overlooking the Aegean Sea and opposite the
island of Lesbos (now Mytilene). A 4th-century temple to Athena,
with 6 columns on the ends and 13 columns viewed from the
sides, adorned the acropolis. It was pillaged by the Byzantines during the campaign of Theodosius to destroy pagan temples, and
later by the Turks. Part of the base, a few capitals, and traces of
black and white mosaic are all that now remain. Two moles still
show above the water. It was probably settled early in the 10th
century by colonists from Lesbos and, though it never had a very
important political role, it was the only harbor along the 50-mile
southern coast of Troas. One of the exports was valonia, dried
acorn cups from an evergreen oak which are used in leather tan-
ning. The harbor is now too shallow except for local boats.

HERMIAS (fl 350 B.C.) was a freed eunuch slave of banker Erboles. Hermias had accumulated considerable wealth as a money-changer and ruled a territory around Assus. He attended the Akademia in Athens along with Aristotle and others. After Plato's death in 347 B.C., Hermias invited Aristotle and Xenocrates to come to Assus, where assistants of Hermias had started a school. Because of negotiations between Philip II of Macedonia and Hermias, the Persians distrusted him. Memnon of Rhodes, who was serving as a general with the Persians, extended a friendly invitation to Hermias which was accepted. He was seized, tortured, and finally crucified in Susa. Assus was then occupied by the Persians.

ARISTOTLE of Stageira (384-322 B.C.) spent three years (347-344 B.C.) in Assus which were very fruitful in that it enabled him to make many biological observations and develop his philosophy. He married Pythias, the niece and adopted daughter of Hermias, by whom he had a daughter, also called Pythias. Aristotle went to Lesbos for two years (344-343 B.C.) and then to Pella, where he tutored Philip's 13-year old son, Alexander.

THEOPHRASTOS of Eresos (372-286 B.C.) was a native of Lesbos and a fellow student with Aristotle in the Akademia. He joined Aristotle in Assus and Lesbos and was destined to succeed Aristotle as head of the Lyceum. He was called "the father of botany" and was the greatest botanist until the 16th century.

CLEANTHES (301-232 B.C.) was born in Assus. He studied in Athens with Crates the Cynic and with Zenon the Stoic, whom he succeeded as head of the school. He wrote a scathing denunciation of Aristarchos and his heliocentric theory of the solar system. He stated that Aristarchos should be tried for impiety.

CALLISTHENES of Olynthus (c 360-328 B.C.). Olynthus, the birthplace of Callisthenes, was a small town at the head of the gulf between the two southern fingers of the Chalcidice peninsula. Callisthenes was a nephew and pupil of Aristotle and was associated with the school in Assus. Through the recommendation of Aristotle, Callisthenes joined Alexander the Great in his Asian campaign as a historian. After his victories over the Persians, Alexander adopted Persian dress and other features of the Persian court, including prostration in his presence. Callisthenes criticized this, which offended Alexander and Callisthenes was accused of conspiracy and executed. Theophrastos commemorated his friend's death in a treatise.

Lesbos

Lesbos (Mytilene) lies just 5 miles south of the Turkish coast at Assus. It is at large U-shaped island, 40 miles long and 25 miles wide, mountainous yet producing lots of olives and grapes. Sardine fishing is an important industry. Greeks from Boeotia are believed to have settled there in the 11th century B.C., with the peak of prosperity about 600 B.C. Its exposure made it vulnerable to attack by the Persians, Athenians, Peloponnesians, Romans, Turks, and Byzantines. In 426 B.C., Athens decreed wholesale execution and slavery of the inhabitants but retracted the sentence and recalled the executioners. Mytilene, the capital, is a mixture of Greek and Turkish, with mosques, churches, olive refineries, and warehouses around the circular harbor. A ruined 14th-century Genoese castle-fortress (*kastro*) occupies the islet which was probably the site of the ancient city, of which there are no remains. There are some ruins about six miles northwest of Mytilene which seem to be of the period 2600-1200 B.C.

TERPANDER (fl 7th century B.C.) was a musician who is regarded by some as the real founder of Greek classical music and lyric poetry. Greek poetry was intended to be sung and the poet composed both the poem and the accompaniment. The instrument was either a flute or, more often, a lyre—hence *lyric*. Terpander is supposed to have increased the number of strings of the lyre from four to seven. He settled in Sparta about 660 B.C.

ALCAEUS (fl 600 B.C.) was a native of Mytilene. In the struggle of the aristocrats against tyranny, he was banished, but later he was pardoned and returned. His lyrics in the Aeolian dialect are thought to be the prototype of those of Sappho, who was a contemporary of Alcaeus and possibly romantically attached to him.

SAPPHO (c 600 B.C.) is the only Greek poetess and one of the most important lyric poets. She was born in Eresos. In the struggle against tyranny, she fled to Sicily. Upon her return, she founded a school for girls, married, and had a daughter named Cleïs. There apparently were eight books of poetry, but except for her "Ode to Aphrodite," only fragments of her poems have survived. These refer to members of her family, pupils, friends, and rivals, and are characterized by simplicity of language and intensity of emotion.

ARISTOLE of Stageira (384-322 B.C.), at the suggestion of Theophrastos, spent two years on Lesbos (344-343 B.C.) studying biology, with emphasis on marine life. From Lesbos he went to Pella to tutor Phillip II's 13-year old son, Alexander.

THEOPHRASTOS (372-286 B.C.) was born is Eresos. His original name was Tyrtamus, but he was called Theophrastos by Aristotle because of his grace of conversation. He was associated with Aristotle in the Lyceum in Athens and succeeded him as head of the school. He wrote two large treatises on plants and was the greatest writer on botany up to the 16th century.

EPICUROS of Samos (341-270 B.C.) taught philosophy in Mytilene for a year (311 B.C.) before going to Lampsacus and to Athens (306 B.C.), where he established a school of philosophy called the Garden. His philosophy of happiness was to do good, live simply and with moderation, and seek the pleasure of friendship.

HERMARCHOS (fl 270 B.C.) was born in Mytilene and studied under Epicuros before the school was moved to Lampsacus in 310 B.C. He succeeded Epicuros as head of the Garden and was executor of his estate.

Pergamon

Pergamon (Bergama) is situated 68 miles north of Izmir at the confluence of three rivers, and 15 miles from the sea. Although it is claimed to have coined money as early as 420 B.C., little is known of it until the time of Lysimachus (355-281 B.C.), one of Alexander's generals who fortified the strategically located 900-foot peak. In time it became one of the most important cities in Asia

Minor and one of the most beautiful and cultural cities in the Mediterranean world.

The territory of Pergamon extended along the western coast of Asia Minor from the Sea of Marmara to the vicinity of Rhodes. After the death of Alexander, it became the domain of Lysimachus. He sent his war spoils amounting to 9,000 talents to Pergamon for safekeeping in the acropolis under the command of Philetaerus. Arsinoë, the wife of Lysimachus, slandered him, and in 283 B.C. he decided to revolt and keep the treasure for himself. He founded the Pergamon kingdom and was succeeded by his nephew and adopted son, Eumenes I (ruled 263-241 B.C.). The first to be proclaimed king was Attalos I (241-197 B.C.), who enlarged the kingdom. Attalos assumed the surname of Soter (Savior) in view of his defeat of the Gauls, pushing them into the section, in the vicinity of modern Ankara, which is now called Galatia. The Gauls were 20,000 mercenaries imported from the north in 275 B.C. by Nicomedes I of Bythinia to bolster his claim to the throne against his brother. However, as soon as they were established, they had ideas of their own. They pillaged cities and raised havoc in the general region for 46 years until subdued in 232 B.C. Attalos brought Antigonos of Carystos to Pergamon from Athens to produce sculptures commemorating the victory and a grandiose 40-foot altar to Zeus was erected on one of the upper terraces of the acropolis. Statues of which such copies as the "Dying Gaul" in the Capitoline Museum in Rome, "The Wounded Gaul" in the Louvre, and the "Gaul Killing Himself After Having Killed His Wife" in the Museo Nationale in Rome are products of this golden age.

During the reign of Eumenes II (197-159 B.C.), the city was enlarged and improved by building a theater, the Temple of Athena, a palace, and a library of 200,000 volumes. This was given by Marc Anthony to Cleopatra (c 34 B.C.) to replace those destroyed during Caesar's occupation of Alexandria in 48 B.C. When Eumenes tried to get Aristophanes of Byzantium away from Alexandria as librarian, Ptolemaios Epiphanes not only imprisoned Aristophanes but forbade the export of papyrus. This obliged the Pergamenians to develop the use of skins of sheep, cattle, and goats. The skins were washed, scraped, smoothed with pumice and dressed with chalk. The hair side is darker but retains the ink better. In various languages it is known as pergamene, pergament, parchemin, and parchment. This material was not suitable for rolls like papyrus and its use introduced the page type of book.

Attalos II Philadephus (159-138 B.C.), a brother, had gone to school in Athens and was the donor of the Stoa Attalos in the Athens agora. He was poisoned by the son of Attalos I, who then took the name of Attalos III Philometor. Like Mithradates VI, Attalos III was so afraid of being poisoned by his subjects that he studied poisonous plants in order that he might develop immunity and antidotes. At the same time, his studies would provide means for getting rid of his enemies, as he did in the case of his uncle. He died childless in 133 B.C. and the kingdom was bequeathed to Rome. They proclaimed the city the capital of the province of Asia.

The summit of the acropolis was crowded with structures. Inherent in any acropolis, access was difficult, but it can now be reached easily by two and a half miles of hard-top road. The chief buildings were on a succession of terraces, with the palace of Eumenes II topmost. Nearby were the cisterns and the storage depot for supplies sufficient to maintain a thousand men for a year. On the terrace below were the library, a long colonnade, and the Temple of Athena. The temple was a six-by-ten columned structure, 42 by 72 feet, surrounded by a U-shaped portico. The open side of the square faced the countryside below. A theater seating 15,000 people was just below the temple. It is still fairly well preserved. Because of lateral space limitations, it is narrower than usual and is probably the steepest of all Greek theaters. There are 82 rows of seats rising up to a height of 175 feet The outlines of the base and a few steps of the famous Altar to Zeus can be seen on a lower terrace. The altar stood on a 30-foot high base, 115 feet on a side. On top was a structure with 8-foot Ionic columns in the shape of an H with a bar across the top. The enclosed rectangular court contained the altar to Zeus. The interior walls were decorated with bas reliefs depicting the story of Telephos, the mythical founder of Pergamon and the son of Heracles. Between the two

THE THEATER AT PERGAMON

PLAN OF THE ALTAR TO ZEUS

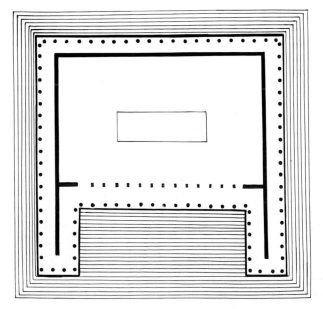

open arms of the colonnade, the base was cut into to provide for 28 steps which were sculptured on their inner faces. The steps varied in height so the pedestrian had ever to be conscious of his steps and hence less likely to have accidents. Encircling the structure near the top of the base was an 8-foot frieze of very high relief depicting historical events but projected by conflicts between mythological gods and giants. The leading artist was Menecrates of Rhodes. Ninety-four slabs and some 2,000 fragments were collected in 1871-73 by Carl Humann for the Berlin Museum. These form a 400-foot display along three walls of an immense room in the Pergamon Museum in East Berlin. The life-size front part of the altar structure on the remaining wall is awesome. Further down the slope were two stoa, two gymnasiums, baths, a stadium, several temples, and other buildings. Modern Bergama overlies the residential part of the Greek city and almost all of the Roman city.

A mile or so southwest of the center of Bergama are the ruins of the Asklepion. The worship of Asclepios was introduced soon after the founding of the town in the 4th century B.C. by a Pergamene who had been healed at Epidaurus. As in all these temples of healing, there were provisions for putting the patient in a good frame of mind with baths, theaters, libraries, storytellers, temples, and dormitories. Over the entrance was an inscription freely translated "The Entrance of Death Is Forbidden." In order that the infallibility of the god not be doubted, when death was imminent, the patient was removed from the premises.

The various buildings of the Asklepion spread over an area of 400 to 500 acres. The circular Temple to Telephorus, about 200 feet in diameter with niches and pools, was where the patients had their healing dreams. The Temple of Asclepios, 80 feet in diameter with a 56-foot-wide stairway, was the holiest place of the cult. Both of these temples were outside the main courtyard. Inside the courtyard and to the right was the library with niches in the wall for the books. Along the sides of the courtyard were 45 columns, mainly Ionic. Most of these are now standing although more or less damaged from being overthrown by an earthquake in 17 A.D. Outside the northwest corner of the courtyard is a theater, partially restored, which accommodated 4,500 people.

Outside the temple area are the Roman ruins of an amphitheater, a circus, and a theater. The amphitheater had a capacity of 50,000 spectators. It straddled a stream so that water shows, or crocodile or hippopotamus fights, could be staged. The theater lies under cultivated land, but it is estimated it could hold nearly 30,000 people. The circus has not been investigated.

APOLLONIOS of Perga (262-205 B.C.) was an outstanding mathematician who is best remembered for his works on conics. He is responsible for the terms *ellipse, parabola,* and *hyperbola* as applied to conic sections. Perga, at the time of Apollonios, was in the kingdom of Pergamon. Although he spent some time in Pergamon, he lived most of his life in Alexandria. Books I and III of his works on conics were dedicated to Eudemos of Pergamon, an otherwise unknown mathematician; Books IV and VIII were dedicated to Attalos I.

SOSOS (fl c 200 B.C.) was a mosaic artist in Pergamon. One mosaic for which he is remembered is "The Unswept House," which showed remnants of food and other "unswept" items in the design. Another showed five doves sitting on the rim of a bowl. One of them was drinking with head bowed and casting a shadow on the water.

SUDINES (fl 200 B.C.) was a native of Pergamon and it is believed that he attended Berosso's school of astrology in Cos. His lunar tables, very likely of Mesopotamian origin, were in use for centuries.

CRATES of Mallos (fl 180 B.C.) spent most of his life in Pergamon, where he was the head of the philological school and director of the Library. He was apparently the first to construct a terrestrial globe. (Eudoxos of Cnidos [408-355 B.C.] introduced the celestial globe.) He wrote criticisms of Hesiod, Euripides, Aristophanes, and Aratus and attempted to show that Homer supported Stoic doctrines. He was one of the early scholars formalizing Greek grammar. While in Rome in 168 B.C. as an ambassador of Eumenes II, he broke his leg in the Cloaxa Maxima, and while convalescing, gave lectures on philology.

NICOMEDES (fl 225 B.C.) is believed to have lived in Pergamon. He invented a curve, called a conchoid, by which it is possible to trisect an angle.

APOLLODOROS of Athens (fl 140 B.C.) is believed to have been a disciple of Aristarchos of Samothrace in Alexandria and then moved (c 146 B.C.) to Pergamon. In his *Chronica,* dedicated to Attalos II, he versified Greek chronology from the fall of Troy to 144 B.C. He wrote commentaries on Greek poets, a Homeric catalogue of ships, and *Bibliotheca,* an elaborate 24-book history of Greek gods and mythology. He died in Athens.

GALEN (129-200 A.D.) was born in Pergamon and was considered the greatest physician of antiquity after Hippocrates. His father was an architect and it is said that Asclepios instructed him in a dream to have his son be a physician. After studying with teachers in Pergamon, Galen spent nine years visiting great medical centers, including Smyrna and Alexandria. He concentrated on anatomy and much of his surgery was learned on the battered bodies of gladiators. Their care was entrusted to him after he had devised a successful dressing for the treatment of ruptured tendons and nerves. Before Galen's time, a ruptured tendon had almost always led to paralysis of the muscle involved. He settled in Rome in 161 A.D. He wrote 500 treatises in Greek describing particularly bones, muscles, nerves, blood vessels, and intestines. He preferred dietetic and prophylactic measures, as it was far better to maintain the body in good health than to try to re-establish lost equilibrium.

Pitane

Pitane was the northernmost member of the Aeolian Confederation and was situated near the mouth of the Caicos River about 20 miles southwest of Pergamon. The village of Chandarli is located on the neck of the peninsula which was the site of Pitane. Little remains except remnants of a city hall, the harbor mole, and the outlines of the theater and the stadium.

AUTOLYCOS (fl 300 B.C.) was an astronomer living in Pitane. Nothing is known about him except his treatises *On the Moving Sphere* and *On the Rising and Settings of the Stars.* These are the only pre-Alexandrian astronomical texts which have been preserved in their entirety. He discussed a theory of the apparent risings and settings of fixed stars. He pointed out that the distances of Venus and Mars from the earth varied in the course of their revolutions and could not possibly describe perfect circles concentric with the earth. This led to discarding the theory of spherics in favor of eccentrics or epicycles. He wrote on spherical astronomy with propositions following one another in logical order, as did Euclid later in his *Elements.* Theodosios of Bythinia (early 1st century B.C.) in his *Sphaerica* proved theorems which Autolycos left unproved.

ARCESILAOS (316-241 B.C.) was a pupil of Autolycos. In Athens he became the head of the Akademia (c 268 B.C.) and changed the policy of the school by reviving the skeptical tendencies of Plato and Socrates. Because of this, and his stand against the Stoics, the school was called the New Akademia, or by the terms Second or Middle.

Cyme

Cyme, or Kyme, was one of the biggest and most important towns of the Aeolian Confederacy. It was located on the coast about 30 miles due north of Smyrna (Izmir). There may have been a pre-Hellenic settlement there as early as 2000 B.C. and the name is believed to have been of Amazonian origin. The Greek city was settled by Aeolians after the Dorians had driven them out of Thessaly. It was dominantly an agricultural state and suffered the usual crises of its neighbors: Persians, Macedonians, Gauls, and Romans. It was still an important town in the Byzantine period but as a result of the Turkish conquest, the walls were torn down and the place abandoned. Namurtköy is a small village on the same site.

HESIOD (c 750 B.C.) was born either in Cyme or in Ascra, Boeotia,* to where his father migrated. His brother, Perses, was

---

The climate in Ascra was reputedly "bad in the winter, oppressive in the summer and pleasant at no time." The expression is mindful of a similar description of Madrid—"seis mesas invierno y seis mesas infierno"*—and of Totontepec, Mexico—"three months of mist, three months of showers, three months of mud, and three months of all three."

indolent and a wastrel; Hesiod was a poet. Herodotus said it was Homer and Hesiod who assigned names, functions, and characteristics to the gods and goddesses. In his *Theogonia,* Hesiod summarizes the mythology, history, and genealogy of the gods. Heroes were fathered by gods, but their mothers were mortals. In the *Astronomical Poem,* of which there are only fragments, the principal constellations are described and their names and myths explained. This is the earliest text of this nature in Greek literature. *Work and Days* was a sort of farmer's almanac with maxims, mythology, and comments on morals. Hesiod tried to shame his brother into doing something with his life, explaining the fundamental law of mankind—justice and honest labor. There is a story of Creation with Prometheus distributing gifts to all living creatures, creating a superior being in the image of the gods to be called man, and stealing fire from the gods for man's service. There is also the story of Pandora, who loosed all the diseases, sorrows, vices, and crimes to plague humanity. In Hesiod's later years, he moved to Oenoë in Locris in disgust over the results of a lawsuit with his brother. He was murdered by the sons of his host.

EPHOROS (c 400-330 B.C.) was a historian and a native of Cyme. His chief work was *Historia,* in 29 books. He was the first historian to divide his works into books and his material according to subject matter instead of according to years. He wrote about the history and antiquities of Cyme in *A Treatise on My Country.*

Phocaea

Phocaea, the modern Focha, 25 airline miles northwest of Izmir, was the most northerly of the twelve Ionian Confederation cities settled at the beginning of the 11th century B.C. The other cities were Smyrna, which was added later, Clazomenae, Erythrae, Chios, Teos, Lebedos, Colophon, Ephesus, Samos, Priene, Myus, and Miletus. The name signifies a "seal" and may have been derived from the shape of the off-shore islands. The Phocaeans were the first to undertake long sea voyages and in the 7th century B.C. settled in such western Mediterranean places as Marseilles (Massalia), Corsica (Cyrnus), and Naples (Cumae). After the capture of Phocaea in 546 B.C. by the Persian general Harpagus, most of the inhabitants embarked under the leadership of Creontiades and sailed ostensibly for Corsica and Marseilles. Some, however, didn't get further than Chios and some returned. The settlement on Corsica got involved with their Etruscan neighbors and after five years settled in Elea, 75 miles south of Naples. This was the site of the Eleatic school of philosophy.

Phocaea continued to exist and in the years following 1421 A.D. the Genoese made their fortune in the rich alum mines in the neighborhood.

Smyrna

Smyrna (Izmir) is said to have been a settlement of pre-Hellenic indigenous people called Lelegians. The name Smyrna is believed to have been that of an Amazon. At the head of a long penetrating gulf and at the terminus of the trade route that passed through Sardis, it has always been a commercial city. In Turkey today, the modern port of Izmir ranks next in importance to Istanbul. It has wide boulevards, a modern residential section, and about two miles of waterfront from which are exported figs, tobacco, olives, raisins, and cotton.

The founding of the city might be said to be by the influx of Aeolians from Lesbos and other Aegean islands in the 11th century B.C. In the 9th and 8th centuries B.C., Ionians moved in from the south, particularly from Colophon, who gained supremacy and initiated a period of great prosperity. It was at this time that Smyrna became the 13th member of the Ionian Confederacy. Since then it has had many periods of destruction and revival: Lydians, Persians, Macedonians, Seleucids, Attalids, Romans, Arabs, Genoese, Turks, Crusaders, Tamerlane, Venetians, Ottomans and earthquakes.

The ancient city was in the vicinity of the northern suburb of Bayrakli. Nearby, on a 1,250-foot peak, are the ruins of a 6th century B.C. acropolis. An ancient circular structure on the outskirts of the town is claimed to be the tomb of Tantalus, the legendary king of Sipylus in Lydia. He was intimate with the gods but abused the privilege and was sentenced to the underworld. Standing up to his neck in water, it would rush away from him when he tried to drink and food hanging above him would waft away when he reached for it. Another claimant for the tomb's location is Magnesia at the foot of Mount Sipylus. Be that as it may, the legend is the origin of the word *tantalize*.

HOMER is claimed to have lived in Smyrna, an honor that is also claimed by Chios. It is quite possible that he—or they, if there were more than one—may have lived in both places at one time or another.

THEON of Smyrna (fl c 125 A.D.) was the author of *Exposition of the Mathematical Subjects Which Are Useful for the Study of Plato.* It consisted of three treatises: Arithmetic, Music, and Astronomy. This is a valuable source of information on Greek cosmology and astronomy. The treatise on astronomy forms a valuable supplement to the *Syntaxis* of Ptolemy.

Clazomenae

Clazomenae, one of the twelve cities of the Ionian Confederation, is situated about 24 miles west of Smyrna, at or near the modern city of Urla. It is believed to have been founded in the 9th century B.C. by Greek Achaeans and was extremely prosperous. When the Persians under Cyrus conquered Asia Minor in 540 B.C., the inhabitants took refuge on an island. This second town of Clazomenae was occupied until the advent of Alexander the Great in 334 B.C., when the people resettled the early site and called it Chytrion. About this time, the island was connected with the mainland by a causeway, a few blocks of which are still visible above the water. A modern successor parallels the old.

Clazomenae developed painted terra-cotta sarcophagi which were the finest examples of Ionian paintings in the 6th century B.C. The town was also celebrated for its temples of Artemis and Apollo.

ANAXAGORAS (499-427 B.C.) left Clazomenae for Athens at the age of 37 and was the first to bring Ionian philosophy and the spirit of scientific inquiry to that city. Nothing is known as to the circumstances under which he developed his philosophy. Possibly nearby Ephesus may have been a source of stimulation. He became an intimate friend of Pericles and, as such, a target of Pericles' enemies. He was charged with impiety for seeking scientific explanations of physical phenomena and was forced to leave. He went to Lampsacus in 433 B.C. and died there at the age of 72.

Chios

Chios is an island lying only 7 miles from the long Turkish peninsula that extends 45 miles westward from Izmir. It is about 30 miles long and from 10 to 15 miles wide. There are stories of its having been settled before the 13th century B.C. by tribes from Asia Minor and Crete. In the 11th century B.C. there was an influx of people from Attica. It was a member of the Ionian Confederation and generally an ally of Miletus. In 540 B.C. when Miletus submitted to Cyrus, Chios submitted; when Miletus revolted, Chios revolted. It joined the Delian League in 479 B.C. and long remained an ally of Athens. It was considered one of the best-governed states in Greece, with the most prosperous period in its history in the 200-year period from 1346 to 1566 A.D. It was during this period that, although it retained the rights of self-government, control was in the hands of the Genoese trading company "Giustiniani." The company was concerned primarily with the mastic trade. Mastic was a combination chewing gum, breath sweetener, tranquilizer, and flavoring for a liquor called *mastika*. It is the product of an evergreen shrub indigenous to the eastern Mediterranean and is grown in Chios for its gum properties Synthetic varnishes and gum have nearly eliminated the market for it.

At one time the island had a population of 110,000, of whom only 6,000 were Turks. Urged on by Samos, Chios rebelled against Turkish rule in 1822 A.D. but was subdued with dire results. The city of Chios and 70 villages were reduced to ashes, 25,000 were slain, and 45,000 were carried off as slaves. Most of the remainder fled to other parts of Greece. At the end of the summer's grim harvest, there were only 2,000 Greeks left.

The island is mountainous and sparsely planted. The current population is 26,000 and declining, as cultivation has deteriorated to the extent that the island is barely self-supporting. The capital, Chios, has a small, safe harbor with broad quays and is a busy town. The fortress, called *kastro,* is a Byzantine structure built in the 9th century A.D. and rebuilt by the Genoese in the 13th century. About six miles north of the city is a sanctuary of the mother-goddess Cybele with her two lions. The mythological story concerns the fleet-footed Atalanta, who was averse to marriage and decreed she would marry only one who could beat her in a foot race. Death was the penalty for losing. One Hippomenes was given three golden apples by Aphrodite with instructions to drop one whenever Atalanta was about to pass. Each time, Atalanta stopped to pick up the apple and Hippomenes won. He forgot to express his gratitude to Aphrodite and both Hippomenes and Atalanta were changed into lions and harnessed to the chariot of Cybele. A statuary group in front of the Madrid post office is familiar to travelers in Spain.

The group of horses above the entrance to St. Mark's Cathedral in Venice came from Chios in the 5th century A.D. via Rome and Constantinople.

Chios had a school of epic poets called Homeridae, which may have capitalized on the interest in Homeric poems. At the same time, it stimulated the claims of Chios that it was the birthplace of Homer. The Homeric Hymn to the Delian Apollo refers to "the blind poet of rocky Chios." However, the uncertainty as to Homer is one that will probably never be settled. The remarkable feature of Greek literature is that it begins "full grown." It is as if the works of Shakespeare constituted the first of English literature. It was an oral literature, recited for information and entertainment as is done today in illiterate countries. Travelers to Marrakech, Morocco, see an example of this in the market place Djemaa el Fna with groups of men huddled around a storyteller or around one who recites the news. The Greek alphabet dates from about 800 B.C. The writing material that would be suitable for the long Homeric poems would be papyrus, which became available in Greece in the 5th, or possibly the 6th, century B.C., although the earliest document now known dates only from the second half of the 4th century B.C.

The events of the *Iliad* and the *Odyssey* took place about 1200 B.C. and any details of that time had to be transmitted by word of mouth for centuries, as the earliest date ascribed to the epics is of the order of 800 B.C. Whether one man, two men, or a composite of several are responsible for the product is an open question which will probably never be answered. If two men, Homer I would take credit for the *Iliad,* and Homer II, somewhat later, for the *Odyssey.* The language is an Ionian dialect with some non-Ionic forms which may be Aeolian. This would suggest a location around Chios, Smyrna, and Colophon.

There apparently were a large number of early Greek epic poems of which the *Iliad* and the *Odyssey* were only two. Or the two may have been combined from a number of Homeric poems. They were recited at the Panathenaean festivals in Athens every four years from the time of Peisistratos, who was a more or less benevolent tyrant in Athens from 541 to 527 B.C. It is believed the form of the *Iliad* and the *Odyssey* was more or less fixed by that time. The method of presentation involving a number of reciters would seem to require a written text, but none has been found. Papyri texts were apparently available at the time Zenodotos of Ephesus was librarian at Alexandria, as his revision was done before 274 B.C. From then on to 150 B.C. ten or eleven papyrus texts have been found which aren't too consistent among themselves. About 150 B.C., Aristarchos of Samothrace, then librarian at Alexandria, brought out his text. From then on, texts were generally uniform.

GLAUCOS (fl c 560 B.C.) invented iron welding.

OENOPIDES (fl c 465 B.C.) is said to have been the first to draw a perpendicular to a given line from a given point, and at a given point to construct an angle equal to a given angle. He also claimed discovery of the obliquity of the ecliptic, from his observations with the gnomon.

HIPPOCRATES (fl c 460 B.C.) was a merchant who had lost his merchandise to pirates and his money to custom officials in Byzantium. He went to Athens to try to recover damages and stayed to teach mathematics. He turned out to be the greatest mathematician of the 5th century B.C. He was the first to attempt to put geometrical theorems in logical order and strengthen the proofs. He determined the area of the lunes formed by the semi-circles drawn on the sides of the right triangle and determined that the problem of duplication of the cube could be reduced to finding two mean proportionals between two lines. He determined that the areas of circles were in the same ratio as the squares of their diameters.

ISOCRATES of Athens (436-338 B.C.) taught rhetoric in Chios (404-392 B.C.) while a refugee from the Thirty Tyrants.

THEOPOMPOS (b 380 B.C.) was educated in Athens and became a famous orator. His extensive writings were principally on history. He was learned but critical of almost everybody.

Teos

Teos is located on the southern coast of the peninsula which extends westward from Izmir toward the island of Chios. About 14 miles west of Izmir, there is a road to the left which leads on to the town of Seferihisar and then on to a fishing hamlet called Sigacik. There is a Genoese castle here and nearby are the ruins of Teos. These are not extensive but do include sections of the wall, parts of the stage of a 2nd century B.C. theater, ruins of a gymnasium, a partially excavated odeon, and traces of a mole.

The city was situated on a small two-mile-wide peninsula and was settled about 1000 B.C. In 544 B.C. nearly the whole town migrated to Abdera to escape the oppression of the Persians. However, many returned and the city prospered. In 302 B.C., some of the inhabitants were transplanted to the new city of Ephesus. The great deity of the Teians was Dionysos, the god of wine and revelry and the patron of the theater.

ANACREON (560-478 B.C.) was a lyric poet who, it is believed, migrated with the Teians to Abdera in 544 B.C. He may have been a tutor of Polycrates of Samos. After the assassination of Polycrates, Anacreon was invited to the court of Hipparchos in Athens. When Hipparchos suffered the same demise, Anacreon may have returned to Teos. He is shown with a lyre on several coins of Teos. His lyrics dealt chiefly with love and wine. A society in London adopted his name and one of their drinking songs was "Anacreon to Heaven," the music of which is that of "The Star-Spangled Banner."

EPICUROS (341-270 B.C.) lived in Teos at an early age before moving on to Mytilene (Lesbos), Lampsacus, and Athens. In Teos, he received some instruction from Nausiphanes, who explained the philosophy of Democritos and provided him with material for one of his important writings, the *Canon*.

APPELLICON (d c 84 B.C.) was a wealthy book collector who became an Athenian citizen. He purchased the libraries of Aristotle and Theophrastos from the family of Neleus, a disciple of Theophrastos. Having been stored in a cellar, the books were in poor condition and the restorations were faulty. Appellicon's library was taken to Rome by Sulla. It included a remarkable old copy of the *Iliad*.

Colophon

Colophon was one of the twelve cities of the Ionian Confederacy. The site is 22 miles south of Izmir and is reached by a poor road which branches off to the right at the Izmir airport. The village of Degirmendre is within sight of the Colophon acropolis. Colophon was settled largely by Cretan-Mycenaean Greeks under the leadership of Andraemon of Pylos. Its harbor was Notion, nine miles distant, and long walls connected the two cities. In the 9th century B.C. many Ionians of Colophon moved to Smyrna and gave that city a period of great prosperity. Colophon was known for its trade, horse breeding, and the pilgrimmages to the temple of Apollo at Claros, eight miles away. Its calvary had the reputation of winning all its engagements; hence the expression "to add a colophon" signified "putting an end to the affair." Early book publishers used to add a colophon at the end of the book giving information relative to its production.

The walls of the lower city were built in the 4th century B.C. and formed a triangle between three hills. The acropolis was on the southwest hill and 650 feet above the plain. There are traces of a stoa and blocks of houses dating from the early 4th century B.C. and beneath these are traces of structures of the 7th and 8th centuries.

In the struggle for power following the death of Alexander the Great, Colophon took the side of Antigonus against Lysimachus. The latter occupied the city in 302 B.C. and deported most of the inhabitants to his city of Ephesus. Apelles and Homer may have come from Colophon.

XENOPHANES (570-480 B.C.) left Colophon when the city was conquered by Cyrus in 540 B.C. and seems to have spent the following years traveling (Egypt and Sicily are mentioned) until he finally settled in Elea in 500 B.C. He is credited with founding the Eleatic school of philosophy, but the real founder was Parmenides.

Ephesus

Ephesus (Efes) is situated 48 miles south of Izmir and adjacent to the town of Seljuk. Nearby was "the Asian mead about the stream of the Cayster" which was destined to bestow its name to the largest continent on earth. This was the site of one of the ancient Seven Wonders of the World—the Temple of Artemis— and nearby was one of the most polished cities of antiquity. The temple site is now but a shallow excavation and the city is still emerging from the silt and debris.

One account says the first temple was built by the Amazons, one of whom was named Ephesus. The temple was dedicated to the ancient mother-goddess Cybele, a fertility goddess represented by a crude many-breasted figure, a copy of which is in the Naples

VIEWS OF EPHESUS

EPHESUS

Museum. In the 11th century B.C. new settlers from Caria built a new temple. Later, these were expelled, or incorporated, by Ionians under the leadership of Androcles, who settled around the acropolis on the heights above the temple and the present-day Seljuk. The deity of the city was Artemis, distinctly different from the Grecian goddess of the hunt and apparently associated with her only because both were goddesses of animals.

Ephesus became the most important Ionian city and grew into a great commercial and financial center. About the middle of the 6th century, it fell to Croesus of Lydia and a few years later to the Persians under Cyrus. Here it remained until the Persian defeat by Alexander the Great. With the silting up of the harbor, the site became marshy and subject to annual floods. Therefore, Lysimachus, one of Alexander's generals who governed after Alexander's death, moved the city two miles westward to higher ground between Mount Pion and Mount Coressus and surrounded it with a wall. The people were reluctant to move up to the new

SCULPTURED BASE DRUM FROM TEMPLE OF ARTEMIS

city, so Lysimachus waited until a downpour and then blocked the sewers, thereby flooding the old city.

In the meantime, the temple, which was now outside the wall, had been destroyed several times. In the 7th century B.C. it was destroyed by the Cimmerians. A new temple was started in 540 B.C. under the supervision of Theodoros, an architect from Samos, and continued by the Cretan architect Cherisphon and his son Metagenes. A marsh was chosen for the temple site, as there would be less likelihood of damage to the temple from earthquakes. This meant that the foundation required special treatment, such as the ramming down of charcoal and fleece. The base, with ten steps instead of the usual three, supported 124 sixty-foot columns. Thirty-six of these, with beautifully decorated base drums, were supplied by Croesus and adorned the front and back of the temple, several of which are now in the British Museum. There were twenty-one columns as viewed from the side and eight from the front and back. There were double rows of columns on the sides and three rows on the ends. In addition there were a number of internal columns. The doors were of cypress and the ceiling was of cedar. The entire temple was 425 feet long and 220 feet wide (359 by 167 feet excluding the steps) and took 120 years to build. It was burned in 356 B.C. by a pyromaniac who wanted to make his name immortal. Twenty years later, Alexander the Great ofered to complete the restoration if he could have the sole honor and have his name inscribed on the architrave of a pillar. The Ephesians declined, saying that it was not right for one deity to erect a temple for another.

Temples were considered sacred precincts and treasures therein were generally safe, even from invaders. However, that didn't deter Nero (1st century A.D.) from removing the images and offerings. In 263 A.D. the Goths destroyed the sanctuary, but it was rebuilt. The religious zeal of Emperor Theodosius in the 4th century A.D. banned pagan cults and provided the justification for the Christians to follow the same destructive instincts which seem to be inherent in the barbarian and the civilized alike. From then on, the temple was used as a quarry for St. Sophia in Constantinople and other

Byzantine and Turkish buildings. The immense dome of St. Sophia rises from eight green jasper columns from the Artemision and two pillars are found in the cathedral in Pisa.

The remains of the city are very extensive and very impressive. The main part lies in a sort of valley but extends up over a saddle to far beyond on this upper level. With colonnaded streets paved with marble, it must have been very lovely. The Arcadian Way, for example, is 1,800 feet long and 36 feet wide, paved with marble blocks and lined with colonnades and porticos under which were shops and statues. The streets were lighted at night. The theater (c 50 A.D.) is Greek in plan and seated over 20,000 people. There were 66 rows of seats topped off with a colonnaded gallery 98 feet above the stage. The length of the topmost row was 495 feet. The 110-foot-diameter orchestra was backed by a stage 48 feet wide and 20 feet deep. A smaller theater, the Odeon, is located up in the saddle and dates from the second century A.D. There are 23 semi-circular rows which seated 1,500. The length of the topmost row is 153 feet. The stadium near the entrance, at the other end of the city, was built at the time of Nero. It had a double colonnade and was 850 feet long and 200 feet wide. These were some of the more evident features of the city. In addition there were four large baths, three gymnasiums, the agora, temples of Serapis and Hadrian, a library, and acres of houses. Near the west wall was the Church of the Virgin Mary, where the 3rd Ecumenical Council was held, in 431 A.D.

The city reached the height of its magnificence as a capital of the Roman province of Asia with a population of 200,000. A terrible earthquake devastated the city in 17 A.D. It was rebuilt but was invaded by the Goths in 263 A.D. and it never fully recovered. During the first half of the 6th century A.D. the city was moved once more, this time to the district where Androcles first settled, namely, around the heights overlooking the present town of Seljuk and the ruins of the Artemision. The hill was fortified with a wall and a citadel. There was a small church on the hill over a 2nd century A.D. tomb claimed to be that of St. John the Apostle. A basilica was built over the tomb utilizing marbles from the Artemision. It was 360 feet long and 130 feet wide; its pillars were massive and faced with marble. An earthquake in the 14th century A.D. partially destroyed the church and it was further ruined by Tamerlane in 1402. In the meantime, by the 10th century A.D. the old city was completely deserted and covered with marshes.

In its long life, Ephesus had its moments of glory and its moments of despair. As an important center of Christendom, it claims the tomb of St. John the Apostle, who is supposed to have written the Fourth Gospel in Ephesus about the end of the first century A.D. There is also the much-questioned story that John brought Mary to Ephesus about 40 A.D. and that she lived here the remainder of her life. St. Paul stayed in Ephesus for two years (56-58 A.D.) preaching in the school of Tyrannus. He was forced to leave to escape persecution by temple priests and the silversmiths who made and sold silver souvenirs of Artemis to pilgrims and tourists. They blamed Paul for discouraging temple worship and pilgrimages and hence jeopardizing their livelihood. An assemblage in the theater gathered to hear their grievance turned into a near riot with the mob yelling. "Great is Artemis of the Ephesians!" A town clerk appeased the multitude by telling them that everyone knew that Ephesus was the servant of Artemis and for them not to do anything rash.

The 3rd Ecumenical Council was called in 431 A.D. to settle two somewhat divergent opinions regarding the divinity of Christ. The Arians taught that Christ was subordinate to God, whereas the Trinitarians held that the Father, Son and Holy Ghost were three distinct personages but "identical in nature" as one God. The Council of Nicaea had convened for the same purpose and half-heartedly adopted the Trinitarian view. However, instead of settling the matter, it paved the way for renewed struggle. The 431 A.D. Council reaffirmed the Nicaean Creed. A Fourth Council was summoned in 499 A.D. to destroy what remained of Arianism (or Nestorism). It was called the "Robber Synod," as it was charged with fraud, coercion, and violence. Violence it produced. For three months there was clamor and bloodshed. Flavian, the primate of Constantinople, was deposed and trampled upon so that he died three days later. In 451 A.D. the Council of Chalcedon annulled the proceedings and canonized Flavian as a martyr—St. Flavian.*

Croesus, Cyrus, and Xerxes were among the early rulers, Xerxes even leaving his children there for safety. Alexander the Great offered to restore the Artemision and here he had Apelles paint his portrait holding a thunderbolt in each hand. At one time or another, the city was visited by every important personage of antiquity.

HERACLITUS (535-476 B.C.) was one of the last descendants of Androcles. Dissatisfied with the ruling power, he withdrew to a secluded estate and devoted himself primarily to philosophy. He was buried in the agora of Ephesus and for several centuries his image continued to be engraved on their coins. His book *On Nature* is the oldest book of Greek prose, but it is poorly written and difficult to read. As all the early Greek literature was transmitted orally from memory, the best form to insure reasonable iteration was poetry. It took the Greeks a long time to develop prose. Heraclitus had a gloomy outlook on life and was called "The Gloomy One." He stated that all knowledge is based on the senses; all knowledge is self-knowledge; only the gods have perfect knowledge. He sought for an intelligible principle of the universe. Fire was the ultimate basis for all existence, which changes continually into water, then earth, and back to fire. The universe was a conflict of opposites controlled by eternal justice. Hot and cold, good and evil, night and day, summer and winter, war and peace, are all inseparable halves of one and the same thing. In spite of the apparent disharmony of the world, underneath was profound harmony, for every change happens in accordance with a universal law. Vir-

---

*The conflict over Arianism had one interesting related incident in Milan. Ambrose, the bishop, had closed all Arian places of worship. Empress Justina, as a widow, had placed herself at the head of the Arians and asked for two churches—one inside the wall and one outside. Ambrose refused. One day while Ambrose was officiating in the basilica, the Arians crowded in but said they had come to pray and not to fight. Ambrose was afraid, however, that they would seize the church at night, so he instituted all-night services. In order to relieve the tedium of the night watches, he taught the congregation to sing hymns composed by himself. This was the start of singing hymns in Christian churches and it was not long before hymns had spread to every corner of Christendom.

tue consists in the subordination of the individual to the laws of universal harmony.

ZENODOTOS (325-234 B.C.) was the first librarian in Alexandria (284-260 B.C.). He undertook critical revisions of the works of Greek poets, including Homer and Hesiod. He divided the *Iliad* and the *Odyssey* into 24 books each and compiled a Homeric glossary and dictionary.

RUFUS (early 2nd century B.C.) was a famous physician who spent a number of years in Alexandria and settled in Rome. He wrote 40 books on anatomy.

ARTEMIDOROS (fl c 100 B.C.) was a geographer and traveler, reaching as far as Spain. He settled in Alexandria and wrote 11 treatises on geography.

SORANUS (early 2nd century A.D.) was considered the greatest gynecologist of antiquity and the earliest authority on infant hygiene and nutrition. He was the author of about 30 books and his works *On Midwifery* and *Diseases of Women* were the source of many books on obstetrics. He is believed to have been the first to turn the child over in the womb for normal delivery. He was the chief representative of a school of physicians, known as Methodists, who sought to heal by restoring the body equilibrium. They regarded the Hippocratic doctrine as "meditation upon death."

Samos

Samos is separated from Asia Minor by only a mile. It is a mountainous island about 27 miles in length and 14 miles in breadth. Percentagewise, there isn't much arable land, but the island still seems prosperous. The valleys are terraced and grapes seem to be the major crop. The capital and main port is Vathy, located on the northeast corner of the island at the head of a long narrow bay and sheltered by the high mountains around it. The population of the city and the suburbs is about 9,000.

A port on the southeast corner was formerly called Tigani but is now called Pythagorian. It was the ancient city of Polycrates (ruled 532-522 B.C.) and is situated on a fairly wide plain between the mountains and the sea. The long mole, or harbor wall, is built on 6th century B.C. foundations. To supply water for the city, Polycrates had Eupalinos of Megara (fl 530 B.C.) construct a tunnel through Mount Ampelos from springs on the north side. It was nearly a mile long with a six-foot cross section and a two-by-two-foot trench in the bottom. It opens out above the city and the water was brought down in clay pipes. Tunneling was started simultaneously on opposite sides of the mountain and several hundred lives were reported lost in its construction. The tunnel can be inspected for about 100 feet. In the general vicinity of the tunnel opening is the site of the ancient theater, with a beautiful view of the city and the harbor. Samos claims to have been the birthplace of Hera and there was a temple erected to her about four miles west of Pythagorion at Cape Colonna. There have been several temples erected at this site, the first dating from the 12th century B.C. The present ruins are from a 6th century B.C. temple, the Heraeion, about 300 feet long and 150 feet wide. Only one unfinished column remains of the original 134. It was the largest temple known at the time of Herodotus. The temple was open to the sky and full of excellent statues. Three colossal statues were by Myron. Marc Antony took them away, but two were restored by Caesar. The one of Zeus was transferred to the Capitoline in Rome.

Samos has had a stormy history. In the 11th century B.C. migrations from Greece to Asia Minor, the island was settled by colonists primarily from Epidaurus. They maintained trade routes with the Black Sea region, Egypt, Cyrenacia, the Greek mainland, and Sicily. Though a member of the Ionian Confederation, it was a bitter rival of Miletus. Samos reached the height of its prosperity under Polycrates when its navy fleet of 150 galleys and a thousand bowmen ruled the waves. He was a pirate chief and a tyrant but at the same time a patron of the arts. Artists and poets always found a welcome at his court. He was invited to the mainland in 522 B.C. by Oroetes, a Persian mercenary general, and crucified.

When Darius came to the throne, he had Oroetes killed for acting too independently. At one time in Egypt when Darius was only an army officer, he admired the red cloak of a stranger. He wanted to buy it but was given it as a gift. The stranger was Syloson of Samos, the brother of Polycrates. After the murder of Polycrates, Syloson reminded Darius of the gift and Darius offered to restore Samos to Syloson. The commander at the time resented being relieved and aggravated the Persians into taking extreme measures against the populace so that the island became almost depopulated. Undeservedly there was the saying "Thanks to Syloson, there is plenty of room." In 479 B.C. the Persian fleet of Xerxes was destroyed at Mycale, on the mainland opposite Samos. At various times, it was occupied by the Persians, Egyptians, Romans, Byzantines, Genoese, and Turks. As a result of the Turkish conquest of Piali Pasha in 1566 A.D., the island was almost depopulated and became no more than a grazing ground for sheep. In the 17th century it was repopulated to some extent by immigrants from Lesbos, Asia Minor, and Albania. It remained under Turkish rule until 1912.

AESOP (c 620-560 B.C.) is said to have been a freed slave of Iadmon of Samos and met a violent death at the hands of the inhabitants of Delphi at a time of widespread pestilence. He was famous for his stories of animals, all of which had a lesson, or moral.

PYTHAGORAS (580-497 B.C.) was born in Samos, but his early life is somewhat vague. The usual story is that he left Samos in order to escape the tyranny of Polycrates (532-522 B.C.). If so, it must have been after his extensive travels in Greece, Egypt, Babylonia, and Crete, as he settled in Croton (Italy) about 530 B.C. Here he founded the Pythagorean Brotherhood, a school of philosophy, mathematics and astronomy. The school was forced to leave Croton in 510 B.C. and moved to Metapontum, where Pythagoras lived until his death.

THEODOROS (fl c 540 B.C.) is believed to have been the chief architect of the Artemision of Ephesus, the gigantic temple dedicated to Artemis. Many construction tools were invented by him, including the lathe, the square, and a level called *diabetes,* which consisted of a triangle with a calibrated crosspiece and a plumb bob suspended from the vertex. He was also a skilled goldsmith and engraver and brought the technique of bronze casting back from Egypt.

ANACREON of Teos (560-378 B.C.) was a lyric poet who may have been a tutor to Polycrates, but at least spent considerable time in his court and wrote many complimentary odes about his patron. He got his reputation from his bacchanalian and amatory lyrics. After the death of Polycrates, he was invited to the court of Hipparchos in Athens and stayed there until the latter's assassination in 514 B.C. Anacreon then returned to Teos.

ARISTARCHOS (310-230 B.C.) was one of the foremost astronomers of antiquity. He studied in Athens (287-279 B.C.) and made observations in Alexandria (280-264 B.C.). He is best known for having proposed a heliocentric solar system and for ingenious methods of determining the relative distances of the sun and the moon and the relative diameters of the earth and the moon.

CONON (fl 260-212 B.C.) was a gifted mathematician associated with the Museum and Library in Alexandria. He wrote seven books on astronomy based on Chaldean and Egyptian observations.

Priene

Priene was the smallest of the twelve towns constituting the Ionian Confederation. It is located on the southern slope of Mount Mycale, a name associated with the defeat of the Persian navy in 479 B.C. South of the town is the wide plain of a river which donated its name to the English language, the Meander. Miletus is across this plain to the south. Priene had its own harbor in ancient days, but the coast is now nine miles away. The city is ten miles from Soke and is reached by a poor road with huge fig orchards on the left. It is laid out on terraces with the rectangular grid pattern of Hippodamos and protected by a 20-foot wall seven feet thick. The Temple of Demeter was at the highest point, about 430 feet above the plain. Above the city on an 800-foot peak was a 4th century B.C. acropolis.

In the center of town was the Sacred Portico, 380 feet long and 40 feet wide. On a foundation with six steps, there were two side rows and a center row of columns supporting a wooden roof. It was built toward the end of the 2nd century B.C. Adjacent to it is the well-preserved Bouleuterium, or Senate House. It is a rectangular building with ten to sixteen rows of seats on three sides and stone benches for the presiding officials on the fourth. The theater is fairly well preserved, although only the lower eight or nine rows of seats have been dug out, the rest having disappeared. The proscenium is well preserved. The agora was relatively large—one-fifth of the city's area. Of the five or six temples in the city, the temple to Athena was the most famous, as it was built in the late 4th century B.C. by the architect Pytheus, the designer of the Mausoleum in Hallicarnassus. It is said to have had a 22-foot statue of Athena modeled after the one in the Parthenon in Athens. Alexander the Great contributed toward the temple's completion. The well-laid-out city, with marble houses, water supply, drainage, temples, theater, and gymnasiums, impresses one as having been a very prosperous and nice place for its 4,000 inhabitants to live.

Its history goes back to the 7th century B.C. and involves the Lydians, Persians, Macedonians, Romans, and Turks. By the 14th century A.D., the harbors had been silted up and Priene was only a small market town.

BIAS (fl 570 B.C.) was, along with Thales, included on the various lists of the Seven Sages of Greece. He is noted for his wise comments and a poem on the best means for making Ionia prosperous. One story concerned advice given Croesus when the latter was building ships to attack the islands. He falsely reported to Croesus that the islands were training a cavalry to attack him. The king replied that nothing would suit him better than for the islanders to attack the Lydian cavalry on land. "What, then," said Bias, "do you suppose they are thinking when they hear you are going to engage them on sea?" Croesus, on second thought, gave up his shipbuilding.

ARCHELAOS (fl 2nd century B.C.) was a sculptor who may have been associated with the Rhodian school. He is known for the relief "Apotheosis of Homer" in the British Museum.

Miletus

Miletus is situated on the Carian coast southeast of the island of Samos, about 20 miles south of Soke near the mouth of the Meander River. It was settled in the 11th century B.C. by Greeks from Pylos at a site already settled by Cretans from a city called Miletus. It became a city of wealth and an important trading and colonizing center. The city had good harbors and was close to the caravan routes which normally ended in Smyrna. It had many colonies, including the Greek trading city of Naucratis on the Nile delta in Egypt. The Black Sea trade was the greatest source of wealth to the Ionian cities and Miletus founded some 60 cities in that region. After the defeat of Croesus, the king of Sardis, by Cyrus in 546 B.C., Miletus came under the domination of Persia but was given favorable treatment and a certain amount of independence. However, it didn't last long, and after Miletus led an Ionian revolt against Persia in 498-494 B.C., the city was sacked and burned and part of the population was transplanted to the mouth of the Tigris in Mesopotamia. It was a terrible blow to the Greeks. When the Athenian poet Phrynichus wrote the tragedy *The Capture of Miletus,* the audience wept so bitterly that the playwright was fined 1,000 drachmas for depressing them and future presentation of the play was banned. After the Greek victory over the Persian navy in 479 B.C. at Mycale, just north of Miletus, the city was rebuilt, but it never fully recovered. The harbors gradually silted up and it became a fever-smitten place.

The city really had four harbors, as Miletus was situated on a peninsula sheltered by islands which are now several miles inland from the coast. Today, Miletus is like an island hill in a 20-mile-wide plain, practically a marsh, in which the river is really not seen, except possibly under flood conditions. A fortified wall guarded the way into the peninsula. The city was about half a square mile in area and was laid out on a rectangular grid by Hippodamos. The theater, which is the most prominent of the remains of the city, was built in the Roman period, about 100 A.D., on top of an older 3rd-century Greek theater. It was characteristic of Greek theaters that, where possible, the audience had a beautiful and interesting background view. In Miletus the theater faced one of the four harbors of the city. The Romans raised the front seats so as to provide entry doors for wild beasts. The ruins of the gymnasium and baths are nearby and other ruins delineate the two market places, the Bouleteurion or Senate House, and temples to Apollo, Serapis, and Asclepius.

THALES (640-546 B.C.). In ancient Greece there were, from time to time, lists of Seven Wise Men noted for their wisdom in politics or philosophy. At the top of all such lists was the name of Thales of Miletus. Herodotus indicated that he was of Phoenician descent, but his mother's name was Cleobuline, which is Greek, and his father's name was Examinus, which is Carian. He was a physician, mathematician, physicist, and the founder of philosophy in Greece. He apparently accumulated wealth through commercial

THE THEATER IN MILETUS
The most prominent of the remains of the city dates from about 100 A.D.

trade and this enabled him to found the Ionian school of philosophy.

In geometry he is credited with several propositions which found their way into Euclid's *Elements,* such as: any circle is bisected by its diameter; the angles at the base of an isosceles triangle are equal; when two lines intersect, the vertical angles are equal; the sides of similar triangles are proportional; two triangles are congruent if they have two angles and the included side equal; and possibly, an angle inscribed in a semi-circle is a right angle. The last had already been determined by the Babylonians. These propositions may seem trivial, but when judged by the state of knowledge at the time, they represented a great contribution in suggesting an abstract geometry and the idea of a logical proof.

Thales is credited with the knowledge that amber will attract light bodies when rubbed with wool. Amber was much used for decoration in antiquity and, in common with silver-gold alloys and gold itself (they have the same pale-yellow color), was called *electron.* He was also familiar with the magnetic properties of lodestone, a magnetite which is said to have been mined near Magnesia on the Meander, 20 miles north of Miletus. The Phoenicians used Ursa Minor for navigation and Thales suggested that Greek mariners should also use this group, which includes Polaris, instead of Ursa Major. He stated that the moon was illuminated by the sun. This is indicative of the state of Greek astronomy at the time, as this had been matter-of-fact information to the Babylonians for centuries. He is credited with predicting, or announcing, the solar eclipse of May 28, 584 B.C., based on Babylonian information. The path of totality of this eclipse passed through Asia Minor and ended in Syria at sundown. A century prior to the above date, a Mesopotamian note indicated that predictions of eclipses were being made. By 500 B.C. their crude tables of the moon and the sun were considerably improved and further improvement was noted by 375 B.C. The records are however almost entirely limited to lunar eclipses. Of course, Thales might have received information about a possible eclipse. If so, he was doubly fortunate—first, that an eclipse occurred and, second, that it was visible in Asia Minor.

Thales thought that the earth was surrounded by the ocean and that the primordial substance of all matter was water. Water is the only substance that exists without difficulty as a gas, a liquid, or a solid, and no life is possible without it.

ANAXIMANDER (611-546 B.C.) was a disciple of Thales and is said to have introduced the gnomon and the sundial to Greece, both of which were Babylonian inventions. Simple measurements with a vertical gnomon will enable an observer to determine the length of the year, the variation in the lengths of the days, local noon, due south, the latitude, the solstices, the equinoxes, and the obliquity of the ecliptic*.

Much of the data was probobly bewildering to Anaximander, as the current model of the earth at the time was a flat disk surrounded by the ocean and floating in space. However, he is said to have proposed that the earth is curved rather than flat and to have prepared a map for navigators. He is credited with having given the true explanation of the phases of the moon.

He conceived of the universe being subject to a single law but objected to Thales' idea of water being the fundamental substance, for how could substances like rock and metals be explained? He therefore avoided commitment by calling it *apeiron*. He dealt with two traditional problems: "How did the world come to be arranged as it is?" and "How did life, especially human life, arise?" The first animals, he thought, were created in water, some of which adapted themselves to living on land. Man must have developed from other animals, for it takes him too long to mature; he would otherwise not have survived.

ANAXIMENES (585-528 B.C.) was a pupil of Anaximander and believed the entire universe was surrounded by a primordial substance from which all material bodies were generated. He believed air to be the fundamental substance: when it expands, it produces fire and when it cools, it produces wind, clouds, water, then earth, and finally rock. The sun, moon, earth, and other planets were disks floating on air, but the stars were fixed on a rotating shell.

*It is of interest to note that the underground kivas of the Mexican and Pueblo Indians enabled them to trace out the sun's image on the kiva floor. The rainy season followed the sun and it was important to burn the brush on their fields and plant their corn just prior to the start of the rains.

HECATAEUS (550-475 B.C.) was a historian, philosopher, traveler, and geographer. He tried unsuccessfully to dissuade the Ionians from revolting against the Persians, but when they were subdued, Hecataeus was instrumental in having the constitution of the Ionic cities restored. He wrote a two-volume book on Europe, Asia, and Egypt entitled *Periodos Ges* and a work on the traditions and mythology of the Greeks called *Geneaolgies*. He maintained that many of the tales of the Greeks were nonsense. His round map of the world centered on Miletus. It showed the Mediterranean emptying into the ocean near Tingus (Tangier). Asia, including Libya (Africa), was shown on the south, the Euxine (Black Sea) and the Caspian Sea toward the east, and Europe, including Scythia, to the north. Around the rim was the ocean.

HIPPODAMOS (fl 450 B.C.) was an architect and city planner, the first person not a statesman to make studies about the best form of government, and the first to lay out towns with a rectangular grid. His plan for an ideal city may have suggested a similar plan to Plato. Hippodamos planned the construction of Athens' harbor at Piraeus (before 466 B.C.), and made plans for Thurii (433 B.C.), Miletus, Priene, Rhodes, and others.

His fondness for distinction led him to wear expensive ornaments on cheap garments. He wore his hair flowing.

LEUCIPPUS (fl 450 B.C.), the originator and joint author with Democritos of the atomic theory, is believed to have been born in Miletus. However, very little is known of his life. He is supposed to have been a disciple of the Eleatic school and to have studied under Zeno. His association with Democritos may have taken place in Abdera. The atomic theory was explained in a book, *The Great World System,* attributed to Leucippus, but it is difficult to ascribe the contribution made by each of the two men. Leucippus probably originated the idea and Democritos developed it. The *atomes* were eternal and indivisible and differ in shape, position, and arrangement. Atoms of a liquid are smooth and round and can roll over one another. Atoms of a solid are uneven and rough and cling together. Compounds are produced according to fixed laws and not by chance. One statement ascribed to Leucippus is:

"Nothing happens without reason; everything has a cause and is the result of necessity." He apparently believed in the geocentric system of the universe with the moon closest to us and the sun most distant. The celestial bodies were set on fire because of their rapid motion.

TIMOTHEOS (446-357 B.C.) was a musician and a poet. He was the author of the earliest known literary papyrus, dating from about the beginning of the 4th century B.C. It was a poem called Persae which has been labeled "a model of designed obscurity." At the dedication of the fourth temple to Artemis in Ephesus about 420 B.C., Timotheos won the first prize for lyric poetry. He increased the number of strings of the zither.

ISIDOROS (fl 540 A.D.) and his uncle, Anthemius of Tralles, were the architects of St. Sophia (Hagia Sophia) in Constantinople.

Halicarnassus

Halicarnassus is the modern Bodrum (corrupt form of the name for Peter—Bedros) and is located about 70 miles south of Izmir and opposite the Greek island of Cos. Bodrum is a city of several thousand people situated in a circle of hills, with the entrance to the harbor guarded by the fortress-castle of St. Peter. The site of the castle—and the site of the ancient city—was originally an island called Zephyra. As the narrow strait filled with sand, the city extended westward to include the Carian village of Salmacis. Bodrum is a poor city with only one street and part of another paved. The rest are of dirt or cobblestones. Traces of the foundations of the city walls, the mausoleum, and the theater are are all that remain of the ancient city. Construction of the Castle of St. Peter was begun in 1402 A.D. by the Knights of St. John from Rhodes. Each commandant left a plaque of his coat of arms imbedded in some prominent place in the wall inside the fortress. The Knights were forced to evacuate in 1523 A.D. and moved, along with the Knights in Rhodes, to Sicily and then to Malta. The castle now houses two museums, one showing Mycenaean art and the other the results of undersea explorations. Shell-encrusted amphorae are plentiful in Bodrum.

The city was founded by Dorian colonists from Peloponnesos about 1000 B.C. For a while it was one of the six members of the Dorian Confederacy, the others being Cos, Cnidos, and three Rhodian cities. About half of the inhabitants were Carian. After being governed for some time by the Lydians, it was ruled by a Carian satrap of the Persians called Lygdamus. He was succeeded in the early 5th century B.C. by his daughter Artemisia I, who ruled over Halicarnassus, Cos, Nesyrus, and Calyndus. She was the first woman admiral in history and commanded her five ships in the battle of Salamis (480 B.C.). During the rout, she escaped with her five ships, but in so doing, she rammed and sank a friendly Calyndian ship. Xerxes, who was watching the battle from the shore, misunderstood the maneuver and is quoted as saying his "men acted like women and his women acted like men." When Xerxes was pondering what to do after the defeat, Artemisia advised him not to risk another battle but to retire from Greece.

A grandson of Artemisia I, named Lygdamus after his great-grandfather, was a tyrant of Caria and was responsible for Herodotus' (484-424 B.C.) leaving Halicarnassus. Prompted by the execution in 454 B.C. of his uncle or cousin, a lyric poet named Panyassis, Herodotus went to Samos and joined an exile group which was successful in overthrowing Lygdamus. Because of unpopularity, which has not been explained, Herodotus left Halicarnassus in 447 B.C. and went to Athens. Denied citizenship because his parents had not been Athenian citizens, he went to Italy in 444 B.C., where he helped found Thurii. Apart from his traveling, he spent the rest of his life there writing his nine-book *Histories*.

Another Persian satrap was Hecatomanus, king of the Carians. He had two sons and two daughters: Mausolus married his sister Artemisia, and Hidraes married his sister Ada. During the reign of Mausolus, Halicarnassus attained its greatest prosperity. Upon his death, his sister-queen Artemisia II succeeded him (353-350 B.C.). The Rhodians tried to take advantage of the death of the king, but their fleet was defeated.

The outstanding event in Artemisia's reign was the construction of a monument which stood halfway up the Hill of Mars on the

ARTIST'S CONCEPT OF MAUSOLUS MONUMENT

STATUES OF MAUSOLUS AND ARTEMISIA
WHICH TOPPED THE MONUMENT

west side of town. It was considered one of the ancient Seven Wonders of the World and gave to the world the term *mausoleum*. Architects Pytheus and Satyrus drew up the plans and sculptors Bryaxes, Leochares, Scopas of Paros, and Timotheos took care of the ornamentation. It had a square base and podium about 100 feet on a side, a second story with ten Ionic columns on a side with an equal number of statues, and a 24-step pyramid on top. A horse-drawn chariot with wheels eight feet in diameter, and ten-foot statues of Mausolus and Artemisia crowned the apex. Some of the sculptures are in the British Museum and one of the reliefs is in the courtyard of the Castle of St. Peter, now a museum. The monument was still in good shape in the 12th century A.D. It is not known in what condition the monument was in 1402 A.D. when the crusading Knights of St. John from Rhodes seized the town, but what was left of the monument went into building the fortress-castle. Many of the statues were burned in 1522 A.D. to make lime.

Artemisia II was also somewhat of a botanist and is credited with discovering and naming several herbs. The bitter aromatic herb *Artemisia* is named after her.

Perhaps the earliest record of the use of letters of the alphabet to indicate numerals is provided by a Halicarnassus inscription (c 450 B.C.).

DIONYSIUS (fl 20 B.C.) was another historian who was born in Halicarnassus. He went to Rome about 30 B.C. and about 8 B.C. finished his most extensive work, *Roman Antiquities*. It was divided into 20 books and covered Roman history from its founding to the First Punic War (246-241 B.C.). This work and that of Livy were the only comprehensive accounts of early Roman history. He also wrote commentaries on literary styles and Attic orators. He died in Rome in 8 B.C.

Cnidos

Cnidos (Knidos) lies at the end of the narrow 60-mile peninsula of Reshadiye, sticking out into the Aegean Sea between the Greek islands of Cos and Rhodes, and about 25 miles south of Bodrum. The road along the peninsula is almost impassable, so

CNIDOS

Two harbors were formed as the strait between the mainland and the island silted in.

that normal access is by boat from Bodrum or Cos. The ancient city was laid out on terraces on both sides of a narrow strait separating a small island, called Triopium, from the mainland. The strait has now been sanded in, forming two harbors. Recently there have been some new excavations and cleaning up but about the only remains of the old city are the outline of the 36-row theater and the retaining walls of the terraces. These extend about 1,000 feet along the valley on both sides of the eastern bay and several hundred feet up the mountainside. Some of the terraces are cultivated in season, but otherwise the only people usually there are several army guards and the lighthouse attendant on Cape Krio. The isolation, as far as land transportation is concerned, illustrates how dependent the Greek cities in Asia Minor were upon the sea. There were only two, or possibly three, of these cities that were not within sight of the coast.

The city was settled by Dorians from Lacedaemonia (Sparta) possibly around the 10th century B.C. Along with Halicarnassus,

Cos, and three Rhodian cities, it was a member of the Dorian Hexapolis. The assemblies were held in the Temple of Apollo on Cape Triopium, where only these Dorian cities could worship. The city was prosperous from trade and their products of fish, wine, and onions. They had a trading post at the Nile Delta city of Naucratis and conducted considerable trade with Tarentum in Magna Graecia. Their Treasury at Delphi had clubrooms which were decorated by Polygnotos. In order to provide better protection from the Persians, they tried to cut off their peninsula by digging a canal but encountered trouble, and the oracle at Delphi advised:

> Fence not the isthmus, nor dig it through.
> Zeus would have made it an island if he had wished to.

Soon after 546 B.C. they submitted to the Persians under Cyrus.

Athens in 394 B.C. won a decisive sea battle over the Spartans off Cape Triopium. The Peloponnesian War had ended in 404 B.C., but Sparta had not seen fit to reward her allies with the fruits of victory. They became dissatisfied and entered into an alliance with Athens. So complete was the rout inflicted by the Athenian admiral, Conon, that Athens regained supremacy of the sea. Both sides were the losers, however, for the war dragged on for eight years and in the end it was Persia that dictated the peace.

In its day, Cnidos was famous as an artistic and cultural center, with a medical school, the school of astronomy of Eudoxos, two theaters, and four temples. From the Temple of Demeter came the statue of Demeter now in the British Museum. The chief deity of the city was Aphrodite, with three temples under surnames of Doritis, Acraean ("warlike") and Euploea ("giver of prosperous voyages"). In the last stood the celebrated statue of Aphrodite by Praxiteles (390-? B.C.). The model was Phryne, a courtesan famous for her beauty. The sculptor had been commissioned by Cos to supply a statue, but the Coans were shocked when they found it was a nude. At the time, nude female figures were not considered proper in Greece. Cnidos acquired it (about 350 B.C.) and it was a great tourist attraction. Nicomedes I of Bythinia offered to pay the public debt of Cnidos for her but was refused. The original statue was removed in the 4th century A.D. to Constantinople, where it was destroyed in the destruction which followed the condemnation of images in 755 A.D.

The medical school at Cnidos was probably founded in the 7th century B.C. This is about a century earlier than the establishment of the school at Cos. They discarded all the traditional association of ailments with magic and superstition and concentrated on diagnosis to determine the cause of the ailment. The adverse criticism was that they overemphasized diagnosis and paid too little attention to the patient. To initiate the scientific development of a new art, it would seem that a study of the fundamentals is the logical first step. Physicians who have been mentioned in connection with the school are: EURYPHON, who may have written or edited the *Cnidian Sentences* discussing diseases and gynecology; CTESIAS, who was a practicing prisoner at the Persian court from 417-398 B.C. and wrote an outstanding history of Persia; and CHRYSIPPOS, who accompanied Eudoxos to Egypt and possibly Sicily.

EUDOXOS (408-355 B.C.) was one of the greatest mathematicians and astronomers of his time. He studied with Plato in Athens, with the priests of Heliopolis in Egypt, and opened a school in Cyzicus. The school was moved to Athens in 378 B.C. Toward the end of his career he spent some time in Halicarnassus before returning home to Cnidos. His observatory still existed in Strabo's time (64 B.C.-21 A.D.).

SOSTRATOS (fl 270 B.C.) was the architect and builder of the Pharos in Alexandria.

AGATHARCHIDES (fl c 180 B.C.) flourished in Alexandria. He wrote a geography and history of Asia in ten books, one of Europe in 49 books, and books on Ethiopia and Arabia. He explained the Nile floods as being due to rain in Ethiopia in the wintertime.

Cos

Cos (Kos) is a dolphin-shaped island a few miles from the Turkish coast near Bodrum (Halicarnassus). The southern part is rather dry, with a few olive trees and cacti. The real productive part of the island is along the northern coast west of the city of Cos. Tomatoes, tobacco, grapes, fish, and tourists seem to be the mainstay of the economy. Cos lettuce gets its name from the island.

The island was settled by the Dorians from Epidauros and belonged to the Dorian League. The early capital was Astypalaea, near the present town of Kefalo. The daughter of one of the early kings, Merops II, was named Kos, and it is from her that the island got its name. The town was sacked by the Spartans in the Peloponnesian War and in 411 B.C. it was ruined by a severe earthquake. The inhabitants then moved over to the other side of the island and built a new capital with the same name.

Cos, or Kos, is a pleasant town with a busy waterfront and a nice residential section with each street lined with a particular type of tree—acacia, pink or white oleander, pine, cedar, et cetera. An earthquake destroyed the town in 1933, so that everything is new. The shops are small, mostly jewelry, hardware, and yard goods. The real activity is on the waterfront, not only because of shipping but for social reasons as well. There are many sidewalk cafes. At one end is a picturesque 14th-century Genoese fortress. The Knights of St. John took over Rhodes, Leros, and Cos with the connivance of a Genoese admiral in 1306 A.D. and the fortress dates from that period. The many plaques of coats-of-arms of the various orders indicate that modifications and additions were made subsequent to the purchase.

Nearby is a large weather-beaten plane tree with its branches propped up. It is claimed to be 2,500 years old, but foresters maintain that no plane tree can live more than 500 years. Close by are the ruins of a Roman agora with temples to Venus and Apollo. On the other side of town are ruins of a parliamentary building, a temple to nymphs, thermal baths, and a baptistry where marriages were performed. South of this place is a small theater with 13 rows of seats. A number of statues were found under the arcade of the theater, including one of Hippocrates which is now in the city museum. These were buried to prevent them from being destroyed by the Romans. At the west end of the theater is a villa of the Hellenistic period with beautiful mosaic floors.

The outstanding attraction in Cos is the Asclepion, about two miles southwest of town. It is a three-terrace affair about 500 feet

VIEW FROM TOP OF THREE TERRACES OF ASCLEPION

STATUE OF HIPPOCRATES
IN THE COS MUSEUM

THE LOWEST TERRACE OF THE ASCLEPION

wide and 800 feet from top to bottom. The first terrace was a
large courtyard with rooms and porticos on three sides. The outlines of some of the foundations are still evident, with some of the
walls intact on one side next to the baths. It was here that Apelles'
painting of Aphrodite hung. Here, too, was a place for the teller
of amusing stories. On the fourth side, against the second terrace,
was a row of fountains. On the second terrace were an altar and
several temples with some of the columns still standing. A grand
stairway of 60 steps leads to the top terrace. Facing the top of the
steps was the Doric Temple of Asclepios, of which there are no remains. From here there is a lovely view of the countryside, Cos,
and the sea. The earliest buildings on the second terrace date from
the 6th century B.C. The temple on the top terrace was of the 2nd
century B.C. It is said that the peak capacity was over a thousand
patients. The sanctuary was destroyed by a severe earthquake in
554 A.D.

Greek medicine may have had its origin at the time of the
Trojan War with a healer called Asclepios, but it was purely a
mystic cult until the school at Cnidos. Gradually there was a
separation of the mystic aspect and the healers, the former being
practiced by the temple priests and the healing by men called
asclepiades. By the time of Cnidos, magic and superstition had
been superseded by diagnosis commensurate with the state of the

art. However, more attention was paid to the disease and the symptoms than to the patient. In Cos, more attention was paid to the patient, putting him in a good frame of mind with pleasant surroundings, fountains, music, and storytellers. Strangely enough, there was no theater.

An International Medical Center is planned for Cos with hospitals, institutes, and laboratories for scientific investigation. It is planned that the main building will have lecture rooms, a library, dining room, and 20 bedrooms. In addition, each nation will provide a separate building. Every five years there will be a Congress on Medicine and Surgery at which doctors of all nations can exchange their views.

HIPPOCRATES (c 460-375 B.C.) apparently was taught by his father, who was an asclepiade. Little is known of him, although it is believed that he traveled and taught in various places around the Aegean. He studied philosophy in Athens and with Democritos in Abdera. He lived on the island of Thasos for three years from 410-407 B.C. Toward the end of his life, he lived chiefly in Thessaly and died in Larissa, where his tomb was to be seen as late as the second century A.D. His personality and contributions have made such an impact on the medical profession that it is evident even to this day. Of the 75 or more books which bear his name, very few are his. His sons, grandsons, and son-in-law were probably the early contributors, followed by physicians over several centuries. A group of books called *Epidemics* gives the symptoms and progress of disease in specific clinical cases and represents the medical experience of a particular group of physicians; there is a long discussion of epilepsy. *Surgical treatises* discusses the treatment of wounds, bandaging, conduct in the operating room (sounds quite modern), fractures, joints and dislocations of the hip, shoulder, and jaw (all almost the same as today). *Aphorisms* are short sentences upon the nature of illnesses and treatment, including sayings, proverbs, and such catch phrases as "Art is long, life is short, opportunity is fleeting." The Hippocratic oath starts off with "I swear by Apollo, the healer, and Asklepios, and Hygeia, and Pandora . . . that according to my ability and judgment, I will keep this oath."

The present form is probably from the 3rd century A.D. Miscellaneous treatises cover diet, exercises, and the influence of climate, water, and topography on the physical and intellectual life of people.

EPICHARMOS (540-450 B.C.) was a comedy poet who spent most of his life in Sicily. He left Cos at an early age and lived in Megara (Sicily) until the city was destroyed by Gelon (484 B.C.), after which he moved to Syracuse. He was the principal exponent of Sicilian comedies. His were of two classes, namely, mythological travesties and comedies involving different classes of the population. A statue of him was erected by the inhabitants of Syracuse.

POLYBOS (fl 400 B.C.) was the son-in-law of Hippocrates and the greatest of his successors. He may have been the author of the treatise *Nature of Man,* a discussion of humors, or the body fluids of man. The balance of four of these determined the health of the body.

PRAXAGORAS (fl 350 B.C.) was the second head of the Dogmatic school of medicine in Athens. He made a clear distinction between arteries and veins, believing that arteries carried blood and the veins, air. This idea is reflected in the names of the veins which drain the upper and lower extremities of the body, viz., the superior and inferior *venae cavae*. After death these veins are empty. His studies of blood vessels led him to investigate the pulse.

APELLES (fl 335 B.C.) was possibly the greatest painter of antiquity. It is not known just where he was born, but it is believed that he lived mainly in Cos and died there. He studied in Sicyon (west of Corinth) under Pamphilos and was the court painter to Philip and Alexander at Pella. After Alexander left, he lived in Cos, Colophon, Ephesus, and Rhodes. He painted many portraits of Alexander; one with a thunderbolt in each hand adorned the Artemision in Ephesus. For this Apelles was paid 20 talents ($21,600). Others include the "Procession of the High Priest at Ephesus," "Antigonos," and "Aphrodite Anadyomene." These were displayed in the Asclepion in Cos. The painting of Aphrodite, "Aphrodite Rising from the Sea" showed her wringing out her hair with falling drops of water forming a transparent veil around her form. The model for the figure is reported to have been Campaspe, Alexander's mistress. The picture was bought by Augustus for 100 talents and placed in the Temple of Julius Caesar in the Roman Forum. There is a story that in a competition involving paintings of horses, the pictures were shown to a group of horses. The only one to which the horses neighed was that by Apelles.

Apelles invented glazing to preserve his paintings and soften the colors.

PHILETAS (340-285 B.C.) was a poet, grammarian, and critic who had been called the founder of the Alexandrian school of poetry. He replaced Straton of Lampsacus in 294 B.C. as tutor to the crown prince who became Ptolemaios II Philadelphus. Others who studied with him were Zenodotos of Ephesus, who was the first librarian in Alexandria, and Theocritos of Syracuse, who was famous as a poet. In his *Atakta* he gives the meanings of rare and obscure words.

BEROSSOS of Babylon (fl 280 B.C.) was a priest of the Temple of Marduk who opened a school of astronomy in Cos about 270 B.C. He came from Antioch, where he had been engaged by Antiochos I of Syria and had written three books on the history of Babylon which were dedicated to him.

PTOLEMAIOS II Philadelphus (309-246 B.C.), the patron of the Museum and Library in Alexandria, was born in Cos. Domination of Cos changed from Macedonia to Egypt about 310 B.C. and the island was used by the Ptolemies as a summer resort

THEOCRITOS of Syracuse (fl 270 B.C.) was considered the creator of pastoral poetry. Very little is known of his life except what is gleaned from his poems. It is believed that he studied with Philetas in Alexandria during the period 277-275 B.C. and spent the rest of his life in Cos. His most delightful poems are pastorals, but he also wrote epics, lyrics, and mimes.

HERODAS (fl 260 B.C.) was the author of short gems of humorous dramatic scenes in verses, of a hundred lines, called mimes.

Rhodes

Homer's *Iliad* speaks of the nine ships manned by the "lordly Rhodians" who came from "Lindos, Ialysos and gleaming Kameiros." If the *Iliad* can be relied upon, Rhodes already had settlements of Achaeans around 1200 B.C. Dorians from the Argos district occupied the cities in the 11th century B.C. and were part of the Dorian Hexapolis along with Cos, Cnidos, and Halicarnassus. The cities were prosperous and founded other colonies, such as Soli in Cilicia, Gela and Agrigentum in Sicily, Arles and Nice (Nike) in France, and Rhoda in Spain. The Rhone River was Rhodamus. In 408 B.C. the three cities agreed to unite to found the city of Rhodos as the island's capital. It was laid out by the city planner, Hippodamos of Miletus. In the years that followed, the island was dominated by Sparta, Athens, Persia, and Macedonia (Alexander the Great).

In 304 B.C. the capital was beseiged by Demetrios Poliorcetes, which ended unsuccessfully when Ptolemaios I of Egypt sent his fleet to aid the defenders. The Rhodians gave Apollo the credit for their deliverance, and of the war machines left behind by Demetrios, they fashioned a hugh bronze statue 105 feet high. It took Chares of Lindos, the architect, 12 years to complete, in 281 B.C. The old Dorian word for statue was *colossos* and as the "Colossus of Rhodes," the statue was one of the ancient Seven Wonders of the World. It was felled by an earthquake in 224 B.C. and the ruins were not removed until 656 A.D., when a metal dealer required 900 camels to haul it away.

The island was sacked by Mithradates VI of Pontus in 88 and again in 69 B.C. In 43 B.C., Rhodes was sacked by Cassius Longinus for refusing to submit to his demands. It was the death blow to its commercial prosperity and the glorious artistic schools of rhetoric, philosophy, painting, sculpture, and astronomy. Its maritime law, however, continued to serve as a basis for marine codes as late as the Middle Ages.

The Crusades were partly "holy wars" to retrieve Jerusalem from the Moslems, partly a "pilgrimage" to the sepulcher of Christ,

RHODES
The harbor entrance viewed from the Crusaders' Castle.

partly an adventure, but behind it all, primarily political. Although
nominally eight Crusades in the two centuries from 1097 to 1291
A.D., it was really continuous warfare, with most of the activity an
internal struggle for power among the crusading participants themselves. Early in the 11th century, a hospital and inn had been rejuvenated by Benedictine monks and when the Crusaders besieged
the city, they were aided by these monks. When Jerusalem fell in
1097 A.D., the order was granted special privileges and organized
as the Knights of St. John the Baptist. It was primarily a nursing
brotherhood, with a rule that the sick gave the orders and the
brethren obeyed. In 1291 A.D. when the capture of Acre ended the
last foothold of the Christians in the Holy Land, the Hospitalers
moved to Cyprus, then under the control of a Genoese admiral. In
1309 A.D., with the help of the Genoese and the approval of the

Pope, they took over the islands of Rhodes, Cos, and Leros from the Byzantines. The Pope felt that as a militant body of Christians, they could do maximum damage to the Moslems and yet they were too far away to cause trouble to Catholic Christendom. The Genoese wanted them there for commercial reasons. Without the Crusades, their policy was dictated primarily by political and commercial considerations. Their antagonism toward Turkey was tempered by the fact that most of their trade and supplies came from the mainland. When Smyrna fell in 1330 A.D., the Knights built the fortress of St. Peter on a small island at the entrance to Halicarnassus. The city is now called Bodrum, a corruption of Bedros, the name for Peter.

The Knights were divided into eight language groups: Auvergne, Provence, France, Aragon, Castile, England, Germany, and Italy. There were five classes: Military Knights, Conventual Chaplains, Serving Brothers, Magistral Knights, and Knights of Grace. The last two were honorary, nominated by the Grand Master. The Serving Brothers were the soldiers, and the Chaplains, in addition to their religious duties, served in the hospital. The Military Knights, from whom the Grand Masters were chosen, had to be of noble birth for at least four generations—the Germans for eight. The Knights were aristocratic, arrogant, brave and ruthless. They lived in Auberges inside the citadel in the Street of the Knights.

Sultan Suleiman the Magnificent besieged the island with 200,000 men for six months in 1522 A.D. His loss was 90,000 men. Nevertheless, when the city fell, he agreed to honorable terms. The 78-year old Villiers de l'Isle Adam, Grand Master, was allowed to sail to Sicily with 180 knights and 5,000 Greeks. After eight years of exile, they finally ended up in Malta, allotted them by Charles V of Spain. Rhodes was saved from the devastation which overtook Moslem cities whenever they were captured by the Christians. It remained under Turkish rule until 1912 and then Italian until 1948, when it was restored to Greece.

Today's city of Rhodes is a pleasant combination of the old, within the imposing wall of the Crusaders, and the modern city outside. The Street of the Knights with the coats-of-arms outside the various inns; the palace of the Grand Master; the hospital, which is now a museum, with the delightful statue of the Rhodian Aphrodite; the buttressed houses in the narrow streets; the two-mile-long city wall with the wide moat on the inland side; the view of the harbor from the hill behind the palace—all lend to make it a picturesque setting. Two miles back from the sea is the acropolis of the ancient city with a few pillars from the Temple of Zeus and the nearby restored theater.

Of the three original settlements, Lindos is the only one now inhabited. Ialysos has practically disappeared, with only a 4th century B.C. Doric fountain and a 3rd-century temple to Athena, both on the acropolis plateau on top of Mount Philerimos, 9 miles west of the city of Rhodes. Kameiros, 20 miles west of Rhodes, has been excavated and shows the foundations, and even walls, of the buildings and an occasional column. There are six columns and their entablature at the top of the valley overlooking the city and the sea beyond.

Lindos is a small village of a thousand inhabitants, 34 miles south of Rhodes. It is situated at the foot of a 400-foot hill on top of which was the acropolis of the ancient city. Here are the remains of a small 3rd century B.C. Doric temple to Athena Lindos, a theater, a ruined Byzantine church, and the fortress of the Knights of St. John. It is a lovely site, but little to show for the cultural art center of ancient days. Prior to the Persian Wars, it was a thriving city of over 100,000 and the mother city of many colonies. It was the capital of the island until 408 B.C., when the capital was moved to the city of Rhodes. In the 6th century B.C. it was ruled by a tyrant called Cleobulos who was the author of the motto "Nothing to Excess" inscribed on the Temple of Apollo at Delphi.

APELLES (fl 335 B.C.), probably the greatest painter of antiquity, lived for a while in Rhodes.

PROTOGENES (fl 335 B.C.) was born in Caunos on the Carian side of the strait between Rhodes and the mainland. He was a painter noted for the minute and laborious detail in his pictures. Apelles said of him that he had only one fault, namely, he didn't know when to remove the brush from the picture. On one picture,

"Ialyssos," he spent seven years. The picture was still in Rhodes at the time of Cicero, but was removed to Rome where it perished in the burning of the Temple of Peace. Another picture, "Satyr," was being painted when the garden in which he was painting was in the midst of the camp of Demetrios Poliorcetes when the city was besieged in 304 B.C. The besiegers altered their plans to save him and his pictures. "Satyr" included a pheasant so lifelife that it detracted from the rest of the picture, whereupon Protogenes painted it out.

EUDEMOS (fl 335 B.C.) was a historian of mathematics, astronomy, and theology. He was a pupil of Aristotle and a contender for the head of the Lyceum, a position which was, however, filled by Theophrastos. A work entitled *Eudemian Ethics,* outlining the philosophy of life taught in the Lyceum, was either written by him or dedicated to him.

CHARES of Lindos (fl 290 B.C.) was the architect of the "Colossus of Rhodes." He was a pupil of Lysippos and founded the Rhodian school of sculpture.

APOLLONIOS of Rhodes (295-215 B.C.) was a Greek-Egyptian born in or near Alexandria. He was librarian at Alexandria from 240 to 235 B.C. and then retired to Rhodes, where he taught rhetoric. He was so popular that he was awarded citizenship and is always referred to as Apollonios of Rhodes. He wrote a poem on the foundation of cities, epigrams attacking Callimachos, with whom he feuded, and an epic poem, *Argonautica,* in four books.

MENECRATES (fl 200 B.C.) was the leading artist responsible for the frieze around the base of the Altar of Zeus at Pergamon.

BOETHOS of Chalcedon was a sculptor who flourished in Lindos about 180 B.C. He is known for the figure of a boy strangling a goose as he embraces it.

APOLLONIOS and TAURICOS of Tralles (fl c 180 B.C.) were adopted by Menecrates. They are the sculptors of the famous "Farnese Bull" group now in the National Museum in Naples and named after the family in Parma, Italy, that owned it. It was found in the Caracalla Baths in Rome and was restored under the supervision of Michelangelo. The group depicts the punishment meted out to Dirce for her treatment of Antiope: Antiope, the daughter of King Nycteus of Boeotia, yielded to Zeus. She fled to Sicyon and married King Epopeus. Her father killed himself after instructing his brother, Lycus, to bring her back. She was imprisoned and tormented by Dirce, wife of Lycus. Antiope's sons undertook to punish Dirce by tying her hair to the horns of a wild bull that dragged her to her death.

PHILISCOS (fl 2nd century B.C.) is believed to be the sculptor of the famous group of nine muses and statues of Leto, Apollo, and Artemis which were found in the Temple of Apollo in Rome.

HIPPARCHOS of Nicaea (190-125 B.C.) was one of the greatest astronomers of all time and an outstanding mathematician. His work is remarkable not so much for his theories as for the precise data and the resulting discoveries. He made observations in Alexandria during the period 161-146 B.C. and in Rhodes from 146 to 125 B.C. His only extant work is his commentary on the astronomical poem *Phainomena* of Aratos, so that most of the information about Hipparchos is from the writings of Strabo and Ptolemy. He rejected the heliocentric theory of Aristarchos and that repudiation was the death knell of that system. He shouldn't be blamed too much, for even Copernicus had to use epicycles and it took a Kepler to make it entirely acceptable. He was not entirely satisfied with either epicycles or eccentrics, although he agreed that either could explain the inequality of the seasons. He was inclined to accept the Pythagorean and Platonic ideas of the cosmos, as it was of divine origin and the only beautiful and rational motion is circular and uniform. However, he felt that the real system could be determined only by careful observations.

Hipparchos made daily observations of the sun and the moon. Comparing the figures of the sun and the stars (principally Spica) with those of Timocharis 150 years earlier and with much earlier Babylonian figures, he noticed that the sun took longer to return to its original position in the zodiac than from equinox to equinox. According to him, the sidereal year was 365 days 6 hours 10 minutes and the tropical year was 365 days 5 hours 55 minutes 12 seconds. The accepted values are 365 days 6 hours 9 minutes 9.5 seconds and 365 days 5 hours 48 minutes 46.08 seconds respectively. He decided the figure for precession was not less than 36″, compared with the accepted value of 50.26″. He also obtained an improved figure for the synodic month, namely 29 days 12 hours 44 minutes 3 seconds.

His catalogue of 850 stars included stellar coordinates, the first of its kind. He also recognized the need for spherical trigonometry and compiled a table of chords* to replace arcs. This was the first of its kind, the chord being equal to twice the sine of half the angle. Chords were not generally replaced by sines for a thousand years.

Much of Ptolemy's *Syntaxis* is based on results obtained by Hipparchos 300 years earlier.

PANAITOS of Lindos (185-109 B.C.) was a disciple of Crates in Pergamon and continued his studies in Athens under Diogenes of Babylonia and Antipatros of Tarsus. He taught in Rhodes and in Rome. He followed Antipatros as head of the Stoic school in 129 B.C. and tried to reject astrology and divination but did not succeed. He was instrumental, however, in extending the attractiveness of Stoic philosophy to the extent that, prior to Christianity, it became the ethical gospel of the more educated people, not only philosophers but statesmen and businessmen as well.

DIONYSIOS THRAX (b c 166 B.C.), so named because his father came from Thrace, was a disciple of Aristarchos of Samothrace in Alexandria and taught rhetoric in Rhodes and in Rome. His Greek grammar, *Techne grammatice,* is the earliest known and the prototype of all later grammars, not only Greek but others as well. It remained the basis of Greek grammars well into the 19th century and was one of the most successful books in the world. Dionysios did for grammar what Euclid did for geometry. It included accent, punctuation marks, pronunciation, syllables, and parts of speech. He was the first to interest himself in Hesiod's *Work and Days.* The Greek text of this work was printed in 1480 A.D.

---

*The term chord stems from the Greek word meaning "intestines." Its geometrical application comes from the resemblance of the chords to the gut strings of the lyre. Muslim astronomers used the Sanskrit word "jiva" for the half-chord, omitting the vowels. In translating into Latin, the wrong vowels were assumed to be the Arabic "jaib" meaning "bay" or "pocket." The Latin equivalent is *sinus.*

PHILON of Byzantium (fl 130 B.C.) was a military engineer who was the first to write on engineering arts. He invented the gimbal mounting used in ships' compasses. Although he spent most of his time in Alexandria, he did spend some time in Rhodes.

POSEIDONIOS of Apamea-Orontes (135-51 B.C.) lived for many years in Athens, where he was a pupil of Panaitos (185-109 B.C.), leader of the Stoa. He was an eloquent proponent of Stoicism and was an important disseminator of that philosophy to the Roman world. In the realm of science, he is known for his work on geography. He traveled extensively around the Mediterranean area and finally settled in Rhodes. In his travels, he visited mines in Andalucia and Galicia and spent a month in Cadiz studying the tides. He learned that there were three periods and was told by the natives about the spring and neap tides. Tides in the eastern Mediterranean are only about a foot, so that tidal periods are not as evident as in the Atlantic. Poseidonios was one of the first to associate tides with the combined action of the sun and the moon. Strabo reported his estimate of the earth's circumference to be 18,000 miles, a figure which may have been more encouraging to Columbus than the 25,000 miles of Eratosthenes. In 74 B.C. he began a universal history covering the period 144-82 B.C. in 52 books.

He went to Rome in 51 B.C. and died there the same year.

GEMINOS (fl 70 B.C.) was a Stoic philosopher and a pupil of Poseidonios. His only extant work is a book on elementary astronomy called *Phainomena,* but his main interest seems to have been mathematics. Only fragments survive of his *Arrangement of Mathematics,* a treatise in six books on the scope of mathematical science. It was the main source of a commentary of Proclus on Book I of Euclid. He divided mathematics into two classes, Pure and Applied. Pure mathematics included Arithmetic (ancient sense) and Geometry. Applied mathematics included Astronomy, Geodesy, Harmonics, Logistics, Mechanics, and Optics. He classified lines as straight, circles, conics, spirals, conchoids, and cissoids.

AGESANDROS, ATHENODOROS, and POLYDOROS (fl 60 B.C.) were the sculptors of the Laocoön group now in the Vatican Museum in Rome. It was set up in the palace of Titus on Equiline Hill in Rome and discovered in 1506 A.D. The right forearm of the boy on the right is a restoration in plaster. The group is fashioned from a single block of marble and the technical difficulties must have been tremendous. Laocoön was a priest of Apollo who offended the god by marrying and having children. He was chosen by the Trojans to propitiate Poseidon in the last year of the Trojan War. When the wooden horse of the Achaeans appeared, Laocoon threw his spear into it and urged the Trojans not to take it inside, saying, "I fear Greeks who bear gifts." Apollo, in the meantime, had sent a serpent to punish Laocoön for the offense against him and it crushed Laocoön and his two sons to death. The Trojans interpreted that as punishment for doubting the sincerity of the gift and took the horse inside. Troy fell.

CLEOMEDES (fl 40 B.C.) often mentions Lysimachia and he may have been born or lived there. The ruins of the town are at the neck of the Gallipoli peninsula, north of the Dardanelles and about 20 miles northeast of the Turkish town of Gelibolu. Cleomedes was a disciple of Poseidonios. Information on the measurements of the earth by Eratosthenes and Poseidonios has been obtained exclusively from his treatise *Cyclice Theoria Meteoron,* "Cyclical Motion of Celestial Bodies." It consists of two books. The first describes the earth as being finite but surrounded by an infinite vacuum. The celestial circles are defined, the five terrestrial zones are defined, and the consequences of the inclination of the zodiac on the equator are discussed. Book II explains the moon's phases, eclipses, discusses refraction and explains that atmospheric refraction accounts for the sun being still visible when it is actually below the horizon.

Perga

Perga is situated on a broad coastal plain 11 miles east of Antalya,* in a section of the southern coast of Turkey called

*Since the highway around the southwest corner of Turkey is extremely poor, it is recommended that access to Antalya from the west coast of Turkey be via Izmir.

PERGA

Pamphylia, which signifies "many races." The nearby Cestrus River provided access to the city from the sea, 6 miles distant. Perga was settled about the 12th century B.C. by a miscellaneous throng who accompanied the Greeks to Troy. The ancient city was probably on a small hill, about a third of a mile across, just north of the present ruins, which date from the Roman era. In Persian times, it may have been somewhat larger. The city readily submitted to Alexander the Great in 333 B.C. and in the Hellenistic era it was an important city surrounded by great walls. It had a famous temple to Artemis which is believed to have stood outside the walls, but no traces of it have been found. In 188 B.C. the city surrendered to the Romans and became prosperous; the theater and many fine buildings were built in the Trajan period (c 100 A.D.). During the Byzantine period, however, it declined in favor of Antalya.

The theater seated about 10,000 people and is fairly well preserved, although the orchestra is cluttered up with the ruins of the stage. There was a covered gallery on top. The horseshoe-shaped stadium was 770 feet long and the track 110 feet wide. The monumental entrance to the stadium is gone, but the barrel vaulting which supported the 12 rows of seats is fairly well preserved. The seating capacity was about 25,000. Both the theater and the stadium were outside the city walls. However, they were near the large entrance gate to the city, from which a colonnaded street led up to the acropolis of the ancient town.

Perga had two important neighbors to the east, Aspendos and Side. Aspendos was a large and important city in ancient days. It was founded by people from Argos in about the 10th century B.C. and was apparently called Estwedia in the 4th century B.C.; at least, that is the name on the coins of that period. The theater (2nd century A.D.) is one of the best-preserved in Asia Minor. There are 40 rows and a 312-foot covered gallery with a seating capacity of 7,500. A series of arched aqueducts is on the north side of town. Alexander the Great exacted a tribute of 4,000 horses from Aspendos.

En route to Side is "bottle town," in which, according to the guide, homes with a marriageable daughter display a bottle on the chimney. There were many there. Side was settled by colonists from Cyme in the 10th century B.C. Since there are no natural harbors on this part of the coast line, moles had to be constructed. Side was the most important city in Pamphylia and had the largest theater. At one time it was the center of pirates and slave trade, until Pompey (c 65 B.C.) burned all their boats, laid waste their settlements, and transferred some of their families to Soli.

An important sea battle took place near Side. Hannibal eluded the Romans in Carthage (196 B.C.) and sought refuge at the court of Antiochos III, the king of Syria. Antiochos, too, was at odds with the Romans and wanted to forestall their eastward movement. He sent an expeditionary force to Greece in 191 B.C. but was defeated at Thermopylae and a naval battle gave the Romans mastery of the Aegean. In order to regain it, Hannibal was sent to Phoenicia, where he outfitted 37 ships and sailed north. Near Side, he met the Rhodian fleet, allied with Rome, and was defeated. It was this victory which was commemorated with the statue "Winged Victory of Samothrace." One of the stipulations of the Peace of Apamea in 188 B.C. was that Hannibal was to be surrendered to the Romans. Hannibal, however, escaped to the court of Prusa in Bythinia, where he later committed suicide.

APOLLONIOS (262-205 B.C.), together with Euclid, dominated mathematics for 2,000 years—Euclid with plane and solid geometry and Apollonios with conics. He spent most of his time in Alexandria but is known to have spent some time in Pergamon and Ephesus. His main work is his *Conics* in eight books, the first three of which are dedicated to Eudemos of Pergamon and the last five to Attalos I. Apollonios applied the terms *parabola, hyperbola,* and *ellipse* to conic sections. He also generalized the theory of epicycles which had been proposed by Heracleides of Pontus, and introduced the theory of eccentrics. These two theories were basic considerations in the Ptolemaic system. He was known to his contemporaries as "The Great Geometer," but little is known of his life and he died in obscurity.

PAUL (1 B.C.-67 A.D.), born in Tarsus, was the principal exponent of Christianity, particularly after 47 A.D., when he preached in Perga independently of Barnabas for the first time.

Soli

Soli is the modern Pompeiopolis, about seven miles west of Mersin in the northeastern corner of the Mediterranean. This section of Turkey is known as Cilicia. It was settled by colonists from Argos and Lindos about 700 B.C., and later by Athenians, who called the town Soli. By the end of the 4th century B.C. it had become very prosperous, with a population of 250,000. Greeks who settled adjacent to people who did not speak Greek developed language peculiarities. Solians got a reputation for their poor Greek and gave the word *solecism* to the English language, meaning "ungrammatical combination of words in a sentence."

The city was destroyed in about 75 B.C. by Tigranes, the king of Armenia, and the inhabitants transplanted to a new royal city, Tigranocertes, on the border between Armenia and Mesopotamia. Soli was rebuilt by Pompey (c 65 B.C.) by settling there such of the pirates captured around Side as were worth saving, and renamed the city Pompeiopolis. An earthquake in the 6th century A.D. destroyed the vast city which extended from the sea into the foothills of the mountains. All that remains of the city of 250,000 people are 15 or 20 Corinthian columns on one side of a road and part of a mole in the harbor. The consoles projecting from the columns supported statuary busts.

SOLI

PHILEMON (361-262 B.C.) was a poet who wrote 97 comedies. He spent most of his life in Alexandria and Athens, becoming a full citizen of the latter city.

ARATUS (315-245 B.C.) was a didactic poet who studied in Ephesus under Menecrates, and in Athens, where he imbibed Stoicism from Zenon of Cition. He was invited to Pella in 276 B.C. by Antigonus Gonatas, king of Macedonia. Here he wrote *Hymn to Pan* and versified the description of the constellations by Eudoxos in a work called *Phainomena*. The last 422 verses had to do with weather based largely on the works of Theophrastos. In 274 B.C., Pyrrhos, king of Epiros, invaded Macedonia and Aratus went to Antioch, where he completed his edition of the *Odyssey*. When Antigonus regained the throne, Aratus returned to Pella.

CHRYSIPPOS (280-206 B.C.) was the third head of the Stoics in Athens (232-207 B.C.). He wrote 750 treatises and the contributions to Stoic philosophy were so great that it was said, "Without Chrysippos there would be no Stoa."

Tarsus

Tarsus lies about halfway between Mersin and Adana in Cilicia, a section along the northeastern coast of the Mediterranean. It is believed to have been settled by the Argives in about the 12th century B.C., but before that it was already an important Hittite town. It was strategically located in that from Tarsus ran the first wide road over the Tarsus Mountains, a road which even to this day is the main highway between this section of Turkey and Ankara. In addition, it had a good harbor, now silted up. The land is fertile and subtropical fruits thrive. Today, it impresses one as a well-kept and very orderly city with hard-top streets. Its population has dwindled to 35,000 and there is little to show of its brilliant past, as most of the extensive ruins are below the city and unexcavated. But it had its share of glory.

During the Seleucid period it became an important educational center and under the Romans it was one of the richest and greatest cities of the East. Cicero was governor between 51 and 50 B.C. In 41 B.C., Cleopatra came here to meet Marc Antony. Plutarch described the craft in which she came: "The stern was golden, the sails were purple, and the oars were silver. These, in their motion, kept time to the music of flutes, pipes, and harps. The Queen of the Nile lay on a couch of gold brocade." Emperor Julian made Tarsus his headquarters prior to invading Persia in 363 A.D. The Arabs invaded Tarsus in 641 A.D., the Turks in 1078, and the Crusaders in 1079. It was part of Armenia for three centuries and finally passed into the hands of the Ottoman Turks, at the beginning of the 16th century.

The people were very devoted to education, with many schools of rhetoric, philosophy, and education in general. Students completed their education abroad, but few returned. Many went to Rome. Tarsus produced three heads of Athenian schools: Zenon was head of the Stoa (207-180 B.C.), succeeding Chrysippos of Soli, Antiparos of Tarsus (fl 140 B.C.) was head of the Garden up to 129 B.C. and Crates was head of the Akademia (131-127 B.C.).

PAUL (1 B.C.-67 A.D.) was born in Tarsus. His Jewish name was Saul. He was converted in 36 A.D. and after he was ordained, he started his first missionary work in Cyprus. He preached in Perga and Antioch and gradually changed his name to Paul. His later voyages took him to Palestine, Asia Minor, and Greece. He was imprisoned in Rome for several years, and beheaded during the great persecution of Christians during the reign of Nero. Paul had never seen Jesus. His knowledge was derived from hearsay of the original disciples, primarily Barnabas. Paul introduced the idea of Jesus as a sacrificial person and so changed Christianity that he was considered its second founder.

Mallos

Mallos, 15 to 20 miles southeast of Adana, was at the mouth of the Pyramus River, near the city of Kiziltahta. It was founded by Amphilochos, who came from Troy after the Trojan War. All the stones of the ancient city, including those of the temple, have been removed and built into houses of neighboring villages. One stone with the inscription MALLOS was found in Kiziltahta, indicating that the city was nearby.

CRATES (fl 180 B.C.) was a grammarian, philologist, and director of the Pergamon Library. He spent some time in Rome as an ambassador from the court of Eumenes II in Pergamon. While there he helped organize libraries in Rome and promoted the Stoic doctrine.

Antioch

Antioch, now called Antakya, is situated on the Orontes River about 15 miles from the northeastern Mediterranean coast. Approaching from the north, one enters a large fertile plain about 50 miles from the city which is the site of the battle of Issus, 333 B.C. It was here that the army of Alexander the Great overwhelmed the Persian army and sent Darius III fleeing on horseback. He left behind not only the remnants of his army but also his harem, slaves, musicians, cooks, and camp followers. It was the second battle with the Persian army since Alexander had started his Asiatic campaign, the first being at Granicus. They were to meet once more, in 331 B.C. at Arbela, near Nineveh.

Antioch was founded on the east bank of the Orontes in 300 B.C. by Seleucus Nicator by transferring 5,300 former Athenian and Macedonian settlers from nearby Antigonia, which Antigonus Monophthalmos had previously founded in 307 B.C. Seleucus named the city after his father, the Macedonian Antiochos. It was strategically located from the standpoints of controlling trade routes and administering Seleucus' empire of Asia Minor, Upper Euphrates, and Palestine. Before his reign ended (305-281 B.C.), the empire extended from India to the Mediterranean and included Persia, Mesopotamia, Syria, most of Asia Minor, and part of Thrace.

Seleucus was assassinated in 281 B.C. by Ptolemy Ceraunos. Ptolemaios I Soter of Egypt had two sons—half-brothers—Philadelphus, who was the younger, and Ceraunos, the older. Laodice, the mother of the older, had been repudiated and Philadelphus succeeded his father in 285 B.C. Ceraunos went to Asia Minor under the protection of Seleucus, who thought Ceraunos might be useful in negotiation with Egypt. However, Ceraunos saw that Seleucus did not intend to reinstate him in Egypt. Seleucus wanted to be king in Pella and had crossed the Dardanelles on his way to win the city, when Ceraunos stabbed him to death outside the city of Lysimachia.

Antiochos I Soter (281-262 B.C.) endeavored to hold the empire together, repelling the Gauls, fighting the Ptolemies in Palestine, and checking the Attalids in Pergamon. Antiochos II Theos (262-247 B.C.) married a cousin, Laodice, but later repudiated her and married Berenice, the sister of Ptolemaios III Euergetes of Egypt. Laodice poisoned her ex-husband and had Berenice and her infant son murdered. This precipitated a reprisal invasion (246-243 B.C.) from Egypt. The greatest cultural advance occurred during the reign of Antiochos the Great (223-187 B.C.), a nephew of Antiochos Theos. He was anxious that Antioch should equal Alexandria with a museum, library, theater, art, and manuscripts. He maintained his empire but lost Asia Minor to Rome and had to sign the Peace of Apamea in 188 B.C. In order to raise money for the heavy indemnity, he plundered the temple of Bel in Elam but was killed by the Persian inhabitants. Antiochos IV Epiphanes (176-164 B.C.) was a patron of the arts but felt that it was his main duty to Hellenize Syria. In trying to get the Jews to give up their religion, he caused the Maccabean revolt. Both Greeks and Jews accused him of sacrilegious crimes and he died insane.

Altogether there were 21 kings who ruled Syria for 229 years, hardly any of whom died natural deaths. It is a record of poisons, assassinations, and murders, many of them by brothers, wives, mothers, and sons. Finally the people of northern Syria got tired of the endless quarrels among members of the Seleucid family and in 83 B.C. invited Tigranes, the king of adjacent Armenia, to rule. The city was comparatively peaceful until 64 B.C., when Pompey invaded and declared the region to be a Roman province.

At one time Antioch was considered the third city of the Roman empire in size and importance. It is little wonder that some of these cities are nothing but ruins when one considers the disasters that befell them. In the case of Antioch there were severe earthquakes in 37 and 115 A.D.; a large part of the population was deported to Persia in 260 A.D. by Shahpur I; Diocletian (c 305 A.D.) persecuted the Christians and destroyed all the churches; an earthquake in 526 A.D. killed 250,000 people; in 540 A.D., Chosroes I with the Sassanid army sent a large part of the population in captivity to Mesopotamia; Arabs captured the city in 636 A.D.; it was captured by the Byzantines in 969 A.D.; it was occupied by the Seljuk Turks in 1084 A.D.; 300,000 Crusaders were finally driven out of the city by disease and famine in 1098; sultans of Egypt and Syria captured the city and razed it in 1268; it was razed by Tamerlane in 1401 so that only 300 houses were occupied; Turkish Sultan Selim I captured the city in 1516; after World War I it was under the French Mandate of Syria from 1919 to 1939, after which it voted to join Turkey.

The history of Antioch is not pleasant reading.

The city played an important part in nurturing Christianity in the early days. In fact, the term *Christian* was first applied in Antioch. St. Paul lived there two years and St. Peter stayed several years. More than 30 synods were held in Antioch in ancient days. The Council of Nicaea accorded it the honor of ranking next after Rome and Alexandria. The hermit Simeon Stylites lived on his pillar for eight years, disapproving of the way of life in Antioch. Arius was a pupil and Nestorius was a monk in Antioch. The Antioch school of Christian thought saw the accomplishment of man's destiny in the union of divinity and humanity in Christ rather than a means to deliver man from the consequences of sin.

Antakya today has a population of 35,000 to 40,000 and combines the old and the new. The east side of the Orontes is the old, with small, dingy shops and poorly maintained streets. A busy bridge spans the river to the new section. Here are found wider streets, big homes and office buildings, and a new archeological museum with a large collection of mosaics. The fortified town was five or six times larger than the Antakya of today. The site of the citadel is three or four miles away and there are occasional towers of the old city wall.

BEROSSOS of Babylon (c 340 - fl 280 B.C.) was a priest of Marduk in Babylon. Antiochos I, anxious to develop a cultural center similar to the one in Alexandria, engaged Berossos to acquaint the Greek world with Babylonian history and astronomy. Berossos wrote three books on Babylonian history which were dedicated Antiochos I: I Origin to the Flood; II The Flood to Nabonassar; and III Nabonasser to the Death of Alexander. The principle that the stars affect the lives of men came from Babylonia. If the fate of a man depended on the position of the planets and stars at the moment of birth, it was necessary to determine these as accurately as possible. This was a function of the astronomers. The more scientific were called mathematicians; the more religious, priests.

Berossos opened a school in Cos in 270 B.C.

Apamea (Orontes)

Apamea on the Orontes is located in northwestern Syria about 125 miles due north of Damascus. It is near the town of Moudiq and is reached over 30 miles of poor road north and west of the town of Hama. The ancient city is being excavated by an archeological group from Belgium. There isn't much left of the old city and what there is, is mostly Roman. An ancient map shows an enlargement of the Orontes at this point into a rather large lake. Apamea was an important city in this region, being second only to Antioch. It was founded by Seleucus I Nicator (c 300 B.C.) and named after his wife, Apama. It replaced a military colony of Macedonia called Pella. It was a natural fortress upstream from Antioch and served as a military headquarters where the Seleucid kings stored their treasure, elephants, and horses. When Antiochos III (223-187 B.C.) was defeated by the Romans, he had to sign the Peace of Apamea in 188 B.C., which put an end to his influence in the Mediterranean. The Romans occupied the city after 46 B.C. and the population at that time was over 100,000. Apamea was destroyed by the Persians (Chosroes II) in the 7th century A.D. and by an earthquake in 1152 A.D.

POSEIDONIOS (135-51 B.C.) was one of the chief proponents of Stoicism and headed up the school in Rhodes. He was a well-known geographer and studied tides and their relation to the sun and the moon. He wrote a history covering the period 144 to 82 B.C. He went to Rome in 51 B.C. and died there the same year.

Phoenicia

Phoenicia was a tract of land between the Lebanon Mountains and the Mediterranean Sea, rarely over 30 miles wide and embracing roughly on the coast of present-day Syria and Lebanon. Homer refers to it as Sidonia. The land to the south, Palestine, was referred to as Ethiopia, the land of Cepheus, Cassiopeia, and Andromeda. Phoinis was the name bestowed by the Greeks; it signified "brightly colored" or "blood red." The main local industry of the Phoenicians was the extraction of a reddish-purple dye from the Murex shellfish. The Latin word for reddish-purple is *punicus,* and as Carthage was a Phoenician settlement, the Carthaginian Wars were referred to as the Punic Wars. Carthage was only one of their many settlements throughout the Mediterranean, as they were the most daring and skillful mariners. From Gades (Cadiz, Spain) they carried on trade with the Canary Islands, Britain, and possibly the Baltic, if that was the source of the great quantities of amber which they sold. Egyptian ships came to the Phoenician port of Byblos with papyrus in exchange for timber, tin, and resin (for embalming). As a result, Byblos became an important export center for papyrus. The Greeks adopted the name *biblion* for the papyrus roll and this in turn led to the word *Bible.*

The native name for the country was Kenaan, or Kna, signifying "lowland," in contrast to the adjoining Aram, the name of the highland of Syria. The name might have been derived from Kinahna, the Babylonian name for the Syrian coast. Although the Phoenicians claimed their cities were established in remote antiquity, they first appear in history about 1550 B.C., when the Egyptian empire began to expand after the Hyksos were expelled. Most of the information comes from the Tell el-Amarna tablets in the 15th and 14th centuries B.C., which mention cities of Acre, Tyre, Sidon, Beirut, Byblos, Simyra, Arvad, and Ugarit. Egypt dominated the country, although after about 1350 B.C. her power declined and ended altogether after about 1100 B.C. For a while the city-states governed themselves, after which the Assyrians ruled (876-605 B.C.), the Babylonians (605-538 B.C.), the Persians (538-333 B.C.), and then the Macedonians and Romans.

The people were an early offshoot of Canaanites. They believed they had originally migrated from the "Erythean Sea," that is, the Indian Ocean. Gradually Canaan included all of Syria and Phoenicia, and when the Israelites invaded Palestine, they applied the term *Canaanite* to all prior inhabitants of Palestine as well. The language was Canaanite, a subdivision of a North Semtic group. The invention of the alphabet must be considered of fundamental importance in the history of civilization and the Phoenicians rendered a great service in its development and diffusion.

UGARIT. The northern coast of Syria and its extension into Turkey was the site of a small empire with a capital and port called Ugarit. The city was mentioned in the Tell el-Amarna tablets (c 1350 B.C.), but until 1928 its location was unknown. About seven miles north of Latakya, near a small fishing-boat harbor called Minet el Beida ("White Port"), a farmer uncovered a stone slab while plowing his field. This disclosed a passage leading to a burial chamber. Among the rubbish, archaeologists discovered remnants of Cypriote and Mycenaean pottery of the 13th and 12th centuries B.C. Excavation of a mound less than a mile away led to the unearthing of the city of Ugarit, known in Arabic as Ras Shamra ("Cape Fennel"). The earliest strata were from about 2000 B.C., but the most rewarding finds were from the 14th to the 12th centuries B.C. Among them were images of the horned god El (the

Mighty One), Baal (Lord), a pseudonym for the chief god of Ugarit, and Anat, the Venus star-goddess. There were burial tombs which showed the Egyptian influence of belief in life after death, a palace, and a library with cuneiform tablets. The excellent museum at Damascus has a room set apart for Ugarit finds, which include ivory carvings, bronze stautettes, and gold trinkets. The most unusual object is a small terra-cotta tablet 3 by 2 by ¾ inches weighing 15 grams with 30 cuneiform symbols written left to right—the Ugarit alphabet. It is claimed to be of the 14th century B.C. Its origin is uncertain, one possibility being that it was an adaptation of cuneiform writing to an existing alphabet. However, there doesn't seem to be any other alphabet sufficiently developed at this early date which Ugarit scribes might have used as a base.

ALPHABET. *It is not possible to trace in its entirety the development of the alphabet prior to the Greek era.* The starting point is probably with the Egyptian hieroglyphic writing. Like Semitic scripts which evolved later, only consonants were written and the direction of the script was from right to left. Since the Middle East area was dominated by Egypt at various times, such influence is not unreasonable. From about 1500 B.C., it was apparently realized in several areas that a simplification of ideographic and syllabic writing would be advantageous.

a) Thirty-six inscriptions in the Sinai Peninsula, dating from about 1500 B.C., are believed to be the work of Egyptians associated with the turquoise mines. Although the inscriptions have not been deciphered, the number of characters is about 30, which indicates an alphabetic system. Seventeen of the symbols are unintelligible. Others are mainly copies of the simple Egyptian hieroglyphs, although there is no relation with the symbols which were used in the alphabetic sense when the Egyptians portrayed foreign words and names.

b) Eleven early Canaanite scripts on fragments variously dated from the 16th to the 13th century B.C. Some of these are in the museum in Jerusalem.

c) The Ugarit (Canaanite dialect) alphabet consisting of 30 cuneiform characters, dated in the 14th century B.C.

d) A pseudo-hieroglyphic script consisting of 114 syllabic signs, about 50 which are similar to certain Egyptian hieroglyphs. It was used for the Phoenician language from 1350 B.C.

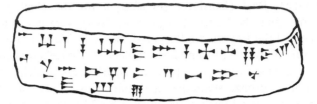

SKETCH OF THE UGARIT TABLET
Showing the 30 Cuneiform Symbols of the Ugarit Alphabet
(Damascus Museum)

THE MOABITE STONE

e) An epitaph inscribed on the 11th-century B.C. Akhiram Sarcophagus found at Byblos (now in the Beïrut Museum of Antiquities) is considered North-Semitic alphabet writing.

f) The Yekhimilk inscription in Beirut, the Gezer Calendar in the Museum of Antiquities in Istanbul, and the Roueisseh spearhead inscription are all of about the 10th century B.C.

g) The Moabite Stone (now in the Louvre) has a 34-line inscription commemorating the successful revolt of King Mesha against Ahab of Israel (c 869-850 B.C.). It was found at Dhiban in 1868.

Although these show a certain amount of activity in North-Semitic scripts striving toward an alphabetic system, there is no straightforward history of the development of the alphabet. But from the North-Semitic family of languages, there developed a 22-symbol consonantal script which was either Phoenician or adopted by the Phoenicians.

A Semitic language was particularly suited to a script without vowels, as the words were generally of one syllable with two consonants and one intervening vowel, or two syllables with three consonants and two intervening vowels. For instance, the Greek letter gamma was the Semite *gimel* (camel), which could be reppresented by the letters *g-m-l*. Omission of the vowels may lead to some misinterpretation but is no worse than what the reader of English encounters every day. The part played by the Phoenicians may have been primarily that of middlemen in perfecting and promoting the system. Because of their being the leading merchants in the Mediterranean area with extensive trade relations, it is possible that they appreciated the advantages of an alphabetic system more than their neighbors did. The alphabet of Tyre was the one used chiefly by the tribes of Moab and Syria. The Semitic names of the letters represent animals or objects common in the daily life of the inhabitants, but nowhere is there an explanation of all the characters.

Tradition, as related by Herodotus, states that the alphabet was introduced to the Greeks by Cadmus, the Easterner. He was a Phoenician, the brother of Europa. In searching for her after her abduction by Zeus, he founded Thebes in Boeotia. The story is that a cow led him to the site. As the head of an ox was the symbol of

GREEK NAME	SEMITIC NAME	APPARENT MEANING	SINAI SCRIPT	MOABITE	THERAEAN	CRETAN	IONIC	CHALCIDIAN	MODERN GREEK	LATIN
ALPHA	ALEPH	OX							A	A
BETA	BETH	HOUSE							B	B
GAMMA	GIMEL	CAMEL							Γ	C
DELTA	DALETH	DOOR							Δ	D
EPSILON	HE	WINDOW							E	E
ZETA	ZAYIN	WEAPON							Z	Z
ETA	HETH	FENCE							H	
THETA	TETH	WHEEL							θ	
IOTA	YOD	HAND							I	I
KAPPA	KAPH	BENT HAND							K	C CH K
LAMBDA	LAMED	OXGOAD							Λ	L
MU	MEM	WATER							M	M
NU	NUN	FISH							N	N
XI	SAMEK	SNAKE							Ξ	
OMICRON	'AYIN	EYE							O	O
PI	PE	MOUTH							π	P
RHO	RESH	HEAD							P	R
SIGMA	SHIN	TOOTH							Σ	S
TAU	TAW	MARK(SIGN)							T	T
DIGAMMA	VAU	HOOK							F	F
UPSILON	VAU								Υ	U
PHI									Φ	
CHI									X	
PSI									Ψ	
OMEGA									Ω	O
	TSADE									
	KOPH									Q

SOME ANCIENT ALPHABETIC SYSTEMS

involved in the development of modern alphabets. It is not possible to trace the step-by-step development of the alphabet prior to the Greek era.

the letter aleph, that letter was put at the head of the alphabet. However, the Phoenicians and the Achaeans were mariners and no doubt there were plently of opportunities for the Greeks to become acquainted with the alphabet. Since the construction of Greek words did not have the Semite form, an alphabet with only consonants was not entirely suitable. Supplying the vowels was a very brilliant step and its importance should not be minimized.

Fourteen letters were taken over directly: beth (beta), gimel (gamma), daleth (delta), zayin (zeta), teth (theta), kaph (kappa), lamen (lambda), mem (mu), nun (nu), samek (xi), pe (pi), resh (rho), shin (sigma), and taw (tau). Five of the consonant symbols which represented non-Greek sounds were changed to vowels: aleph (alpha), he (epsilon), vau (upsilon), yod (iota), and 'ayin (omicron). Four symbols were added: phi, chi, psi, and omega. There were several Greek alphabets which differed slightly from each other. The earliest was from the islands of the southern Aegean—Thera, Crete, and Melos. The two main divisions were the Ionic, or Eastern, and the Chalcidian, or Western. The Ionic, which was the one generally used, took the symbol H to represent the long e (eta) and gave up V and W. This alphabet was officially accepted in Athens in 402 B.C. At first only capital letters were used and it was not until the 7th or 8th century A.D. that small letters were introduced. The earliest extant Greek inscription was found on the island of Thera. This and other inscriptions engraved on stone date from the 8th century B.C. Writing from right to left was used because this was more convenient for a right-handed stonecutter. Later, in a period of indecision, alternate lines were right to left and left to right. The 6th-century civil code in Gortyn, Crete, employs this "as the ox plows" method called *boustrophedon*. For handwriting, left to right is more convenient for right-handed writers and by the 6th century B.C., that method was finally adopted. This probably coincided with greater use of records on papyrus, although the earliest extant documents date from the 5th century B.C.

Immigrants from Chalcis in Euboea to the Greek settlement at Cumae introduced the alphabet to Italy. This was not identical to the Ionic alphabet, so they retained the old signs for *L* and *S* and the older values of *H, F,* and *Q. Y* and *Z* were reintroduced about 100 B.C. The letter *C* originally represented a different sound, but when *K* was abandoned, *C* took its place. *G* was then invented to replace *C,* except for abbreviations. Letters *J* and *V* were originally used as initial letters for *I* and *U.* Later, they were assigned to distinct sounds, *V* in the 10th century A.D. and *J* in the 15th century A.D.

Cyrene

Cyrenacia is a small bulge of Africa projecting into the Mediterranean along the eastern coast of Libya due south of the mainland of Greece. The country seems prosperous, with much construction along the narrow strip of land between the desert and the sea. This is probably due to revenue from the newly developed oil fields.

Cyrene is located north of the town of Beida, about 135 miles east of Benghazi along the coastal highway. Cyrene itself is only a crossroads settlement called Shahat, but the ruins are extensive. They are situated on two terraces on a plateau which is about 1,800 feet above sea level and within sight of the sea eight miles away. The city was founded by Greek immigrants from the island of Thera (Santorin) about 631 B.C. A severe drouth over a number of years sent the leaders to the oracle of Apollo at Delphi for advice and they were told to found a colony in Libya. All Africa was called Libya at that time. Some 200 men under a leader, who took the name of Battus, sailed to Crete to pick up a pilot and then continued on to Libya. Their first settlement on a small island was not satisfactory and they moved on to the mainland to a site near a spring named after a nymph called Kurana, Kurene, or Cyrene. The economy of the colony depended on corn, wool, dates, olives, and, primarily, a herb called silphium.

Battus ruled for 40 years and was succeeded by his son Arcesilaos. For eight generations, the names of the kings were alternately Battus and Arcesilaos. Uprisings against the rulers seemed to be a customary thing, including the republican form of govern-

CYRENE
The Fountain and Sanctuary group on a terrace below the commercial group.

ment which was set up in 440 B.C. About 325 B.C. a Spartan adventurer called Thibron arrived with 7,000 mercenaries, which led to an intervention by Egypt. In 300 B.C., Magus, the stepson of Ptolemaios I, was installed as governor and ruled for 50 years—after 283 B.C., as king. His daughter Berenice married Ptolemaios III Euergetes. A new city was founded to replace the silted-up Hesperides and named after her. It is now called Benghazi. Cyrenacia was ruled by the Egyptian Ptolemies until 163 B.C., when the brother of Ptolemaios VI Philometor broke a ruling partnership and was given Cyrenacia and Cyprus as his own realm. When Philometor died in Palestine in 145 B.C., the brother succeeded to the Egyptian throne. Since he had apparently gotten obese in Cyrenacia, the disrespectful Alexandrians called him Physcon ("potbelly"). A mistress, Irene, had borne him a son who, as Ptolemy Apion, was Cyrenacia's last Greek ruler. In 96 B.C. the Romans took possession.

Jewish revolts (115 A.D.) marred the Roman rule, with some 200,000 people killed. The land was littered with corpses and soaked in blood, with the cities half destroyed. Reconstruction was

begun under Hadrian and contemporary inscriptions hailed him as
the founder of Cyrene. But it was not until the end of the 2nd
century that restoration was complete. The exception was the
Temple of Zeus, the columns of which had been overturned by the
Jewish rebels. A severe earthquake and tidal wave in 365 A.D. was
particularly disastrous for Cyrene and a number of temples and
what was left of the Temple of Zeus were desecrated as an act of
purification. Arabs overcame the Byzantine garrisons in 643 A.D.
and they in turn were overcome by new Arab conquerors. When
western Arab lands revolted against Cairo in 1046 A.D., rugged
uncultured tribesmen were given a camel and a piece of gold and
told to "go west." The industrious and peaceful population could
not hope to resist the mass migrations of desert tribesmen and
Cyrenacia's economy declined.

The partial excavations of the city may be grouped in three
areas. The city was situated on top of a plateau overlooking a
rolling plain of red earth out toward the sea, eight miles distant.
The Roman group on top of the plateau includes the great rectangular Forum, with internal porticos and a temple to Bacchus in the
center. Behind is the Odeon filled with rubble, a stoa with 13
defaced or weather-worn figures of Hermes and Heracles, and a
group of buildings surrounding the Greek agora. To the left of the
Forum are a Roman theater and the ruins of numerous small
structures, including the official palace, temples, and administrative
buildings.

The Fountain and Sanctuary group lie on a terrace below the
commercial group described above. In this area are a number of
fountains, baths, a number of small temples, and, most conspicuous of all, the Temple of Apollo. The temple had eleven unfluted
Doric columns viewed from the side and six from the ends. Seven
are standing. At the western end of the Sanctuary terrace is a large
theater. Originally it was of the usual Greek pattern and of it only
the upper rows of seats survive. In the Roman period, the theater
was rebuilt to make it more suitable for gladiatorial combats and
spectacles involving wild beasts. The lower row of seats were
eliminated to provide protection for the spectators. Seats were

provided on the seaward side, but these have since collapsed.

About half a mile to the northwest of the areas described are the ruins of a hippodrome and the Temple of Zeus. The temple was 225 feet long and 104 feet wide and is believed to date from about 500 B.C. Jewish rebels in 115 A.D. undercut and overturned the outside rows of columns and they were never re-erected. Reconstruction of the interior of the temple involved removing the twin Doric interior colonnades and erecting a colossal seated statue of Zeus. It was completed in 185 A.D., but the structure was destroyed by an earthquake in 365 A.D. and later by the Christian population, which wrecked everything that remained visible. The statues were chopped up and the whole interior was burned. The temple remains are a few scattered pillar drums, capitals, and one re-erected column.

Nearby is a small but very interesting museum with several copies of the "Three Graces," a restored copy of the "Aphrodite of Cyrene" (the original is in the Terme Museo Nationale in Rome), and other objects from the excavations.

THEODOROS (b c 470 B.C.) was a Pythagorean philosopher in Cyrene who was introduced in Plato's *Theaetetus* as a famous mathematician. It is believed that both Plato and Theaetetus were taught by Theodoros. The Pythagoreans determined that the square root of 2 could not be expressed by a simple number; it was not rational. Theodoros determined the square roots of 3, 5, 6, 7, 8, 10, 11, 12, 13, 14, 15, and 17 were also irrational. Numbers of this type did not fit into Pythagorean philosophy. Eudoxos showed that they could be represented as the limit of a converging series of fractions.

ARISTIPPUS (435-356 B.C.) was the founder of the Cyrenaic school of philosophy. While in Athens, he became a pupil of Socrates. Socrates held that virtue was the only human good but admitted that happiness did play a part. Aristippus based his philosophy on happiness alone, denying that virtue, logic, and physical sciences had any value. Virtue was good only in so far as it produced pleasure. Pleasure was the only criterion of "goodness," and bodily pleasure, being simpler, was preferred. However, he did temper his philosophy by holding that true pleasure can only be achieved by one who is self-controlled and master over himself. His daughter Arete and her son Aristippus the Younger (*ho metrodidactos*, "mother-taught") carried on after his death. Later, the teachings were modified so much by Anniceris that the school was called Annicerian.

CALLIMACHOS (c 310-240 B.C.) was a poet and grammarian who opened a school in the suburbs of Alexandria and was appointed librarian in 260 B.C. His principal achievement was cataloguing the books of the Library. He also laid the foundation of the history of Greek literature.

ERATOSTHENES (276-194 B.C.) was Cyrene's most illustrious son. He was educated in Athens and was appointed a Fellow in the Museum in Alexandria in 244 B.C. Nine years later he became the Librarian. His greatest achievement was his measurement of the circumference of the earth. He endeavored to establish the chronology of Greece from the time of Troy.

CARNEADES (213-129 B.C.) was the founder of the Third, or New, Akademia. His main philosophy seems to have been his opposition to the Stoicism of Chrysippos. He was sent as an ambassador to Rome on a mission and gave a series of lectures that attracted much attention. His audience was attracted by his reasoning and the fluency of his language. His reputation was so high in Greece that other philosophers attended his lectures.

Tarentum

Tarentum (Taranto) is located in the top-inside of the heel of the Italian boot. It is the most enterprising city in southern Italy— a busy port, a naval base, with considerable industry, and well laid out and provisioned. Its population is about 200,000. The city occupies a peninsula through which a channel was cut during the time of Ferdinand of Aragon (c 1500 A.D.) to provide access between the two harbors. It is guarded by a castle-fortress of about the same period. Nearby is the only Greek relic of the past — two fluted columns of a Doric temple. There is, however, an excellent museum with interesting sculpture pieces, a large collection of pottery, and an outstanding collection of most extraordinary 4th century B.C. jewelry. An unusual feature of the harbor is the cultivation of mussels, with the beds mounted on networks supported by rows of poles. The tarantula gets its name from Taranto.

There was a permanent Greek settlement in Tarentum when a group of Spartans came there in 708 B.C. During the Messenian War (735-715 B.C.), with the Spartan soldiers away from home, slaves and others fathered children by Spartan women who became known as Partheneioi (offspring of maidens). They were rejected at home and so, led by Phalanthus, they migrated to Tarentum. The city became a democracy in the 5th century B.C. and reached the peak of its prosperity in the 4th century B.C. At that time it was the first city in Magna Graecia in its wealth and artistic culture. Friction developed between Tarentum and Rome in 282 B.C. and, knowing that she was no match for Rome, Tarentum invited King Pyrrhos of Epiros to assist. Pyrrhos was anxious to head an empire and eagerly accepted. In 280 B.C. he landed with 25,000 men and several hundred elephants. Pyrrhos won, but the victory was dearly bought. When he was congratulated on his victory, he replied that one more such victory would be his undoing.

PHILOLAUS (b c 480 B.C.) was either a member of the Pythagorean Brotherhood in nearby Metapontinon or well acquainted with their doctrines. They did not commit any of their doctrines to writing and it is believed that the first publication is that of Philolaus. His book *Physios* may have formed the basis for part of Plato's *Timaeus*. He pictured the universe as being spherical with a central fire at the center. To explain why this fire was not apparent at night, he proposed an anti-earth which shaded the earth from it. This seems to have been unnecessary, as it was on the back side of the earth and couldn't be seen anyway. The earth with its shadowing anti-earth and other celestial bodies revolved around the central fire. The orbital period of the earth was 24 hours; that of the sun, one year. Although far from representing an accurate picture, there were two ideas that had an element of novelty not prevalent at the time, namely, that the central fire was the center of the universe and not the earth, and that the earth and anti-earth turned on an axis once a day.

Following the disbanding of the Pythagorean Brotherhood about 450 B.C., Philolaus taught in Thebes for a while. After his return to Tarentum, he had Archytas among his pupils.

ARCHYTAS (fl c 400 B.C.) was a general, a politician, a philosopher, a mathematician, and the elected governor of Tarentum seven times. Plato visited with him on his trip to Syracuse in 388 B.C. Although the information was known to Thales, Archytas is credited with knowing the relationship between the sides of a right triangle and the segments of the hypotenuse produced by a perpendicular to the hypotenuse from the vertex. He distinguished harmonic progression from geometric and arithmetric. His solution of the duplication of the cube involved a cylinder, a torus, and a cone. He is claimed to have invented the screw, the pulley, and a wooden pigeon that could fly. Aristotle wrote the special treatise *On the Philosophy of Archytas*. Archytas is reported to have died in a shipwreck in the Adriatic.

ARISTOXENES (fl c 335 B.C.) was associated with the Lyceum in Athens and was one of the contenders for head of the institution when Aristotle retired. He is remembered primarily for introducing semi-tones in the musical scale. He wrote 453 books on music, philosophy, history, and education. He was considered the greatest musicologist of antiquity.

HERACLEIDES (fl c 75 B.C.) trained in the Herophilean school of medicine in Alexandria. He was the most famous physician of the ancient Empirical school, which made use of the new anatomical and physiological developments of the time. He wrote the earliest work on veterinary medicine and experimented with drugs, including opium. He reconciled theory with experience and, because of his wisdom, the school produced some of the leading physicians of antiquity. He wrote a most important work on pharmacology, therapeutics, and dietetics called *Materi Medica*.

Metapontinon

Metapontinon (Latin, Metapontum; Italian, Metaponto) is located on a wide coastal plain 24 miles southwest of Taranto.

METAPONTINON VIEWED FROM THE MUSEUM
This was the site of the Pythagorian School 510-450 B.C.

The name stems from *Metabos,* signifying "the place between two rivers," the Brandanus and the Casuentas. Its symbol was a spike of barley. There are several legendary tales regarding its original settlers: veterans from the Trojan War who had sailed with Nestor; Achaeans from northern Peloponnesus and Boeotia; Daulios, a tyrant from near Delphi; and an Achaean named Leukippos, whose head adorned their money. The colony was wiped out by the Samnites, a warlike tribe in southern Italy who were an offshoot of the Sabines. The city was resettled in 700 B.C. by Achaeans from Sybaris and Croton as a buffer between Taranto and Sybaris.

The city expanded during the 6th century B.C. and increased in importance. The hexagon-shaped city was laid out with a rectangular grid of streets inside a four-mile city wall. The agora was in the center and the main avenue ran approximately north and south. Near the center were a theater and a Doric temple dedicated to Apollo Lyceios. The temple measured 186 by 92 feet, but only the foundations are left.

Two miles north of the city walls, on the main coastal highway, is the excavation of Tavolo Palatine with a Doric temple (c 500 B.C.) dedicated to Hera. The temple base measures 110 by 46 feet and had 12 columns on the sides and 6 as viewed from the ends. Of these, a group of 10 on one side and of 5 on the other are standing. The site is well kept up, very attractive, and has a small but excellent museum.

It was to here that Pythagoras moved his school from Croton in 510 B.C. He died in 497 B.C. and was entombed in the wall of the theater. The tomb was still there in the 2nd century A.D. The Brotherhood was entirely disbanded about 450 B.C. It had lasted about 80 years.

In the Second Punic War, Metapontinon sided with Carthage and its fortunes faded with Rome's victory (202 B.C.) Aerial photographs taken ten years apart (1950-1960) show that even in that short time, the inroads of agriculture have obliterated many traces of the ancient city, such as roads and the theater.

Sybaris and Thurii

Sybaris and Thurii were located in the western corner of the instep of the Italian boot. Sybaris was founded by the Achaeans in 720 B.C. between the Crathis and Sybaris rivers. The main reason for its being was to avoid the tolls, pirates, and navigational hazards of shipping through the Strait of Messina. Transportation to the western coast of Italy was overland to some port, such as Paestum (Posidonia) or Laus. The city prospered and the people lived in such affluence that *sybaritic* became known as a synonym for luxury. It ruled over four tribes and twenty-five subject cities. The population of the community must have been considerable, as in the war with Croton it mustered an army of 300,000.

In 511 B.C. a man by the name of Telys brought charges against 500 of the most wealthy and influential citizens and persuaded the Sybarites to confiscate their estates. The men fled to

Croton and took refuge in the temples near the agora. Telys demanded their return but was refused and Sybaris declared war. Croton's 100,000 troops under the command of Milo, the athlete, routed the Sybarites and many perished. Sybaris was plundered and laid waste, with the course of the Crathis diverted to obliterate the last trace. Fifty-eight years later (452 B.C.), former Sybarites and their descendants tried to resettle the site but were driven out by Croton. In 444 B.C. they tried again at a site near a spring called Thuria.

Athens supported the new community. Herodotus, the historian, helped found the new city. Hippodamos of Miletus did the city planning, and Protagoras provided the constitution. Internal strife soon became evident, however, as the former Sybarites were assigning the most important offices to themselves. They were outnumbered by the new citizens and in the end practically all of the original Sybarites were put to death.

The railway station at Sybaris stands alone in an expansive valley with widely scattered farmhouses. If one inquires where the town of Sybaris is, the reply is: "Sybaris? This is it!" And so it is —only a railway station. Thurii and Sybaris were deeply covered with earth eroded from nearby hills that it was not before 1953 that coring tools brought up some potsherds. Some tombs were found under 25 feet of heavy clay soil. There are some excavations 2 miles southeast of the railway station but the sites are mainly under water.

HERODOTUS of Halicarnassus (484-424 B.C.) was a famous historian who started his career by traveling extensively in Greece, Asia Minor, Persia, Babylonia, the Black Sea region, Phoenicia, Palestine, Egypt, and Magna Graecia. He left Halicarnassus in 447 B.C. for Athens, where he became the intimate friend of Sophocles, Pericles, and others. He was not eligible for citizenship in Athens, but he was so popular that the city awarded him the sum of ten talents. He joined a group of colonists and helped found Thurii in 443 B.C. From then on, he seems to have been involved in finishing his *Histories,* comprised of nine books: I History of Croesus and War with Persia; II Egypt; III Conquest of Egypt by

Persians; IV Conquest of Darius Against Scythians and Libyans;
V Persians Invasions of Thrace and Ironian Revolt; VI Persian In-
vasion of Greece; VII Death of Darius and Invasion of Greece by
Xerxes; VIII Salamis and Withdrawal; IX Defeat of Persians at
Mycale and Plataea.

Croton

Croton, the modern Crotone, is a busy city of 87,000 inhabi-
tants near the ball of the Italian boot, with the picturesque Castello
Carlos overlooking the port. The dominant industry is chemical.
It prides itself on being "La Citta di Pitagora." It wasn't always so.

There is a story that veterans returning from the Trojan War
stopped at the mouth of the nearby Neaethus River for inspection
and supplies. The Trojan women were weary of the voyage and
burned all the ships. Croton in 710 B.C. became an Achaean colony, led by Mysceles. It was eminently successful in athletics and
in one Olympian festival the seven men who surpassed all the
others came from Croton. The most famous was Milo (c 520 B.C.),
who was crowned six times at Olympia for wrestling, and six times
at the Pythian games in Delphi.

When the Sybarites attacked Croton in 510 B.C. because of
the latter's refusal to give up 500 wealthy citizens who had sought
refuge in Croton, the Sybarites were defeated and their city was
razed. The victory stimulated warlike spirits in Croton and in their
conflict with Locri in 480 B.C., an army of 130,000 Crotonians was
routed by 10,000 of the enemy. The loss was so great that it
marked the beginning of the decline, and Croton became a prey
to succeeding invaders. In 277 B.C. when the Romans occupied
Croton, the city walls were 12 miles long, but more than half of
the area had ceased to be inhabited. After Hannibal's victory over
the Romans at Cannae in 216 B.C., Croton revolted against Roman rule and Hannibal made his winter headquarters there for
three years. The city finally capitulated to the Romans in 193 B.C.

Nothing is known of the exact site of the ancient city or its
remains. However, about six miles out on a mountainous peninsula
of gray rock and terminating in Capo Colonna, there is a single

column still standing of the Temple of Hera Lacinia. It was a 5th century B.C. structure with 48 fluted Doric columns 27 feet high. In addition, some of the building foundations have been excavated.

PYTHAGORAS of Samos (580-497 B.C.). Very little is known of the early life of Pythagoras. The usual story is that he studied with Thales at Miletus, and traveled extensively in Greece, Egypt, Babylonia, and Crete before settling down in Croton about 530 B.C. at the age of 50. Having an attractive personality and pretending to have divination powers, he gathered some 300 young men and formed a brotherhood which ever since has served as a model for secret societies. They practiced abstention from certain kinds of foods, lived simply, and avoided woolen clothes, a custom he learned in Egypt. Women were admitted as well as men and all wore distinctive garments and went barefooted. Their symbol was a five-pointed star with the points labeled Hy-g-e-i-a.

They regarded earthly life as a hiatus in the real life. The soul could leave the body and could, temporarily or permanently, transmigrate to the bodies of other men or animals. For many, the Brotherhood was a religious sect, as they did not understand the philosophical and scientific aspects. Destruction of Sybaris by Croton may have been instrumental in the Pythagoreans' seeking a voice in the civic affairs of the city. But it only caused trouble and the Brotherhood moved to Metapontinon in 510 B.C. After the death of Pythagoras, persecutions increased and the group succumbed about 450 B.C. Although the school lasted only about 80 years, the direct and indirect effects upon Western civilization are still evident. Plato spoke of the Pythagoreans but never of Pythagoras. Apparently all information was issued in the name of the Brotherhood rather than of any individual.

Much of their mathematics dealt with numbers. Since even the use of letters for numbers was not yet known, pebbles were used. The root of the word *calculate* signifies "pebble." As the first numerologists, the Pythagoreans were devoted to associating their philosophy of man and nature, harmony and soul, good and evil, and the cosmic order, with numbers. The two main divisions of numbers were the *odd* and the *even*. Odd numbers were either prime or factorable. There were two classes of even numbers. One class encompassed numbers that could be successively divisable by a number of 2's, for example 16 which gave successively quotients of 8, 4, 2, and 1. Adding these up gave the original number minus 1, in this case 15, or 16 — 1. Then there was a class which were divisable by 2 only once, such as 2, 6, 10, 14, 22 etc. These had the characteristic that of the divisor and quotient, one was even and the other odd, for example 30 = 5 x 6.

Even numbers could also be classed as excess, deficient, or perfect. In the case of excess, the sum of the fractional parts is greater than the number. For example, with the number 24, the fractional parts 1, 2, 3, 4, 6, 8, and 12 add up to 36. With a number like 14, the fractional parts 1, 2, and 7 add up to 10, or less than the number. For a number like, 6, the sum of the fractional parts 1, 2, and 3 equals the number 6. These perfect numbers are very rare, only four less than 10,000, namely 6, 28, 496 and 8,128. The fifth is 33,550,336. They discovered that a square number was equal to the sum of all the odd numbers that were less than twice its root; e.g., $25 = 5^2 = 1 + 3 + 5 + 7 + 9$.

Another problem which interested the Pythagoreans was that of the *application of areas*. This involved drawing upon a given line a figure of the same area but of a different shape than another. The base would either fit, fall short of, or exceed the length of a given straight line. For these cases, the terms *parabole, ellipsis,* and *hyperbole* applied. The method provided a geometrical solution of a quadratic equation and was employed by Apollonios in his treatment of conic sections.

They may have proved, or at least they knew that the interior angles of a triangle total two right angles. The so-called Pythagorean theorem, that the square of the hypotenuse is equal to the sum of the squares of the other two sides, was known to the Babylonians long before Pythagoras. The Babylonians may even have developed a formula for computing simple triads in which this relation holds. However, a geometric proof may be due to the Pythagoreans. The problem may have come up in connection with the determination of the length of the diagonal of a square. They were dismayed to learn that the square root of 2 was not a finite number. How could numbers be so irrational? It upset their philosophy of numbers and they were only reconciled by Eudoxos' statement that it could be represented by the limit of a series of fractions.

They knew 11 different kinds of means but studied only 3: the arithmetic mean, $a - b = b - c$ or $b = (a + c)/2$; the geometric mean, $a : b = b : c$ or $b^2 = ac$; the harmonic mean, $1/a - 1/b = 1/b - 1/c$, which reduces to $b = 2ac/(a + c)$.

Their interest in various kinds of series led to the development of the diatonic musical scale. It was well known that the combinations of certain tones were pleasing. From the strings of musical instruments, they knew that the shorter string produced tones of higher pitch and that pitch was a function of the number of vibrations per second. They were aware of the phenomenon that by "stopping" the vibration of a string in the middle, a higher-pitched tone could be heard. This is the first harmonic, an octave higher. The step-by-step development might have proceeded somewhat as follows:

Step	Relative Frequency								
1	1							2	Fundamental and an octave higher
2	1				3/2			2	The sonant combination
3	1			4/3				2	If 3/2 is a good ratio, what ratio multiplied by 3/2 = 2? *Ans.* 4/3
4	1		5/4						A very sonant combination
5			5/4				15/8		A tone which is 3/2 higher than the 5/4 tone
6				4/3		5/3			A tone which is 5/4 higher than the 4/3 tone
7		9/8			3/2			9/4	A tone which is 3/2 higher than the 3/2 tone and an octave below

The net result is a series of frequencies which have been developed from the simple ratios 2/1, 3/2, 4/3 and 5/4, to which letters of the octave have been assigned:

1	9/8	5/4	4/3	3/2	5/3	15/8	2
C	D	E	F	G	A	B	C'

Combinations of these tones gives us:

First major chord

1	5/4	3/2	2	ratio of frequencies
C	E	G	C'	notes on the scale
4	5	6	8	relative frequencies

Second major chord

1	4/3	5/3	2
C	F	A	C'
3	4	5	6

Third major chord

9/8	3/2	15/8	9/4
D	G	B	D'
3	4	5	6

Note that the relative frequencies of the notes of the chords follow the general pattern 3, 4, 5, 6. This is the diatonic scale developed by the Pythagoreans. The next step was taken by Aristoxenes, attached to the Lyceum in Athens. He computed semi-tones, thirds, fourths, and fifths of tones. In the final analysis, only the semi-tones were used, but since they vary slightly in the various scales, compromise values had to be chosen. Twelve tones were selected in the octave range with an interval ratio of 1.059. This is called an evenly tempered scale.

Their idea of harmony extended also to the universe. The earth was spherical because it was a perfect solid; the motions of the planets were circular and uniform; their distances from the earth were in accord with simple ratios. The "music of the spheres" even entered into Kepler's speculations with his planetary system 2,000 years later: Saturn by a very low G and Mercury by an E seven octaves and a major sixth higher.

DEMOCEDES (fl 520 B.C.) was the first Greek physician of note. He is said to have served Polycrates in Samos (ruled 532-522 B.C.) and to have been detained in the court of Darius in Susa. By strategy, he effected his departure and returned to Croton. His daughter was married to Milo, the athlete.

ALCMAION (fl 500 B.C.) was the first teacher in the first medical center in Greece. He was a disciple of Pythagoras. He investigated the sense organs and was the first to attempt a surgical opera-
tion on the eye.

Cumae

Cumae was one of the first cities to be settled in Magna Graecia, the period being early in the 8th century B.C. It was located
about 12 miles west of Naples. Though no scientists are known to
have been associated with Cumae (Kyme), it is of interest because
the city was inadvertently involved in bestowing the name of
Greece. Among the settlers were some from Boeotia who worshiped the Graeae, or at least were associated with them in the
minds of the indigenous people. The Graeae were three horrible
sisters who possessed but one eye and one tooth among them. To
the indigenous people surrounding Cumae, all Greeks were Graeci.

Elea

Elea is the present-day Velia, about 75 airline miles south of
Naples. The excavation covers an area only about 300 feet square
on the land side of the railroad tracks and about a quarter of a
mile from the sea. Apparently there are no traces of the three-mile
city wall. There is no real harbor. In fact, there is no natural harbor on the west coast of Italy south of Naples. On top of a 400-
foot hill to the north of the site is a medieval castle, Castellamare
della Bruca.

There seems to have been an early Phoenician settlement here
called Hyele. The name was changed by the Phocaean colonists
to Elea, possibly after a spring called Ele, or after a river called
Elees, (Alento), or after the Asia Minor town of Elea, not far
from Phocaea. After the capture of Phocaea by the Persian general
Harpagus in 546 B.C., most of the inhabitants embarked with their
whole families on their light boats under the leadership of Creontiades. Some didn't get any further than Chios, but most sailed on
to Cyrnus (Corsica) and Massalia (Marseilles), where they already had flourishing colonies. In Corsica they plundered their

Etruscan neighbors, who fought back. The Phocaeans won, but both participants suffered and after five years they left for Hyele.

XENOPHANES of Colophon (570-480 B.C.) left his home town when it was conquered by Cyrus and apparently spent most of his life traveling before finally settling in Elea sometime after 500 B.C. In his travels he is reported to have found sea shells in mountainous strata and fossils of fish and seals in the quarries of Syracuse, indicating that the land had once been under the sea. His theosophy was more pantheistic than monotheistic but definitely not polytheistic. Theophrastos summed it up as "The All is One and the One is God." Xenophanes started the Eleatic school, but the real founder was Parmenides.

PARMENIDES (b c 510 B.C.) is considered to be the real founder of the Eleatic school. He was a metaphysicist and believed that absolute truth could be attained only by logic. Because our senses are imperfect, observations and experiments might lead us astray. He was the first to classify the temperature zones of the spherical earth into a broad equatorial zone, two temperate zones, and two arctic zones. In physics and astronomy, the philosophy was similar to that of the Pythagoreans. He conceived the universe to consist of spherical shells concentric with the earth and reasoned that the earth was at the center because there was no reason for it to go elsewhere.

The influence of the Eleatic school on physics and mathematics was considerable. They were the first to submit thought to critical examination. The distinction between perception and reason was emphasized and phenomena had to be reconciled with the laws of logic.

ZENO (b c 480 B.C.) followed Parmenides as head of the school. He is remembered primarily for the paradoxes he proposed, one of which is the story of Achilles chasing the tortoise. Even though Achilles ran much faster than the tortoise, if space and time were divided into infinitely small parts, he would never catch it. As soon as Achilles reached the point where the tortoise was a moment ago, the tortoise would have moved on just a little, and so on ad infinitum. Another was that of an arrow in flight: since it occupies space, it must also be at rest.

Syracuse

Syracuse was the chief city of ancient Sicily and was founded in 734 B.C. by Greeks from Corinth. Led by Archias, they settled on an island called Ortygia. For over 200 years, its history is rather fragmentary. In 485 B.C., Gelon, tyrant of Gela, took possession of the city, but his rule was mild. His brother and successor, Hieron (478-467 B.C.), was greedy and cruel, but he did encourage poets and philosophers. The people rebelled and for 50 years they had a democratic government. Spurred by the ill advice of Alcibiades, the Athenians sent an expedition to Syracuse in 415 B.C. in an attempt to establish an empire in Sicily. With the help of Corinth and Sparta, the Athenians were defeated. Few of those who sailed, either with the original or with the relief expedition, ever returned. Seven thousand Athenians were interned in the city's quarry to slave and to die.

By questionable means and mercenaries, Dionysius I emerged as a tyrant in 405 B.C. and remained in power for 38 years. He was the cruelest tyrant that Hellas ever produced. But Syracuse prospered and grew in size, population, and grandeur. Its fleet was the most powerful in the Mediterranean. There are two stories about Dionysius which bear repeating. When Damocles, one of his courtiers, spoke in lyrical terms about the life of a tyrant, Dionysius invited him to make merry at a banquet with a dagger suspended by a horsehair over his head. In the story of Damon and Phintias, the latter was condemned to death but requested a delay that he might put his personal affairs in order. Damon offered to be security for his friend's return. When Phintias did return, Dionysius was so impressed by their faithfulness that he freed them both. Dionysius claimed to be a philosopher and welcomed Plato on a visit in 388-387 B.C.

His son Dionysius II was advised in 367 B.C. by his uncle, Dion, to bring Plato to Syracuse for a second visit. However, there were others in the court who advised against reform. Dion was banished and Plato escaped with difficulty. Dion lived for a while in Athens and returned in 357 B.C. and gained control. He was assassinated three years later. Corinth was appealed to for a new ruler and Timoleon gave them a popular government for 20 years. After his death, a splendid monument with porticos and a gymnasium was erected in his honor. Revolutions, oligarchies, tyrants, and the Carthaginians kept Syracusans occupied. Rome controlled the entire peninsula of Italy by 272 B.C. and, later, all of Sicily except Syracuse.

Independence was insured under Hieron II by making a treaty with Rome. An equitable tax system was developed, new buildings were constructed, the Greek theater was rebuilt, a temple to Athena with doors of ivory and golden doorknobs was erected, the Venus Anadyomene in the National Museum in Syracuse was sculptured and science prospered under Archimedes.

With Hannibal's success in Italy, Hieronymus, the grandson of Hieron II, decided to ally himself with Carthage, but a popular outbreak ended with the murder of him, his family, and many of the conspirators. However, the Carthaginian faction got the upper hand. The Roman pro-consul, Marcellus, marched against the city in 213 B.C. and a year later the siege was over. Marcellus gave the city up to plunder and Archimedes perished in the confusion.

At the height of its splendor in the 5th and 4th centuries B.C., Syracuse had a population of 300,000. Today it is a modern city of about 100,000 but has preserved a number of interesting vestiges of the past. The 5th century B.C. theater is one of the largest and best preserved of ancient Greece. It was hollowed out of solid rock and the 59 rows of seats were shaped for the comfort of the spectators. It is 440 feet around at the top and has resonant chambers to improve the acoustics. The Roman amphitheater is of the 2nd century B.C. and the entrances and covered gangways for the animals and the gladiators can still be seen. The cathedral (640 A.D.) is built on the site of the Temple of Athena (460 B.C.) and incorporates 28 of the original 36 columns with masonry between some of the columns. The fresh-water Fountain of Arethusa is separated from the salty Mediterranean by only a roadway.

EPICHARMOS of Cos (540-450 B.C.) was a comic poet. He left Cos at an early age and spent the rest of his life in Sicily. He first lived in Megara, until that city was destroyed by Gelon (484 B.C.), and then moved to Syracuse. He was the principle exponent of Sicilian comedies based on the lives of different classes of the population and on mythological travesties. The people of Syracuse erected a statue of him.

AESCHYLUS of Eleusis (525-456 B.C.) is considered the father of Greek drama. No one surpassed him in the number of times his plays won in competition. He was invited to the court of Hieron I in 476 B.C. on the occasion of the founding of a new town called Aetna on the site of present-day Catania. For this, he composed the play *The Women of Aetna*. On a second visit, in 472 B.C., *The Persians* was produced. Aeschylus returned again to Sicily in 458 B.C. and died two years later in Gela.

HICETAS (5th century B.C.) was a Pythagorean astronomer who asserted that the earth turned on its axis once every 24 hours.

THEOCRITOS (fl 270 B.C.) was considered the greatest poet of the Hellenistic age. Very little is known of his life except that he studied in Alexandria (277-275 B.C.) and spent the rest of his life in Cos. He wrote delightful pastorals and also epics and lyrics.

ARCHIMEDES (287-212 B.C.) was primarily a mathematician and a physicist. He spent some time in Alexandria with his friend Eratosthenes, but lived mostly in Syracuse. He had many inventions to his credit, among them the hydraulic screw still used in Egypt for irrigation, compounded pulleys, a hydraulic organ, ballistic machines, an endless screw (cochlias), and an orrery which demonstrated eclipses. He is said to have used large concave mirrors for reflecting the sun's rays on enemy ships, perfected grappling hooks, designed catapults, and strengthened the defenses of Syracuse.

The treatise *On the Sphere and the Cylinder* discusses mensuration of spheres, cylinders, and cones. The area of a sphere is shown to be equal to four times the area of a great circle, that is, $4\pi r^2$. In *The Measurement of the Circle,* π is determined to lie between 3 1/7 and 3 10/71 (between 3.142 and 3.141). This was determined by inscribing and circumscribing regular polygons up to 96 sides. These methods had been used by Antiphon (c 430 B.C.) and Bryson (c 430 B.C.). He suggested a scheme of numer-

THE ARCHIMEDES SCREW
An Egyptian method of irrigation.

ation for large numbers in the *Sand Reckoner* with numbers arranged in octads, or the eighth powers of 10 (10^8). This provided for numbers up to 10^{80} and made multiplication possible by the equivalent of adding exponents. The system was applied to estimating the number of grains of sand in a sphere the size of the universe.

On Floating Bodies treats of specific gravity and shows that the loss of weight of a submerged body is equal to the weight of the displaced liquid, and a floating body diplaces its own weight of the liquid. There is the story of his problem to determine whether Hieron's crown was all gold or whether the goldsmith had introduced some silver. While taking a bath, either the overflow or the buoyancy suggested the solution and he ran through the streets exclaiming "Eureka! Eureka!" ("I have found it"). The overflow, or the difference in the weight of the crown in and out of water, enabled the volume to be determined and from that the specific gravity.

In his *Equiponderance of Planes* he devolped the principle of the lever and an expression is attributed to him: "Give me a fulcrum on which to rest and I will move the earth." His *Quadrature of the Parabola* shows the area of a segment of a parabola to be two-thirds that of a circumscribed parallelogram. He also wrote on Spirals, Conchoids, Spheroids, Paraboloids, Hyperboloids, Ellipses of revolution, and the Theory of Mirrors.

When General Marcellus, the Roman pro-consul for Sicily, besieged Syracuse in 212 B.C., Archimedes was killed by a Roman soldier. One story is that the soldier suspected Archimedes of carrying gold; another, that he was working on a problem and refused to obey the soldier until he had finished. Marcellus was much disturbed by the incident and endeavored to make some amends to Archimedes' kindred.

On his tombstone was inscribed the figure of a sphere and a cylinder, since he regarded this field as his greatest contribution.

Akragas

Agrigento, the ancient Akragas, is located in about the middle of the southern coast of Sicily and about two miles from the sea. It was founded about 582 B.C. by settlers from Gela and in time came to rank second to Syracuse in importance, and possibly first in wealth and splendor. When the Pythagoreans were driven out of Croton in 510 B.C., some found refuge in Akragas. Throughout its history, it has found itself in the path of war: internal Sicilian, Carthaginian, Roman; and in World War II, American amphibian forces landed at Port Empedocles. It is still an important commercial city, with a population of nearly 50,000, and is the capital of the province. Nevertheless, the center of interest is in the ruins of the ancient Greek city of "Golden Akragas." It was fabulous in wealth, its joy of luxury a byword and its beauty fatal. It was said of it that the people built as if they were to live forever and feasted as if they were to die on the morrow.

There are ruins of no fewer than ten temples in the city:

Demeter, Hera Lacinia, Concordia, Heracles, Zeus, Castor and Pollux, Hephaestus, Asclepius, Athena, and an unnamed temple. These are among the earliest and the largest temples in classical Greece. The temple of Zeus, 361 feet long and 173 feet wide, was the largest in the Greek world, outranking the Artemision at Ephesus by a few feet. There were 38 columns, 62 feet in height and 14 feet in diameter. A man could stand in the flutings. Huge male figures called Telamones, 25 feet high, stood on consoles between the columns and appeared to support the entablature. The foundation supports went down 29 feet. The temple was still unfinished in 405 B.C. when the Carthaginians plundered the city, and in 1756 A.D. many of the limestone blocks were used to build the harbor moles in Port Empedocles.

The temple of Heracles dates from about 510 B.C. and is believed to be the oldest of the Agrigento temples. Its length was 220 feet and its breadth 85 feet. Eight of the thirty-eight 33-foot columns have been raised and the others are a jumble of ruins.

The Temple of Concord was built as a Temple of Hera between 450 and 440 B.C. It is the most massive, most majestic, and best-preserved of the Doric temples in Sicily. Its present name is from an inscription nearby. Its length is 130 feet, its breadth 55 feet. The temple is very similar to the Temple of Hephaestus in the Agora in Athens; both with 6 and 13 columns facing the front and sides respectively, the structures are intact except for the roof, and they were erected about the same time. One characteristic of Sicilian temples which differs from the ones in Greece proper is that they were not constructed of marble but have a stucco facing. In most cases, the stucco has nearly all disintegrated.

The Temple of Hera Lacinia dates from about 460 B.C. and gets its name from the Temple of Hera Lacinia in Croton.

EMPEDOCLES (c 492-433 B.C.) was a physician, physicist, orator, poet, social reformer, and philosopher. He assumed the elements of all animate and inanimate life to be fire, air, water, earth, love, and hate. He taught that at first, everything was a mixture held together with love. Strife separated the elements, and eventually love will prevail and things will again be a chaotic unit.

He stated that blood issues from the heart and flows back to it. He taught that the highest form of human life was the prophet and the physician; and in some respects, he was both. His skill in medicine and natural philosophy enabled him to do things which were passed off as miracles. He had marsh lands drained and he reformed the government.

He went robed in purple with a sash and sandals in gold, wore a Delphic laurel-wreath crown, and was followed by a train of attendants. Eccentric though he was, he apparently served Akragas well, for he was urgently invited to be her king. He refused.

He is said to have ended his life by jumping into the crater of Mount Etna. His name is perpetuated in the name of Agrigento's port, Port Empedocles.

PART THREE

EGYPT

EGYPT is at the southern end of the Fertile Crescent and consists of the Nile Delta, a 10- to 15-mile strip of arable land along a thousand miles of the Nile, and the desert. This seems surprisingly little to develop and support the wealth and culture of ancient Egypt. Not only does it seem little at best, but prosperity was dependent on the not always dependable flooding waters of the Nile every June to October. Evidently it was adequate, and for an indefinite formative period of a thousand years or so before 3100 B.C., communities developed from an intermingling of Paleolithic hunters, nomadic Libyans, Nubians and southwestern Asians. These gravitated into the Upper and Lower reaches of the Nile.

Egypt's history begins with Mena (King Narmer), the first pharaoh of the united kingdom, with the capital at Memphis. Little is known of the first two of priest Manetho's 32 dynasties before Alexander the Great. They lasted until 2686 B.C. A hieroglyphic form of writing was developed during this period and also a cursive script for use with the newly invented papyrus writing material. Egypt's history from then on is usually divided into three distinct eras of prosperity: the OLD KINGDOM (2686-2270 B.C.), an intermediate period; the MIDDLE KINGDOM (2160-1786 B.C.), a second intermediate period; and the NEW KINGDOM (1567-1085 B.C.). Then followed a period of decline with ten foreign dynasties down to Cleopatra (30 B.C.), the last of the Ptolemaic dynasty. After that, the nation came under the domination of the Romans, the Moslems in 640 A.D., and the Turks in 1517-1919 A.D. Some of the outstanding rulers and events during this long history are outlined below.

OLD KINGDOM, 2686-2270 B.C. Memphis was the capital of Egypt throughout most of its early history. It was an unimportant town when first selected, with a local god, Ptah. In keeping with the importance of a capital city, Ptah was raised to the top of the Egyptian pantheon, and a name for the city was Hakeptah, home of the *ka* of Ptah. The name Egypt is believed to be a Grecian corruption of Hakeptah. In the VI Dynasty, the white walls of the palace and pyramids may have suggested the name Men-nefer, which gradually became Memfi and the Latin form Memphis. Once

STEP PYRAMID OF SAKKARAH

one of the great cities of the world, 15 miles in length along the Nile and 3 miles wide, there remain but an alabaster sphinx and a prostrate statue of Rameses II.

The Step Pyramid of Sakkarah was erected during the reign of King Zoser, who headed the III Dynasty. This is the oldest free-standing man-made masonry structure in the world. The architect was Imhotep, Zoser's grand vizier and physician, who was later deified under his own name. SNEFRU built two pyramids, a step pyramid in Maidun and another at Dashur. He initiated a large ship-building program. There were three kings in the IV Dynasty: KHUFU (Cheops), with the largest pyramid at Giza which took 20 years to build (c 2650 B.C.), KHA-EF-RE (Chephren), and MEN-KAU-RE (Mycernius). This was the age of great pyramids and the lion-bodied Sphinx, representing Cephren, which was carved from bedrock. The grandeur of the art of this period was formalized and remained the pattern for a thousand years. The V Dynasty kings worshiped Re, the sun, rather than Horus, as their ancestor.

THE GIZA PYRAMIDS AND THE SPHINX

One of the best of the pyramid temples is that of SAHU-RE. In the
VI Dynasty, PEPI II reigned for 94 years (2364-2270 B.C.), the
longest reign in the history of the world.

INTERMEDIATE PERIOD, 2270-2160 B.C. Little is known of the
VII to X Dynasties of this decadent period. Kings of Heracleopolis
(70 miles south of Cairo) ruled the Nile Valley north of Abydos
and princes of Thebes (Karnak) ruled the south. Several rival
pharaohs ruled at the same time.

MIDDLE KINGDOM, 2160-1786 B.C. The princes of Thebes
founded the XI Dynasty, which gradually occupied the whole country. The XII Dynasty was started by Minister of State AMENEM-
HET I. He had to reorganize the country and removed the capital
to Lisht, near Memphis. During his 30-year reign, there was great
building at Thebes and foreign expansion into Nubia and Syria.
AMENEMHET IV died childless and his sister-wife Sebeknefru married a commoner. The eight rulers of the XII Dynasty had ruled
for 213 years. Upper Egypt seceded and Dynasty XIII and XIV

HATSHEPSUT MONUMENT AT THEBES

ruled at the same time. When the country was near exhaustion, the horse-drawn chariots of the Hyksos (Greek for "shepherd king") from Syria conquered and ruled Egypt for 200 years.

INTERMEDIATE PERIOD, 1786-1567 B.C. The history of the Hyksos dynasties, XV, XVI, and XVII, is very obscure. They were finally forced out of Egypt into the Sinai Peninsula by SEKENENRE. The Rhind Mathematical Papyrus was copied during this period (c 1650 B.C.).

NEW KINGDOM, 1567-1085 B.C. This period is characterized by the building of grand palaces, tombs and temples around Thebes. The XVIII Dynasty was founded by AHMOSE I, a stepson of Sekenenre. It is the best-recorded and a most important period in the history of Egypt. TUTHMOSIS I, grandson of Ahmose I, conquered Nubia and lands northeast as far as Syria. He added to the Temple of Amon at Karnak, which in time became the greatest of the existing temples in the world. A son, TUTHMOSIS II, succeeded with his wife and half-sister HATSHEPSUT but ruled only two or three years. During this time, he placed his son by a concubine, TUTHMOSIS III, on the throne while he warred in Nubia. When Tuthmosis II died (c 1500 B.C.), Hatshepsut assumed power, ruling in masculine attire and wearing a false beard. Egypt prospered under her rule. She extended the empire with trade, restored worship in the temples, which had not recovered from the Hyksos rule, continued the expansion of the Karnak temple of Amon, and built the most elaborate and impressive temple on the west bank of the Nile at Thebes. In his 22nd year, Tuthmosis III came to power. After the death of Hatshepsut, a violent reaction set in and essentially all inscriptions and sculptured figures of her were defaced. Tuthmosis III is possibly the greatest ruler in the history of Egypt. He subdued revolting city-states in western Syria as far as Carchemish on the Euphrates, was an efficient administrator at home, educated the children of subdued vassals in Asia who were held as hostages, and established the empire on a sound basis.

AMENHOTEP III, great-grandson of Tuthmosis III, came to the throne at the height of Egypt's glory. He married a non-royal lady called Taia. The earliest of the letters known as the Tell-el-Amarna tablets date from this period (c 1400 B.C.). The temple at Luxor and the avenue of the rams are a product of his reign. He lived in great luxury at Luxor and did everything to enhance his position. Statues of himself exceed those of every other pharaoh. Two of them at Thebes were called the Colossi of Memnon by the Greeks after an Ethiopian king killed by Achilles in the Trojan War. The top of the northern one toppled over as the result of an earthquake and every morning as it was heated up by the sun's rays, a sharp twang would be heard. This was said to be Memnon's voice greeting the dawn. The phenomenon ceased when the statue was remounted. AMENHOTEP IV (1375-1357 B.C.) was married to the oft-portrayed Queen NEFERTITI. He was effeminate and given to mysticism and philosophy. One story is that his mother, of Syrian birth, was opposed by the priests and she may have influenced her son. Another is that he endeavored to establish a religion which could be adhered to throughout his empire. He renamed himself AKHNATEN, abolished hundreds of Egyptian deities in favor of Aten, the Sun, and established a new capital, Akhetaten (now Tell el Amarna), about halfway between Luxor and Cairo. The site has been the source of many cuneiform clay tablets in the Akkadian

PART OF TEMPLE AT LUXOR

international diplomatic language. He was succeeded by his son-in-law TUT-ANKH-AMON (1353-1344 B.C.), who restored the old religions and moved the capital back to Thebes. He died at the age of 18 and his queen Ankh-Es-En was pressurized by the old priest AY to marry him so that he might rule. She shrank from it and wrote a letter to the Hittite king Suppiluliumas offering to marry one of his sons. The Hittite prince was ambushed at the Egyptian border and Ay usurped the throne. A northern general and commoner HAR-EM-HAB seized control after a few years, re-established a strong government, and ruled for 20 years.

The XIX Dynasty (1320-1205 B.C.) was founded by RAMESES I (General Pa-Ramessu), who ruled for two years and planned the great colonnaded hall at Karnak. His son SETI I ruled for 21 years and suppressed invaders in Palestine, furthered building at

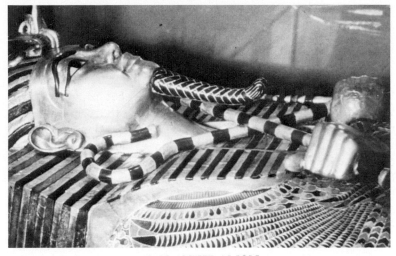

TUT-ANKH-AMON
GOLDEN HEADPIECE FROM COFFIN (1344 B.C.)
Note the shepherd's crook and the flail, symbols of the god Osiris. He
was probably of Syrian origin and taught the Egyptians agriculture.
(Egyptian Museum, Cairo)

Karnak, and restored damaged monuments and inscriptions of
Akhnaten. His son RAMESES II (1298-1232 B.C.) was a great
builder of palaces, temples, monuments, and a family. He had 7
queens, 79 sons, and 31 daughters. He completed the Karnak temple and carved out the Temple of Abu-Simbel. He made treaties
with the Hittites and commerce flourished. Israelites came to
Egypt because of a famine in Canaan. They prospered, but Rameses oppressed them to the extent that they returned to their land.
Towards the end of his long reign, and in the reigns that followed,
there were many petty invasions throughout the empire, particularly from Libya and Asia Minor. A Syrian, SETNEKHT, founded the
XX Dynasty (1205-1085 B.C.) and his son RAMESES III spent
much of his reign halting these invasions. He was the last of the
great pharoahs. (Pharoah is the Hebraized form of the Egyptian

Per-o, which means "royal palace.") There was too much peace and prosperity, the country degenerated, the pharoahs became lazy, the officials neglectful, and the peasants unhappy. The priestcraft, in the meantime, acquired much of the property of Egypt (it was estimated at 15 percent). Nine other kings by the name of Rameses followed in an 80-year period. But they could not cope with the increasing strength of the Amon priesthood and the dynasty was finally overthrown by the high priest, HERITHOR.

LATE EGYPTIAN PERIOD, 1085-30 B.C. This period is characterized by kings of Ethiopia, Nubia, Assryia, Persia, and Greece. During the XXV Dynasty under TIRHAKA, Assyrians under Essarhaddon invaded Egypt and captured Memphis (671 B.C.). The administration was entrusted to native chiefs with a single Assyrian garrison. Tirhaka soon returned and Essarhaddon organized a second expedition (668 B.C.) but died on the way. His son Assurbanipal did return and sacked Thebes (663 B.C.) so that it never recovered. King NECHO of Sais on the Delta and Memphis headed the reinstated governors and founded the XXVI Dynasty (663-525 B.C.), followed by his son PSAMMETIK. By 655 B.C., the Assyrians had lost control. They were victorious everywhere but at the cost of complete exhaustion. By the end of Psammetik's reign (610 B.C.), Egypt had regained part of its prosperity. Trade with other nations brought in new ideas, the arts flourished, and piety increased. Psammetik's son NECHO II (610-594 B.C.) set out to regain Syria and other lands to the north but was disastrously defeated by Nebuchadnezzar at Carchemish. In 525 B.C., Egypt was conquered by Cambyses of Persia. Under Persian rule there were four puppet dynasties before Alexander's army seized Egypt in 332 B.C.

After Alexander's death, his general in Egypt, PTOLEMY (367-283 B.C.), ruled as regent and after the murder of Alexander's son, assumed the throne in 306 B.C. as PTOLEMAIOS I SOTER. He was considered to have been a half-brother of Alexander, as his mother Arsinoë had been a concubine of Philip before she married Lagus. He was a good soldier and administrator, and the creator of Egyptian prosperity. He initiated and gave both moral and financial support in the founding of the famous cultural center in Alexandria. He was first married to Eurydice, the daughter of Antipater, by whom he had one son, Ptolemaios Ceraunos. Eurydice had brought her niece Berenice along with her to Egypt. Berenice was the widow of a Macedonian soldier, Phillipus, by whom she had one son, Magus, who later ruled Cyrene. Eurydice was repudiated and Ptolemaios married Berenice. There were three offspring: Arsinoë II, Ptolemaios II, and Argaeus. He reigned until 285 B.C., when, at the age of 82, he abdicated in favor of his second son.

PTOLEMAIOS II PHILADELPHUS (285-247 B.C.) was first married to Arsinoë I, the daughter of Lysimachus, one of Alexander's generals, and his first wife Nicaea. There were two children, Ptolemaios III and Berenice Syra, who married Antiochos II. Arsinoë I was accused of plotting to kill her husband and was banished to Upper Egypt. Ptolemaios then married his sister, Arsinoë II. She was a woman of extraordinary beauty and intelligence and was considered one of the greatest of Hellenistic queens. She had been the second wife of Lysimachus. After his defeat and death in 281 B.C., she married her stepbrother Ptolemaios Ceraunos in his scheme to rule at Pella, but he immediately banished her to Samothrace. He died shortly thereafter and Arsinoë fled to Egypt. Before her death in 270 B.C. she was deified as Arsinoë Philadelphus. The surname Philadelphus properly belongs only to her and applies to her husband only by courtesy. Cities were named for her and a temple, Arsinoë Aphrodite, was dedicated to her on the promontory of Zephyrium east of Alexandria. In the 38-year reign of Ptolemaios Philadelphus, he did his utmost to enrich the Library at Alexandria and attract productive scholars to the Museum. He brought the corpse of Alexander from Memphis and entombed it in Alexandria. Incidentally, he introduced camels into Egypt. Although Egypt during his reign rose to a high rank among nations in power and wealth, behind the glittering facade of Alexandria the country was poor in spirit and hardly knew happiness. Theoretically the Pharaoh was the sole owner of Egypt, but practically he had been merely the head of a country where property and private rights were respected. The Ptolemies took the theory at face value and placed everything under the state, confiscating earnings by excessive taxation and penalties. To maintain such a system, hordes of officials were required. As a result, there was a feeling of dull despair; revolts only resulted in massacres.

PTOLEMAIOS III EUERGETES (Benefactor) (247-222 B.C.) brought the dynasty to a climax in his 25-year reign. His wife was Berenice, the daughter and successor of Magus, king of Cyrenacia. Her sister-in-law, also named Berenice, was married to Antiochos II, king of Syria. Upon his death, his former wife, Laodice, murdered Berenice and her infant son. Ptolemaios. In order to avenge his sister's murder, ordered an expedition to Syria (246-243 B.C.) and his queen vowed to dedicate her tresses to the Goddess of Beauty if he returned safely. On his return, Queen Berenice's hair was accordingly deposited in the Temple of Arsinoë at Zephyrium. When it later disappeared, the astronomer Conon consoled the pair by publicly announcing that Zeus had taken the queen's locks and placed them in the heavens as Coma Berenices. It has been said that our word *varnish* stems, through variations, from the name Berenice because of the resemblance of the color of varnish to her amber-colored tresses.

Decline set in during the reign of PTOLEMAIOS IV PHILOPATER from 222-205 B.C. Like all the Ptolemies who followed, he was corrupted by luxurious living. He was a debauchee, murdered his mother, and was ruled by his courtiers and mistresses. He married his sister Arsinoë III, who was burned to death in a deliberately set palace fire.

PTOLEMAIOS V EPIPHANES (ruled 205-180 B.C.) was only five years old when he succeeded to the throne and much of his reign was under a series of regents. He married Cleopatra, the daughter of Antiochos III, and had three children: a daughter Cleopatra, a son who became Ptolemaios VI Philometer, and a younger son, who became Ptolemaios VII Euergetes. Philometer married his sister Cleopatra and ruled in Egypt. Euergetes was assigned to rule in Cyrenacia. Philometer was killed in a battle near Antioch in 145 B.C. Philometer's infant son was proclaimed king, but Euergetes rushed from Cyrenacia, killed the infant, seized the throne and married his sister, the widowed queen. They had one son, Memphites, whom Euergetes murdered. He then married Philometer's daughter, also named Cleopatra. He was loathsome and bloodthirsty and was nicknamed Physcon, signifying "potbelly." Despised by the Greeks, he seems to have had the support of the native population and reigned for 29 years (145-116 B.C.). He and the second Cleopatra had two daughters, Selene and Cleopatra, and two sons, Soter and Alexander I. He had one illegitimate son, Apion, to whom was bequeathed Cyrenacia.

The rule of PTOLEMAIOS VIII SOTER (nicknamed Lathyros) (116-80 B.C.) was characterized by a joint rule with his mother and an interim rule by his brother Alexander, PTOLEMAIOS IX, who had married Soter's daughter Berenice. During the latter part of Soter's reign, a native rebellion resulted in the destruction of Thebes. On the death of Soter, an illegitimate son of Alexander murdered his cousin and stepmother, Berenice, but was himself killed by an enraged people.

An illegitimate son of Soter was then chosen to be king as PTOLEMAIOS XI. He was nicknamed Auletes, "The Flute Player." He was driven into exile by popular hatred, during which time his daughter Berenice ruled. She sent to Syria for a husband but couldn't stand his coarseness and vulgarity, so had him strangled. Restored to power by the Romans, Auletes murdered his daughter. He died a few years later (51 B.C.), leaving the kingdom to his son and his daughter, Cleopatra (69-30 B.C.). The son deprived Cleopatra of her royal authority. In the struggle which followed, the son was killed and Cleopatra was restored to the throne along with another younger brother, whom she had murdered by poison. Allied with Rome, first with Caesar and later with Marc Antony, she lost out to Octavian and committed suicide by exposing herself to the bite of an asp.

PRE-ALEXANDRIAN SCIENCE

MANY of the accomplishments of Egyptian civilization were seemingly bypassed in the development of Western science. However, no one can tell what rumor, suggestion, or hearsay may have inspired others to develop the ideas which later turned out to be in the main stream of progress.

First of all, they developed a written language which, through devious routes, contributed to the formation of our present alphabet. The invention of papyrus, without which ancient science could not have progressed, the 365-day calendar and the 24-hour day, the measurements of geometry, medicine, the techniques of building marvelous temples and pyramids, and the techniques involved in the perfection of their art treasures are outstanding features of their science.

Their natural science was not one of discovering scientific principals but rather one of the solving of practical problems. Arithmetic was required for trade; geometry was needed to re-establish property boundaries after Nile flooding, to run irrigation and drainage canals, and in the constuction of their pyramids and temples; astronomy was studied to determine the time of Nile flooding, to determine when to celebrate their festivals, to determine the time of day, and to orient their pyramids and temples; medicine was needed to heal.

Information on Egyptian mathematics is derived from the Rhind, Moscow, Berlin, and Kahun papyri, a short leather manuscript in the British Museum, and two wooden tablets in the Cairo Museum. Astronomical information is derived from scenes on temple walls and ceilings, from coffin lids in which the sky is shown only incidentally, from the orientation of monuments, and from calendars. The Smith, Ebers, and Berlin papyri are devoted to medicine.

Written Language

PAPYRUS. A written language presupposes that materials are available to write upon and with. Stone and chisel provide a permanent record, but the method is not suitable for long narratives nor suitable for distribution. The clay tablets of Mesopotamia were reasonably permanent when fired. They were portable but bulky and not conveniently stored. However, they were quite suitable for that area, as clay was plentiful, reed styluses were convenient, and the product was not affected by the molds and mildew associated with a humid climate.

Egypt solved her problem by inventing a paperlike material made from the papyrus plant. Although our product paper, made of pulp, was invented in China, the word itself stems from *papyrus*.

The material is made from the pith of a tall reed, *Cyperus papyrus,* which was abundant in the marshes of the Delta region. Strips of the pith were laid side by side, on top of which was laid a second layer at right angles. There was usually enough stickiness associated with the pulp so that under pressure a firm sheet was produced. If not, a flour paste with vinegar was used. The sheets varied in size but were usually from 10 to 18 inches wide. These could be pasted together to form rolls which, fortunately, insured continuity. The longest roll which has been found measures 133 feet long and 16½ inches wide. The writing was usually on the side with the horizontal strips. This was on the inside when rolled up. In order that the title and other identifying information be on the outside, the outside sheet was reversed. This was the first sheet to be unrolled and the Greeks called it *protocollon,* from which we get our word *protocol.* Thousands of papyri have been discovered, the richest site being on the western side of the Nile Valley at El Bahnasa, 110 miles south of Cairo.

Papyrus writing material made its appearance at a very early date, probably concurrently with the development of hieratic cursive script, by the end of the II Dynasty. In Greece, however, it was not in common use before the 5th century, B.C.

As with all primitive languages, written Egyptian starts out with picture writing, in which the picture really means what it depicts. It is difficult to convey abstract ideas by picture writing alone, so pictures are sometimes used to represent ideas as well; as for example, a dove might signify "peace." For such use, the symbol is called an *ideogram*. In order that the secondary meaning be intended, an unpronounced symbol called a *determinant* is added to the word sign. For example, a pair of walking feet added to the symbol for "house" will indicate "to go out." Along with the ideograms, an infusion of pictograph symbols called *phonograms* is used to denote sound only, as in a rebus.

The Egyptian hieroglyphic written language consisted of about 700 signs, many pertaining to animals or parts thereof. Of these there were about 100 phonograms, of which 75 involved two consonants and 24 were uniconsonantal. To these, half a dozen *homonyms* (similar in sound but different in meaning) were added. No vowels were indicated. This might introduce some ambiguity, as the symbol *bd* might be pronounced bad, bed, bead, bid, or bud. However, this may not have been serious, as the reader could probably tell the correct word from the context. In any case, it probably was no worse than the English language, where, although we have vowels, they are often the wrong ones. It was not a syllabic language, in the sense that the syllables had no significance by themselves. Some difficulty was encountered in representing names, particularly foreign ones, and for this purpose some symbols were given the status of alphabetic letters. Their use was, however, limited to foreign words and names. The development of a complete alphabet was left to others.

By the time of Mena, the first dynastic king, about 3100 B.C., the written language had been reduced to the hieroglyphic form. It was a beautiful, decorative script and appropriate for the short inscriptions for monuments and temple walls. For over 3,000 years it remained intact, with relatively few changes. But it was ill suited for practical daily use. By the end of the II Dynasty, a cursive handwritten script called *hieratic* had been developed primarily for use by the priests in recording rituals and inventories on the newly invented papyrus. As more people became involved in trade, a simpler form of the hieratic developed which was called *demotic,* meaning in Greek "for the people." This took place about the time of the XXV Dynasty (700 B.C.). In neither the hieratic nor the demotic did the characters bear any resemblance to the original hieroglyphics. From this time on, there were three styles of Egyptian writing: hieroglyphic, for monuments and temples; hieratic, for priestly use; and demotic, for the daily life of the people. Hieroglyphs gradually died out, although one example found at Philae was dated 394 A.D. The Egyptian spoken language continued to be used by the Christianized Egyptians called Copts (the name is the degenerate form of the Arab *gupts,* from Aegyptus) until the 16th century A.D., when it was replaced by Arabic. The Egyptian Christian church still celebrates mass (Korban) in the language of the Pharaohs, or the debased form spoken in the 5th century A.D.

The key to the decipherment of the hieroglyphs was a black basalt slab, approximately 45 by 30 by 11 inches, accidentally dug up by an engineering group of Napoleon's army in 1799 near the Rosetta mouth of the Nile. British intervention brought about a collapse of Napoleon's campaign and the Rosetta Stone ended up in the British Museum. The trilingual inscriptions consist of 14 incomplete lines of glyphs, 32 of demotic cursive, half of which are incomplete, and 54 lines of Greek, half of which are mutilated at the ends. The Greek text stated that the priests of all Egypt had assembled at Memphis to do honor to Ptolemy Epiphanes in the ninth year of his reign (196 B.C.) because he had respected the temples and protected the priests and that the recording was to be in sacred, demotic, and Greek languages.

Then followed 20 years of attempts to decipher the two inscriptions other than the Greek, which of course could be read.

In 1802, a Swedish diplomat and philologist, J. A. Akerblad, identified in the demotic each of the proper names mentioned in the Greek and also the words for *temple* and *Greek.* Physicist Thomas Young worked out a provisional translation of the demotic in 1814. He reasoned that a scribe would be likely to represent foreign names phonetically and picked out the name *Ptolemis.* In 1815 a bilingual stone was excavated at Philae, an island near the old Aswan dam. Young detected the names *Berenice* and *Cleopatra* in the cartouches. By 1819 he concluded that the cartouches con-

THE ROSETTA STONE

records a decree by the priests of Memphis conferring divine honors
on Ptolemaios V Ephiphanes, king of Egypt 196 B.C. The inscription
is in classical Egyptian hieroglyphs, in the Egyptian demotic form,
and in Greek. This provided the clue to the decipherment of the
Egyptian characters. (British Museum)

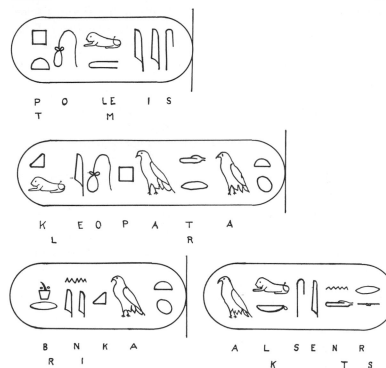

P   O   LE   I   S
T   M

K   E   O   P   A   T   A
  L   R

B   N   K   A   A   L   S   E   N   R
  R   I   K   T   S

tained royal names beginning at the rounded end and that some of the symbols were phonetic rather than symbolic.

Jean François Champollon (1790-1832), a young professor at Grenoble, encountered a name in a papyrus which he thought might be *Cleopatra* and which was confirmed by the Philae obelisk. Another name determined to be *Alksentrs* (Alexander) added three more signs. In a matter of weeks, he had deciphered over 100 cartouches. In some pre-Greek cartouches, he got the names of *Rameses* and *Tothmes*. By 1822 he announced the key to the decipherment of the Rosetta Stone and stated that the hieroglyphs were both phonetic and symbolic.

However, Champollon did not leave a complete analysis of the written language and for years there was considerable skepticism as to the value of his translations. In 1866 a German scientist, Karl Richard Lepsius, discovered in the vicinity of Tanis, another bilingual inscription, called the Decree of Canopus (237 B.C.), which extolled the virtues of Ptolemaios III and accorded him the title of Euergetes. By its translation and analysis, Lepsius clarified the Egyptian system of writing. Samuel Birch and Edward Hincks explained the determinatives. Contributions were made to the vowelless script by a number of other philologists, with the accepted principles of translation due primarily to the school of Adolf Erman.

Mathematics and Mensuration

The Egyptians had no science of mathematics but merely worked out certain rules which enabled them to deal with certain practical problems of daily life. Our information comes from one leather roll and five papyri, of which the Rhind and the Moscow papyri are the most important.

The Egyptians had a decimal system from the very beginning with vertical bars for units, inverted U's for tens, and variations of C's for hundreds. They had no zero, but left a space. Their multi-

I	II	III	IIII	'II	III	∩	I∩	I∩∩	9	₤
1	2	3	4	5	9	10	11	21	100	1000

plication and division consisted of successive additions. Except for a special symbol of ⅔, unit fractions were employed. For the fraction ¾, for example, they added ½ and ¼. They knew how to compute the areas of triangles and rectangles. For circles they used Area $= (8/9d)^2$, which is the equivalent of having $\pi = 3.16$. For laying out right angles, a knotted rope with twelve divisions was employed so that a 3-4-5 sided triangle could be formed. The surveyors who employed this were called *harpedonaptae* by the Greeks, literally 'rope stretchers." They knew how to run a straight "level" line over elevations and around bends.

The Rhind Mathematical Papyrus, now in the British Museum, is the largest of the ancient Egyptian mathematical papyri known, and was found in Thebes in 1858. Originally it was a single scroll about 18½ feet long and 13 inches high, of which the Rhind portion constituted all but a foot and a half. This portion has been practically restored from fragments. The papyrus was copied by a scribe named Ahmose ("The Moon-God Is Born") about 1650 B.C. from a document dated about 200 years earlier. It is the principal source of information as to how the Egyptians counted, computed, and measured, and consists of mathematical exercises and examples. It starts out with the evaluation of fractions with a numerator of 2 and odd denominators of 3, 5, 7, 9, 11, 13, 15, 17, 97, 99, 101. Ordinarily the Egyptians operated only with unit fractions, and every fraction, except ⅔, for which they had a special symbol, had to be expressed as a sum of a series of fractions, all with the numerator 1. The following is a table of the fractional equivalents of the numbers 1 to 9 divided by 10.

1	1/10	4	1/5 + 1/5	7	2/3 + 1/30
2	1/5	5	1/2	8	2/3 + 1/10 + 1/30
3	1/5 + 1/10	6	1/2 + 1/10	9	2/3 + 1/5 + 1/30

The fraction 2/17, for example, is arrived at by seeing what unit fractions of 17 add up to 2:

$$1/3 \text{ of } 17 = 5 \quad 2/3 \qquad\qquad\qquad \text{too much}$$
$$1/6 \text{ of } 17 = 2 \quad 5/6 \;= 2 + 1/2 + 1/3 \qquad \text{too much}$$
$$1/12 \text{ of } 17 = 1 \quad 5/12 \quad \text{which lacks } 7/12 \text{ of being 2,}$$
$$\text{or } 1/4 \text{ and } 1/3$$
$$1/68 \text{ of } 17 = 1/4$$
$$1/51 \text{ of } 17 = 1/3$$

The whole fraction 2/17 would then be $1/12 + 1/51 + 1/68$.

Their system of fractions was ingenious, but it would also have been ingenious if they could have extended their decimal system to fractions as well. That system, however, was not to be until about 1600 A.D., 3,000 years later. (Decimal fractions, Stevin 1585; decimal point, Pitiscus 1608.) Since the Egyptian method of dealing with fractions was more involved than the Mesopotamian method, it was natural that the Greek mathematicians, Ptolemy for example, chose to use the latter method.

For multiplication, the Egyptian could only double. To do this, he twice wrote down the numerals of the original number and substituted a 10-symbol for ten units and a 100-symbol for ten 10-symbols. To multiply by 3, he would double and add the original number; to multiply by 9, he would double three times and then add the original number. To multiply by 10, the unit symbols were replaced by those for 10 and the symbols for 10 were replaced by the symbol for 100. Division was performed by doubling and redoubling the divisor and adding until the dividend was reached.

The Rhind Papyrus continues with 85 problems. Forty of these involve simple arithmetic manipulation, for example, problem No. 24: A quantity and its 1/7 added together equals 19; what is the number? Answer: 16 + ½ + 1/8. Twenty problems involve mensuration of volumes, and areas, followed by 25 miscellaneous problems in arithmetic, multiplication of fractions, division of loaves of bread into unequal proportions, geometric progression, measurement and division of grain.

The Moscow Mathematical Papyrus dates from the middle of the 19th century B.C. It is about 18 feet long and 4 inches high. The text consists of 25 mathematical problems and their solutions, similar to those found in the Rhind Papyrus. One problem is to find the volume of a truncated pyramid with a vertical height of 6 and sides of the bottom and top bases, 4 and 2 respectively.

The construction of the pyramids and temples is a marvelous feat even by modern standards and warrants the highest admiration. In the pyramids are huge blocks of Aswan granite that fit so well that one cannot insert a sheet of paper between the blocks. The deviation of the pyramid bases from perfect squares is negligible and their orientation with regard to true north varies but a few minutes. The astronomical equipment may be crude and their observations inaccurate, but one cannot criticize their structures.

The earliest pyramid is the Step Pyramid at Sakkarah (2700 B.C.), on the west bank of the Nile about 30 miles south of Cairo. It is the oldest free-standing stone masonry structure in the world.

It measures 400 feet by 350 feet at the base and 200 feet high. An impressive three-tier pyramid at Maidum, 50 miles south of Cairo, is a transitional form between the step pyramid and that of Khufu (Cheops). The Khufu Pyramid at Giza is 481 feet high and measures 756 feet on a side. It is oriented 3′ 43″ west of north. The star Thuban (a Draconis) was 3° 51′ from the pole at the time the pyramid was constructed and could be seen at night from the bottom of a 380-foot shaft inclined 26° 17′ to the horizontal whenever the star was directly below the pole. The latitude of the pyramid is 30° North. In view of the great precision with which this immense structure was constructed, it must be assumed that the design was carefully worked out by the architects. The basis for the selection of the dimensions is not known but there are two deductions from the dimensions which are of interest. The ratio of a side (755.55 feet) to half the height (481/2) is 3.14158, essentially the accepted value of pi (π). Hence the perimeter of the base is equal

PYRAMID OF KHUFU

GIZA (CAIRO) EGYPT

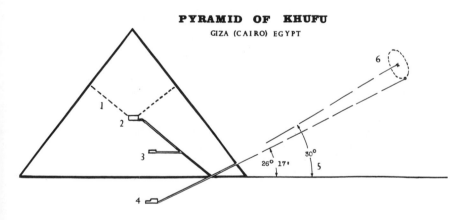

SECTIONAL VIEW OF THE PYRAMID OF KHUFU

1. Air shaft. 2. King's chamber. 3. Queen's chamber. 4. Subterranean chamber. 5. Elevation of the pole is the same as the latitude of the pyramid. 6. Daily apparent circular path of Thuban around the celestial pole at an angular distance of 3°51′.

to the circumference of a circle with a radius equal to the height of the pyramid. However, this is no solution to the ancient problem of "squaring the circle;" perimeters are equated — not areas. Secondly, the slope-angle of the pyramid (51° 51') is indeed very unique. The tangent of the angle is 1.272 and in a triangle with a base 1 and altitude 1.272, the hypotenuse is 1.618. From this it can be computed that the area of a face of the pyramid is equal to the area of a square with the height of the pyramid as the dimension of a side. The computation can be carried further to obtain the Golden Section relationship (1 : .618 = .618 : .382) which represents the division of a line so that the ratio of the whole is to the larger segment as the ratio of the larger segment is to the lesser. Since the Renaissance art period, this division has been considered a principle of pleasing composition. Two vertical lines, each spaced about 38% from the respective edges of the canvas, and two similar horizontal lines, indicate the most effective positions for important elements of a picture. A division very near the middle or one less than a quarter is displeasing.

For the pillars which supported the light roof of the early dwellings, the primitive Egyptian employed several bundles of papyrus stems lashed with several turns of a cord below the heads and at the base. The same motif was employed in the stone pillars of the temples and palaces. However, it wasn't practical to copy the papyrus heads. Instead, the buds of the blue lotus were used for the capital. The short lengths of papyrus stems which held the lashing taut are simulated in stone. The roofs of the temples were made of slabs of stone, so that in order to support the weight, a pillared hall became a forest of columns.

Astronomy

The most important purpose of Egyptian astronomical observations was to determine the helical rising of Sirius, as that was associated with the Nile flooding. The next in importance was the necessity of prescribing the times for celebrating religious festivals in accordance with the lunar calendar. Their instruments were limited to a slotted palm frond, a plumb line, a crude sundial, and an inaccurate water clock. Their instruments were crude, the observations were simple, and their aim was not academic. Practically all the information pertaining to the calendar comes from 2nd-millennium inscriptions on tombs and coffin lids. After the 6th century B.C., astronomy was dominated by the Greeks.

The year was divided into three seasons: Inundation (Akhet) from July to November, Emergence (Peret) from November to March, and Drouth (Shemu) from March to July. The 365-day solar calendar consisted of twelve 30-day months plus five additional feast days. Since their solar year was ¼ day short, after four years the helical rising of Sirius (first morning appearance of the star before sunrise) came one day late. In 1,460 years, the solar calendar would again be in step with Sirius. This is called the Sothic cycle, after Sothis, the popular Graeco-Egyptian name for Sirius. Theon of Alexandria (fl 360 A.D.) stated that in 139 A.D. it was recorded that New Year's Day coincided with the helical rising of Sirius. The previous occurrences would be 1321, 2781, and 4241 B.C. It is possible that the calendar was inaugurated on one of these dates. Records indicate that the 365-day calendar was in use during the V and VI dynasties, so that 2781 B.C. seems to be the most reasonable. Allowing for the secular motion of the sun and the proper motion of Sirius, this figure may be in error by a few years, but that is not too important.

Their lunar calendar enabled them to predict the phases of the moon. In order that the lunar calendar be reconciled with the 365-day solar calendar, 9 intercalary months were inserted in every 25-year period (9125 days) so that with 16 years of 12 lunar months and 9 years of 13 months, there would be 309 lunar months. It should be emphasized that the solar year was assumed to be 365 days. The 365¼-day year was not introduced until 45 B.C., at the time of Julius Caesar. The length of the lunar month is 29.5306 days.

The 24-hour day is of Egyptian origin, although the hours varied in length with the seasons. It started with a system called *decans,* so named by the Greeks because of a ten-degree spacing of the stars. It was a method of keeping track of Sirius. Sirius first rises in the early dawn after a 70-day interval when it is too close to the sun to be seen. The origin of the decans is a matter of speculation, but it seems to be tied up with following the heavens during the period when Sirius is not visible. The region of the zodiac was divided into 36 divisions, each representing the movement of the stars, or the sun, in ten days. Stars, which have not been identified, were chosen as the division points and the time of night could be judged by the time of rising of the pilot stars. At the time of the equinoxes, half of these should be visible at night at any one time, and during the night 18 decan stars should theoretically rise. However, in the summertime, allowing for evening and morning twilight, only 12 decan stars should rise. In the wintertime, the sundial would function only during the equivalent of 12 decans. This led the Egyptians to divide the day and night into 12 hours each, but the length of the hours varied with seasons. During the longer nights in winter, the length of the nighttime hour was longer and that of the daytime hour, shorter. In the summer, the opposite was true. The Babylonians had a similar system of 36 stars (Creation Epic c 2000 B.C.) but divided the whole day into 12 equal divisions of 30 *gesh* each. So from the Egyptians we derived the 24 divisions of the day and from the Babylonians, the idea of equality of the divisions.

Temple ceilings and coffin lids frequently depict groupings of stars, but it is a hopeless task to find groups that match the stars in the sky. The most picturesque of these is the Denerah Zodiac which decorated the ceiling in the temple of Hathor and is now in the Louvre. It is about eight feet in diameter and portrays a circular disk supported around the periphery by the 24 upstretched arms of twelve female figures. Figures representing constellations are pictured in the central portion counterclockwise around Polaris. Since the plaque is comparatively recent, 34 B.C., the twelve signs of the zodiac are readily recognizable. Among the others are Hydra, Sirius, Corvus and Orion. A peripheral row of figures may represent the 36 decans.

Sirius is the only star that is known for certainty and a hieroglyph for a dog appears on many temple walls throughout the Nile

Valley. Its helical rising, which is now the middle of August, was associated with Nile floods and its worship dates from about 3000 B.C. It was worshiped as *Isis Hathor* in the form of a cow with a disk between the horns, and is so depicted at Sakkarah (2700 B.C.) and in the Temple of Hatshepsut in Thebes (1500 B.C.). On the Denderah Zodiac, Sirius is represented by a cow with a star between the horns, resting in a boat. As *Toth,* its helical rising was associated with the sacred ibis, and the star and the bird often appear together on temple walls. It was worshiped as *Sihor,* the Nile star, and more commonly as *Sothis,* the Bright Star of the Waters.

There are other constellatory and stellar associations which have been claimed, but these are more or less speculative and are doubtful.

The planet Mars was instrumental in naming the city of Cairo. In the first Arab invasion of Egypt in 641 A.D. by the Omayyad Moslems, the conqueror Amr pitched his tent at a site which became a Moslem capital called El Fostat. When the Fatimite Moslems conquered Egypt in 968 A.D., Mars, known as Kahir the Victorious, was prominent in the night sky and the city was named El Kahira. The modern Egyptian name is spelled El Qahira.

Medicine

Because of the all importance of the human body to the individual and the need to correct structural and functional deficiencies, medicine and the physician are of great importance in every stage of society. Egyptian medicine is believed to have been well along early in the 2nd millennium, even though the principal papyri are from the period 2000-1300 B.C. These are believed to be copies of older treatises. The earliest Egyptian physician mentioned is Imhotep (c 2700 B.C.), who was also the architect of the Step Pyramid at Sakkarah. The rules for treatment seem to have been prescribed early and it was apparently the practice to follow directions religiously. If the patient died in so doing, the physician could not be held responsible, but if he varied the treatment, he might be subject to punishment. However, some alteration was allowable after the fourth day.

There were no schools for physicians, so the art had to be handed down on a personal basis—often from father to son. Wounds and surface diseases were evident and treatment was more or less straightforward. The art of bone surgery was exceptionally well developed. They had very little information regarding the anatomy of the body, and internal diseases were considered to be caused by supernatural spirits—a natural enough statement to cover up their ignorance. These diseases required a magical prayer which in many cases might be partially effective in that the patient was put in the proper frame of mind to promote healing. The Ebers Papyrus lists 877 remedies for various symptoms, including over 100 remedies for eye diseases and 21 different cough mixtures. Honey is a frequent component of prescribed remedies; castor oil was used as a purgative. Liver (vitamin A) was prescribed for night blindness. In some cases, bile of birds, pigs, turtles, and other animals was prescribed. This is a source of cholic acid, the basis of cortisone. Many of the remedies seem ridiculous, but some had an ingredient which is known today as an effective treatment for some ills.

The Smith Papyrus prescribed near-scientific treatment for bone surgery, including fractures and dislocations. It was recognized that the beating of the heart had some connection with the pulse felt at various places on the body. There were vessels from the heart to every limb, but they had no idea of the mechanism . . . they might possibly carry air.

Although the art was rather primitive, it nevertheless was sufficiently advanced to warrant that Hippocrates, Galen, and other physicians study their methods and their medical texts in the Temple of Imhotep in Memphis.

Chemistry

Chemistry had its origin in Egypt and gets its name from an ancient name of the country, Kemi, or Khemi, signifying "black" and suggested by the black alluvial soil of the Nile Valley. They pioneered in metallurgy and developed a blast furnace for smelting copper and gold. Glass is believed to be a product of Egypt, starting first with glass beads and then with glass bottles around 1550

B.C. Tin oxide was used to make glass opaque and copper to color it turquoise blue. Pressed and molded glass appeared about 1200 B.C., but the blowpipe wasn't invented until after 300 B.C. The industry gravitated toward Alexandria, from which traders carried glass products to all the countries of the Mediterranean. Remains of a glass factory have been found in Wadi Natrun.

Extensive deposits of natron, that is, sodium carbonate, and of sodium bicarbonate are found in Wadi Natrun. It is a valley about 20 miles long, six or seven miles wide and 60 feet below sea level, situated halfway between Alexandria and Cairo on the desert route. There are a number of monasteries in the area.[1]

Ammonia was first distilled, as ammonium chloride, from the camel dunghills of the Temple of Amon at the oasis of Siwa. Siwa is located about 300 miles southwest of Alexandria, but is reached by the somewhat longer route via Matruh. It was the site of the famous oracle of Zeus Amon.[2]

[1] Wadi Natrun is the home of monasticism, Egypt's gift to the Christian church. Monasticism existed before the Christian era in India and other parts of Asia and among certain sects of the Jews. St. Anthony seems to have started this in the Christian church (c 270 A.D.) by withdrawing from the world and living out in the desert. The words *monk* and *hermit* signify "alone" and "desert" respectively in Greek. The movement was promoted in the 4th century A.D. by Pachomius, a military man who was converted while watching the endurance of martyrs during persecution. He designed the tunic with the girdle and cowl and prescribed the minute details of the life with prayers and meals in common. Wadi Natrun was known in the 4th century A.D. as "The Valley of the Monks." At one time there were ten monasteries and as many as 2,400 monks. There are now only four monasteries.

[2] Although there were many oracles in the Greek world, the first three and the most important were the ones at Siwa, Delphi, and Dodona. The last was near Joaninni, in northwestern Greece. The god's answer at Dodona was delivered via the rustling of oak leaves. The Delphic oracle involved an elderly woman sitting on a tripod over the identical crack where the serpent Python once made its den. The priestess would fall into a trance, possibly induced by the fumes of burning laurel leaves, and mutter some unintelligible sounds which the priests would interpret. A thespiode would then put the god's answer into verse. The advice was usually ambiguous, but they knew their business and the advice was usually good.

When Hercules visited Libya in search of the Golden Apples of Hesperides, he visited the oracle at Siwa and demanded to see Zeus. Zeus, or the priest to avoid exposure, did not wish to show himself but killed a ram, covered himself with the fleece and held the ram's head in front of him. Since then, the Egyptians represented Zeus Amon with the face and the horns of a ram.

Alexander spent three weeks at the temple. He alone was permitted to pass into the temple in his usual dress. The rest had to change their clothes. The oracular responses were in nods and tokens. Alexander was told he was the son of Zeus, and Alexandria minted a coin in 326 B.C. with a portrait of Alexander with a ram's horn behind his ear.

Art

Egyptian art is characterized by its dignity, simplicity, and durability. The relief sculptures are particularly beautiful and in many respects have never been surpassed, although they date from 1500 to 1200 B.C. Painting, though not to be compared with that of the Renaissance, nevertheless excelled that of other lands. Polygnotos, who flourished in Athens about a thousand years later (c 450 B.C.), still used only tinted outlines on a colored background without shading and without perspective.

They were supreme in metalworking, particularly in gold, with beautiful jewelry appearing as early as 2500 B.C. They maintained their supremacy at least up to the Renaissance and some of their work must be listed among the world's masterpieces even today.

THE NARMER PALETTE

A ceremonial slate palette which celebrated the victory over Lower Egypt and is the oldest historic work of art (c 3100 B.C.). It is far from primitive and shows most of the features of later Egyptian art. (Egyptian Museum, Cairo)

ALEXANDRIA

THERE is little or nothing in modern El Iskandariya to remind one of the many historical associations which file across the pages of its history. Founded by Alexander the Great in 332 B.C., it has hosted the Ptolemaic dynasty of pharaohs, Aristarchos, Euclid, Eratosthenes, Archimedes, the Septuagints, Cleopatra, Caesar, Antony, St. Mark, Ptolemy, and many others. It grew to be a city of 300,000 and second only to Rome in the Roman Empire. Following sieges by the Persians and the Arabs, the building of Cairo in 969 A.D., and the discovery of a shipping route around the Cape of Good Hope, the city declined and in the early 19th century A.D. its population had dwindled to around 4,000.

It is now a city with a population approaching two million. Its harbor is the center of eastern and western commerce. Its waterfront boulevard is very impressive, but a few blocks back, conditions are nearly slum-like. In the central part of the city are large decorative buildings of the Victorian era. Most cities have new construction in progress, with new buildings replacing the old. This is not the case in Alexandria.

Neither is the city itself a tourist town. Even the Ras-el-Tin Palace is now a presidential palace and is not open to the public. However, east of the city are a number of beaches which are very popular in the summertime. Alexandria is rapidly developing industries, and large irrigation projects are under way east of the city on the desert route to Cairo. Fields are already being planted in anticipation and a number of large buildings, possibly apartment houses, have been constructed.

When Alexander the Great entered Egypt in the autumn of 332 B.C., he sought a site on which to build a capital city which would reflect Greece—and himself. The capital of Egypt at the time was Memphis, which was too far inland for the seafaring Greeks and

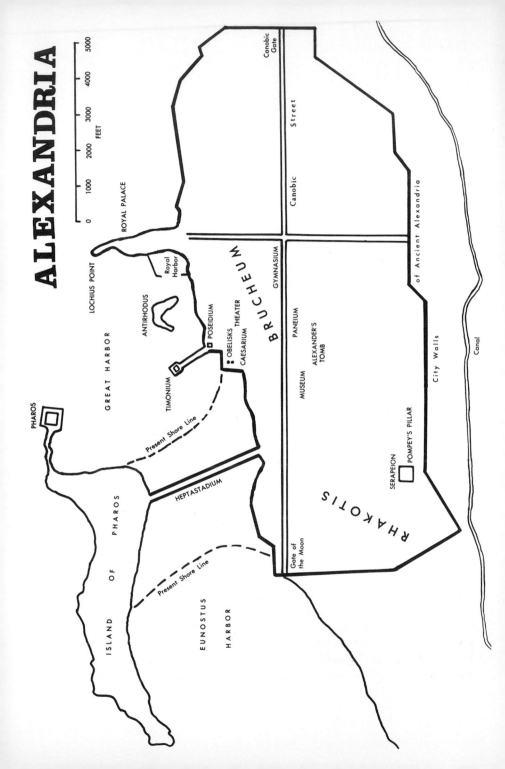

too Egyptian. Naucratis, a city which had been allotted to Greek merchants, was too disreputable. His choice was the small settlement of Rhacotis on a narrow strip of land between the Mediterranean and Lake Mareotis, about 35 miles west of the Rosetta mouth of the Nile. The section was originally inhabited by fishermen and pirates and at that time if Greek mariners wanted to settle, they had to live in Rhacotis. The site was far enough away from the Nile so that silting of the harbor was not a problem and access to the Nile was provided by a canal from Lake Mareotis to Cairo. The patron founder was Ptolemaios I Soter, who provided both financial and moral support to build a large cultural city.

The city was laid out on the rectangular grid plan which Hippodamos of Miletus was recommending a century earlier. The wide and long Canopic Way, running east and west, was pillared from the Gate of the Sun at one end to the Gate of the Moon at the other. A wide but shorter street ran perpendicular to it, thus dividing the city into four sections. A fifth section, at the western end of the city, retained the old name, Rhacotis. Some of the streets were colonnaded for shelter for pedestrians and for adornment. The center of activity was in the vicinity of the present Raml Station. Here were the Temple of Poseidon, a temple built in Marc Antony's honor called the Caesarium, the two obelisks* from Heliopolis, one of which ended up on the London Embankment and the other in New York's Central Park, and a theater. A few blocks further inland—that is, south—were the Museum, the Library, and the tomb of Alexander. The original sarcophagus was of gold, but it was plundered by Ptolemy XI Auletus. In the time of Strabo it was of alabaster. Along the waterfront to the east was a peninsula shutting off the harbor on the east. It was called Lochias and had a royal palace with a private harbor. Nearby was an artificial island, called Antirhodos, with a royal palace. Projecting out into the middle of the harbor from the vicinity of the Temple of Poseidon, was a mole with a lodge at the extremity built by Marc Antony, which was called the Timonium.

On a hill in the southwest part of the city stands a monument

---

*Early Greek uses for iron were money (*obol*) and a roasting spit (*obelos*); the term "obelisk" stems from the latter.

ALEXANDRIA
The distant Sultain Bey Fort is built on the base of the Pharos lighthouse.

known as Pompey's Pillar, presumably to note that Pompey, in his
flight from Caesar, was murdered in Alexandria. One story is that
it was erected by the fanatical Bishop Theophilus to commemorate
the destruction of the Serapeion in 390 A.D. The Serapeion was a
library adjunct to the main library near the center of the city. Another story is that the pillar was erected in 292 A.D. to commemorate the beneficence of Diocletian toward the inhabitants who had
revolted against his rule. In this same general area were a stadium
and the hippodrome.

About a mile off shore opposite the western part of the city
was Pharos Island, which includes the site of the present Ras-el-Tin
Palace and the El Anfusi section. On the eastern end of Pharos
Island was a little island on which stood the famed lighthouse, now
occupied by the ungarrisoned Qait Bey Fort. A mole, called Hepta-
stadium, connected the mainland with Pharos Island, thus forming
two harbors, Great Harbor on the east and Eunostus Harbor, the
Harbor of Happy Return, on the west. Since then, land has been
filled in on both sides of the mole so as to form a peninsula almost
as wide as the island was long.

The lighthouse was built on a small solid-rock island off the
eastern end of Pharos Island during the reign of Ptolemaios II Philadelphus (c 270 B.C.) by the architect Sostratos of Cnidos. It was

still in service in the 7th century A.D. and remains of the tower
were still visible as late as 1375 A.D. An earthquake tumbled it into
the sea shortly after. Its beam was said to be visible 20 miles out
at sea, so its height must have been over 300 feet. The base of
huge blocks of Aswan granite was 18 feet above sea level. The
tower itself was constructed in three sections with an inside circular ramp wide enough for two horsemen abreast. The lower had
a square cross section of about 125 feet on a side and 200 feet
high. The second section was octagonal with 32 steps and the
cylindrical top had 18 steps. Donkeys were constantly ascending
loaded with wood. The Arabs called the Pharos *Manar*—"The
Place Where Fire Burns." The use of *manar* to describe a tower
is the basis for the familiar *minaret* associated with mosques.

The literary and scientific activity of Alexandria was centered
in the Museum and the Library. The term *museum* signifies a
temple of the Muses, who were daughters of Zeus and Mnemosyne
(memory). Clio was the Muse of history; Euterpe, song; Thalia,
comedy and pastoral poetry; Melpomene, tragedy; Terpsichore,
dancing; Erato, love poetry; Calliope, heroic poetry; Polyhymnia,
religious poetry; and Urania, astronomy. The scientific research
was carried on in the Museum and the Library was the center of
humanities.

Strabo, who saw it in 25 B.C., said the Museum was connected
with the royal palaces with a colonnaded walk "with seats where
philosophers, rhetoricians, and others who delight in studies, can
engage in disputation." There were accommodations for its members, a large dining hall, a dissection theater for physicians, and
observatories for its astronomers. Teachers were meant to devote
all their time to research and discussions with colleagues and distinguished visitors. At its height, there were several hundred philologists concerned with the principles of grammar and language,
and philosophers devoted to mathematics, astronomy, geography,
and medicine. It was a community of scholars, the elite among the
learned.

The first need was to collect manuscripts for the Library.
Agents were sent to all parts of Greece and Asia Minor to purchase

manuscripts or to borrow manuscripts which could be copied. Often, apparently, the copies were returned instead of the original. Travelers were required to surrender any books which were not already in the Library. If the manuscript was in a foreign language, it was translated and both the original and the translation were placed in the Library. Thousands of papyri discovered in Egypt indicate the type of literary contents of the Library. Homer exceeded the total of all the rest, which included works of Demosthenes, Euripides, Aeschylus, Meandres, Xenophon, Sophocles, Pindar, Sappho, Aristotle, and Herodotus. By the time of Caesar, the collection had grown to 300,000 volumes in the main Library and an additional 200,000 in the Serapeion. The city was brilliant and famous the world over for its intellectual achievements. The Library was the greatest university of its time and stimulated similar institutions in other cities, such as Antioch, Pergamon, Rhodes, and Ephesus. When the activities were temporarily curtailed during the reign of Ptolemaios Euergetes, Rhodes and Pergamon received many of the Museum's scientists.

When Caesar besieged the city in 48 B.C., the main library was destroyed. Marc Antony is reported to have presented 200,000 volumes from the Pergamon Library to Cleopatra (c 34 B.C.) in recompense. During the reign of Aurelian, the greater part of the main library was again destroyed, the Romans being accused of transporting a significant portion to Rome. Toward the end of the 4th century A.D., Alexandria was under the control of Christian bishops who looked upon the Library as a citadel of disbelief and immorality. Under Theodosius the Great (emperor 379-395 A.D.), the Libray was destroyed in 390 A.D. by order of Theophilus, the Bishop of Alexandria. By 416 A.D., the Library was essentially non-existent.

When the Moslems took Alexandria in 640 A.D., they reportedly completed the destruction. Their philosophy was that if the material was in the Koran, it wasn't necessary; and if it wasn't, it should be destroyed anyway. However, there wasn't much left to destroy.

The foundation of the Museum and the Library was the work

of three men: Ptolemaios I was the patron, Straton of Lampsacus was the technical organizer, and Demetrios of Phaleron was the administrator. The librarians were Zenodotos of Ephesus (284-260 B.C.), Callimachos of Cyrene (260-240 B.C.), Apollonios of Rhodes (240-235 B.C.), Eratosthenes of Cyrene (235-195 B.C.), Aristophanes of Byzantium (195-180 B.C.), Apollonios Eidographos (180-160 B.C.), and Aristarchos of Samothrace (160-145 B.C.), after whom no librarian is mentioned.

DEMETRIOS of Phaleron (345-283 B.C.) was the first administrator of the Museum and Library. In Athens he had been a student at the Lyceum and made a collection of Aesop's fables in ten books. He was the representative of Cassander and head of the administration of Athens from 317 to 307 B.C. With a change of rulers, he was forced to flee to Egypt. He was associated with the Library until 284 B.C., when the new king, Ptolemaios II, exiled him to Upper Egypt, where, it is said, he died of a snake bite.

STRATON of Lampsacus (fl c 300 B.C.) was a pupil of Aristotle and went to Alexandria as tutor to the crown prince who became Ptolemaios Philadelphus. He may have been the one who originally suggested the idea of the Library and Museum to Ptolemaios I and he took a major role in their founding and organization. In 286 B.C., he was called to Athens to head the Lyceum.

ZENODOTOS of Ephesus (325-234 B.C.) was a pupil of Philetas of Cos and the first librarian at Alexandria (284-260 B.C.). He undertook the major task of collecting and revising the works of Greek poets, principally Homer. He divided the *Iliad* and the *Odyssey* into 24 books each and compiled a Homeric glossary and a dictionary of foreign words. Hesiod's *Theogonia* was critically revised and some of the poems of Pindar and Anacreon were corrected.

CALLIMACHOS of Cyrene (310-240 B.C.) left Cyrene early in life. He studied in Athens and opened a school in a suburb of Alexandria called Eleusis where he taught grammar. He succeeded Zenodotos as librarian in 260 B.C. and held that position until his death 20 year later. He compiled a catalogue of the Library that filled 120 rolls. It covered dramatists, poets, legislators, philosophers, historians, orators, rhetoricians, and miscellaneous writers. The classification covered only the literary section, as possibly the science volumes were housed in the Museum proper. He wrote 800 works in prose and verse, the longest and most famous being an elegy called *Causes.* The best-known was *The Lock of Berenice.* He was greatly admired by the Roman poets. He taught the three librarians who followed, namely, Apollonios of Rhodes, Eratosthenes of Cyrene, and Aristophanes of Byzantium.

SEPTUAGINT: ("The Seventy"). Shortly after the city's founding, large numbers of Jews settled in Alexandria, principally in the northeastern section of the city. Their language was Alexandrian-Greek. In order that the Hebrew scriptures might be made available to them, Ptolemaios II, acting on the advice of his librarian, requested the high priest of Jerusalem to select six interpreters from each of the 12 tribes to translate the scriptures into Greek. About 280 B.C. the 72 scholars were housed on Pharos Island and apparently in 70 days, the translations were completed, a remarkably short time for such an undertaking. The Septuagint is faithful in substance but not in detail. The various books were apparently parceled out to various translators without an over-all review to maintain consistency.

The Psalms are fairly well produced, but the versions of Jeremiah are poor compared with later Hebrew manuscripts. Nevertheless, the translation represented the sole written version of the Old Testament for centuries. The Septuagint continued to be the basis for the sacred text of the Christians. St. Jerome translated it into a Latin Vulgate version in Bethlehem (386-404 A.D.). The first printed text of the entire Hebrew Bible was a limited edition in 1490 A.D. in Soncino (near Cremona) Italy. In the 2nd century A.D., Jewish scribes in Palestine prepared the "text of the Sopherim." Between the 7th and 10th centuries A.D., certain Jewish scholars called Masoretes, resident chiefly in Tiberias, added the vowel sounds and interpretations. This was the text followed by the Jews.

This was the situation regarding source material until the recent find of the Dead Sea Scrolls. These may be the remnants of the library of the Essenian monastery at Khirbat Qumran which was occupied from about 120 B.C. to 68 A.D.

EUCLID (fl c 300 B.C.) is probably the best-known of the mathematicians and scientists associated with Alexandria, yet very little is known of his personal life. As his *Elements* has appeared in well over a thousand editions, and even today is the basis for geometry textbooks, he is the most successful textbook writer the world has known. Nothing is known of his life except that he founded a school and taught in Alexandria during the reign of Ptolemaios I, that he was associated with the Museum, and that he was known to Archimedes. This would indicate that he was active during the first half of the 3rd century B.C. His most important work, *Elements*, consisted of 13 books: I Fundamentals, II Geometric Algebra, III Circles, IV Inscribed and Circumscribed Polygons, V Proportion, VI Similar Polygons, VII-IX Arithmetic Treated Geometrically, X Incommensurables, XI-XIII Solid Geometry. Book XIV with seven propositions on regular polyhedrons is usually attributed to Hypsicles (c 180 B.C.). Books I, II, IV, and VI reflect Pythagorean mathematics. Some credit is due Hippocrates of Chios for Book III and for the method of presenting the propositions. Proclus credited Eudoxos with providing much of Book V.

Other works of Euclid include *Phaenomena,* dealing with the celestial sphere in 25 geometric propositions, and *Optica,* dealing with the Pythagorean theory of vision, perspective, and possibly mirrors. Euclid may also be the author of *Katatome Kanonos,* a discussion of the Pythagorean theory of music.

An anecdote ascribed to Euclid is his answer to a student who asked what he would gain by learning geometry. Euclid told his slave: "Give this man an obol, since he must have a profit for what he learns."

ARISTILLUS of Stageira and TIMOCHARIS (fl 280 B.C.) were the first to ascertain and to record the positions of the chief stars by means of numerical measurements of their distances from fixed positions in the sky, rather than by more or less vague verbal descriptions. They may therefore be regarded as producing the first real star catalogue. A century and a half later, these measurements indicated to Hipparchos that the equinoctial points had changed. For example, in 129 B.C. he found Spica to be 6° from the autumnal equinox, whereas the measurement in 283 B.C. indicated 8°, or an annual precession of nearly 47″.

MANETHO of Sebennytus (fl 280 B.C.) was a priest from the eastern part of the Nile Delta who was requested by Ptolemaios Philadelphus to write the history of Egypt up until 323 B.C. He classified the rulers into 32 dynasties.

ARISTARCHOS of Samos (310-230 B.C.) had been a pupil of Straton, who at the time (287-279 B.C.) was head of the Lyceum in Athens. He was keenly interested in physics, optics, and astronomy. He invented the *scaphe,* a sundial with a hemispherical concave surface with a vertical gnomon. He observed in Alexandria during the period 280 to 264 B.C. In his treatise *On the Magnitudes and Distances of the Sun and Moon* he described an ingenious method for deriving the relative distances of the sun and the moon. Consider the triangle formed by the sun, the moon, and the earth when the moon is half full. He assumed correctly that the angle at the moon is then a right angle. By measuring the angle at the earth between the sun and the moon, the shape of the triangle is fixed and hence the relative lengths of the sides. For those versed in trigonometry, the relative distance of the moon to that of the sun is the cosine of the angle at the earth (side adjacent divided by the hypotenuse). Aristarchos measured the angle to be 29/30 of a right angle, or 87°, and arrived at the sun's being 19 times as far away as the moon. Actually the angle is 89° 50′, almost a right angle, and the relative distances are 400 to 1. Considering the difficulties of determining when the moon is exactly half full and of measuring an angle close to 90° where a small error makes a large difference, it is not surprising that the results were poor. The importance of the measurement lies in the fact that this is the first time a value was arrived at by measurement instead of by guess.

By observing the relation of the diameters of the shadow cast by the earth during a lunar eclipse to the diameter of the moon, he decided the earth's diameter to be about three times that of the moon, which compares favorably with the true value of about 3.7.

Archimedes is the authority for the views of Aristarchos about the universe: ". . . Aristarchos of Samos has published certain hypotheses . . . that the fixed stars and the sun are immovable but that the earth is carried around the sun in a circle which is in the middle of the course. . . ." Aristarchos pointed out that the stars must be very far away, otherwise their brightness would vary as the earth revolved around the sun. He also held the view that the earth rotated on its axis west to east, once in 24 hours. These views were quite contrary to the thinking of his day. Cleanthes of Assus, a famous Stoic, called the plan blasphemy. The earth being the heaviest of all celestial bodies, it must necessarily sink to the bottom, the center of the universe.

It wasn't apparent that the irregularities in the motions of the sun and the planets could be explained by the simple system of Aristarchos, so it did not find acceptance. Later when Hipparchos, the most famous of the ancient astronomers, also turned it down, the system was given the death blow. Eighteen hundred years later, the argument was settled by Kepler.

HEROPHILOS of Chalcedon (fl 280 B.C.) was the foremost physician of his day and the founder of systematic anatomy. He studied in Athens under Praxagoras of Cos, the second head of the Dogmatic school of medicine. He was a shrewd observer and made the most of the facilities of the Museum. He gave a detailed description of the brain, the cerebrum, the cerebellum, and the membranes. The point where the four great venous sinuses meet inside the skull is known today as the *torcular Herophili.* He regarded the brain as the center of intelligence, thereby rejecting Aristotle's view that it was the heart. He distinguished between nerves and tendons, described the eye, including the retina and the optic nerve, the duodenum (the length was the breadth of 12 fingers), the liver, the salivary glands, the pancreas, the genital organs, the vascular system, and the difference between the veins and arteries.

ERASISTRATOS (b 304 B.C.) was born in Iulis on the island of Kea, one of the Cyclades about 40 miles southeast of Athens. He studied in Athens under Chrysippos of the Stoic school, Metrodoros, and Theophrastos. He was a most eminent physician and physiologist. He named the trachea and made a thorough study of the nervous system, bones, pancreas, liver, spleen, and embryology. He was the first to distinguish between sensory and motor nerves. He studied the arteries and veins and appreciated that it was the heart that caused the blood to flow but didn't entirely discover the circulatory system. The catheter was invented by him. He preferred preventive hygiene to therapy.

APOLLONIOS of Rhodes (295-215 B.C.) was a Greek-Egyptian born near Alexandria. He was a pupil of Callimachos of Cyrene and feuded with him, primarily because Callimachos rejected his four-book epic poem *Argonautica*. He succeeded Callimachos as librarian (240-235 B.C.). He was called a Rhodian because he was granted citizenship after his retirement to that city. In Rhodes he taught rhetoric and revised his *Argonautica*. He wrote epigrams (attacking Callimachos) and other critical poems. *Krises* dealt with the foundations of cities.

CONON of Samos (fl 260-d 212 B.C.) was a gifted mathematician who won the admiration of Archimedes and Apollonios of Perga. Book II of *Conics* by Apollonios was partly based on his work. He wrote seven books on astronomy. He is best known for his story of his naming the constellation of Coma Berenices. It has been said that men like Conon are the usual heralds announcing the approach of genius.

ERATOSTHENES of Cyrene (276-194 B.C.) was educated in Athens, came to Alexandria in 244 B.C. as a fellow of the Museum, and followed Apollonios of Rhodes as librarian from 235 to 195 B.C. He was considered one of the greatest scholars of antiquity, a poet, a librarian, an arithmetician, and the first prominent geographer. His most important geographical treatises are *On Measurement of the Earth and Hypomnemata Geographica*. The poem *Hermes Trismegistos* explained his views on scientific subjects; *Catasterismoi* described the constellations and their mythology; *Anterinys* described Hesiod's death and the punishment of his murderers. *Erigone,* an elegy, told the story of Icarus and his daughter. In *Chronographia,* he endeavored to establish the chronology of Greece on a scientific basis back to the time of Troy.

His measurement of the earth was an outstanding achievement. He had heard that at Syene (Aswan) at noon at the time of the summer solstice, the sun's rays were reflected from the bottom of the deepest wells and that vertical sticks cast no shadows—the sun being directly overhead. Syene and Alexandria were thought to be on the same meridian (actually about a 3° difference) and about 5,000 stadia apart. A measurement of the sun's altitude at

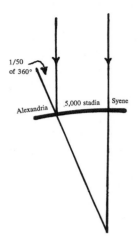

Alexandria indicated an angle of about 1/50 of a great circle of 360° (7° 12′). Reasoning that 1/50 of the earth's circumference was equivalent to 5,000 stadia, he obtained a value of 250,000 stadia for the circumference, or 694 stadia per degree. Figures for the length of the stadium vary somewhat (originally, the distance a man could run on one breath) but assuming about ten stadia per mile, the overall circumference comes out to be 25,000 miles.

His map of the world was obviously based on speculation and hearsay, but he did employ a grid of unspecified parallels and meridians. The map ranged east and west from the mouth of the Ganges to Portugal. North and south, it extended from Britain to the southern end of the Red Sea. It was much criticized by Strabo two centuries later, but Strabo's map wasn't much different. Eratosthenes established geographic climatic zones. From measurements of the solar angles at summer and winter solstices, he estimated the distance between the tropics to be 48° which is equivalent to 24° for the obliquity of the ecliptic.

The contribution of Eratosthenes to arithmetic was his "sieve" for listing prime numbers. This he did by writing all the odd numbers and then canceling the successive multiples of each.

APOLLONIOS of Perga (262-205 B.C.) lived in Alexandria and is known to have visited Pergamon and Ephesus. His most important work is *Conics,* in eight books. Books I-III contain "elementary principles" of material which was largely known. Much of this information came from Euclid. Book I gives, however, more detailed development of curves and their properties. Book IV also deals with elementary principles but is mostly new. Book V treats of normals to a curve. Book VI discusses the equality and similarity of conics and Book VII discusses diameters and rectilinear figures described on those diameters. Book VIII is missing except for fragments but seems to be a continuation of Book VII. The first three books were dedicated to Eudemos of Pergamon. Together with Book VI, these have come down to us in Greek. Books IV to VII were dedicated to King Attalos I of Pergamon. The last three have survived only in Arabic. Lacking the advantages of current notation, the descriptions and explanations are rather involved and do not make for easy reading. However, the arrangement and reasoning are unexceptional.

Menaechmos (350 B.C.) used conic curves in his solution of the duplication of the cube. He obtained his curves by passing a plane perpendicular to the side of a cone and varying the apex angle. For acute, right, and obtuse vertical angles, the curves would be ellipse, parabola, and hyperbola respectively. Apollonios achieved his curves from a single cone by varying the angle of incidence.

Apollonios applied the terms *ellipse, parabola,* and *hyperbola* to conic sections. Before his time they were called a section of an acute, right, or obtuse-angled cone respectively. The terms ellipse, parabola, and hyperbola were used by the Pythagoreans in a classification of numbers and in a method called application of areas, as in the construction of a figure with a known side and area. There are three possibilities: there would be a fit, it would fall short, or it would exceed the length of a given line. In the case of conic curves, if the length of the rectangle equaled a given line, it was called a *parabola.* Ellipse was used to indicate a deficiency, and *hyperbola* an excess. The application to conic curves is illustrated by the following equations:

Parabola	$y^2 = mx$	area of square on ordinate equal to area of rectangle (abscissa times latus rectum)
Ellipse	$x^2/a^2 + y^2/b^2 = m$, or	
	$x^2/a^2 = m - y^2/b^2$	(a deficiency)
Hyperbola	$x^2/a^2 - y^2/b^2 = m$, or	
	$x^2/a^2 = m + y^2/b^2$	(an excess)

Commentaries by Pappus indicate that Apollonios also wrote *On Cutting Off an Area, On Cutting Off a Ratio, On Determinate Section, Inclinations, Plane Loci, Tangencies,* and a work which proposed a system of notation based on 10^4 instead of the 10^8 base proposed by Archimedes in his *Sand Reckoner.* Other works of Apollonios are *On the Burning Glass* (the parabolic mirror), *On the Cylindrical Helix,* and *Okytokion,* in which he showed how to get closer limits for π than obtained by Archimedes.

Heracleides has been mentioned as having proposed epicycles to explain the irregularities in the motions of Mercury and Venus and that Apollonios generalized the idea to include Mars, Jupiter, and Saturn. He also suggested the idea of a movable eccentric in which the sun and the exterior planets revolved around a point external to the earth and the point revolved around the earth once a year. Either method could explain the retrograde motions of the exterior planets and the differences in the lengths of the seasons. But epicycles would still be required for Mercury and Venus, so the eccentric theory was abandoned.

Apollonios deserves a very high place in the development of mathematics. Without Euclid, he could not have attained such prominence, but in turn he paved the way for Hipparchos and Ptolemy. After his death, no great mathematician appeared before Diophantus, about two centuries later.

ARISTOPHANES of Byzantium (257-180 B.C.) was a pupil of Zenodotos and Callimachos and followed Eratosthenes as librarian for the period 195-180 B.C. He was primarily a grammarian, lexicographer, and philologist, perhaps the greatest of classical antiquity. He improved editions of Homer, Hesiod, and other literary

giants, helped organize Greek grammar, compiled a Greek dictionary, and standardized punctuation and accents. Before his time
there was not only little use of accentuation and punctuation, but
even no word spacing. Punctuation was not generally adopted until
the 16th century A.D.

Eumenes II, king of Pergamon, tried to induce Aristophanes
to become librarian of the Pergamon Library, whereupon Ptolemaios Epiphanes put Aristophanes in prison and forbade the export
of papyrus.

CTESIBIOS of Alexandria (fl c 200 B.C.) was, according to
Vitruvius and others, a barber, engineer, craftsman, and inventor.
He invented a forced water pump with the three essentials of
cylinder, piston, and valve; a water organ, and improved water
clocks. Water clocks (clepsydras), had been in use in Egypt for
a thousand years but measured a certain length of time as a whole,
like an hourglass. Ctesibios improved them so the water head was
kept constant and the outflow would be steady. Time was measured
by the level of the water in the collecting vessel.*

SERAPION (fl 200 B.C.), along with Philinos of Cos, was a
leader in founding a new school of medicine, called the Empirical
school, which made full use of the anatomic and physiologic work
done at Alexandria during the 3rd century B.C. Surgery was the
only real improvement over the Hippocratic school, but in that
field it was revolutionary.

ZENODOROS (fl c 180 B.C.) studied polygons and stated that of
all regular polygons with equal perimeters, the one with the greatest
number of angles or sides has the greatest area. He also stated that
the area of a circle is greater than the area of a polygon with equal
perimeter and that the volume of a sphere is greater than that of
any polyhedron of equal surface. The spherical shape of bubbles
and droplets is Nature's demonstration of the efficiency of that
conformation.

AGATHARCHIDES of Cnidos (fl c 180 B.C.) was a Peripatetic
philosopher who flourished in Alexandria. He wrote a 10-book

*On a visit to Fez, Morocco, in 1955, a water clock, consisting of half a
dozen units, was pointed out on the side of a building wall in one of the
main streets of the city. No one seemed to know how it worked.

treatise on the geography and history of Asia and a 49-book work
on the geography and history of Europe. He also wrote a mariners'
manual for the Red Sea. He explained the summer floods of the
Nile as due to the accumulation of waters in Ethiopia in the wintertime.

HYPSICLES (fl c 180 B.C.) is credited with being the author of
Book XIV of Euclid's *Elements,* containing eight propositions on
the more complex polyhedrons. He had no knowledge of trigonometry. His prime interest was in astronomy and he wrote a
treatise on the risings and settings of the signs of the zodiac. About
this time, the Greeks were beginning to follow the Babylonian plan
of dividing the circle into 360° and a definite use of sexagesimal
fractions. Hypsicles was the first to apply degrees to the ecliptic.

ARISTARCHOS of Samothrace (217-145 B.C.) is the last librarian in Alexandria mentioned, serving from 160 to 145 B.C. He was
one of Greece's great philologists and his commentaries and critical
treatises filled 800 rolls. He was one of the first to recognize nine
parts of speech (noun, pronoun, participle, verb, adjective, ad-
verb, preposition, conjunction, and article) and strove to extract
and systematize the grammar of the Greek language from the literature. He wrote critical recensions and commentaries on Hesiod,
Anacreon, Pindar, and others. Before Aristarchos, there were many
varied editions of the *Iliad* and the *Odyssey.* He divided the epics
into 24 books each, as Zenodotos did, with explanatory notes based
on detailed acquaintance with Homeric poems and Greek literature.
These have since been the basis of all the later editions, including
present-day texts.

Conditions in Egypt and the Library were deteriorating after
the accession of Ptolemaios VII (Physcon), so that Aristarchos
decided to leave. He went to Cyprus, where he died of dropsy.

ARTEMIDOROS of Ephesus (fl c 100 B.C.) was a traveler and
geographer. After settling in Alexandria, he wrote a work on geography in 11 books.

PHILON of Byzantium (fl c 130 B.C.) spent much of his time
in Alexandria and some in Rhodes. He was a military engineer,
the first to write on the arts of war. He wrote on the use of the

lever, the construction of harbors, engines for shooting, the fortification of walls, and methods of besieging. Air was shown to be a material body which fills space, and a vacuum cannot exist; if air is withdrawn from an upturned chamber in a basin of water, the water will follow it. He discussed siphons, water wheels, and water pumps. He invented the gimbal mounting used with ships' compasses, which was resurrected by Girolamo Cardano (1501-1576 A.D.).

SOSIGENES (fl c 50 B.C.) is best known for his part in the revision of the calendar. Prior to the 5th century B.C., the Roman calendar was a 12-month lunar affair. At that time, the twelve ruling magistrates, the Decemvirs, decreed a solar year, leaving the regulation in the hands of the priests. It was so mismanaged that by the time of Julius Caesar it was 80 days out of line and radical measures were necessary for its reform. Following the advice of Sosigenes, Caesar decreed that the year 46 B.C. should have 445 days and that thereafter every year should have 365 days, with an extra day every four years. This is the Julian calendar and the years will average out 365.25 days. This is slightly longer than the true value of 365.2422 days. By 1582 A.D., the calendar was 13 days off.

The Council of Nicaea in 325 A.D. fixed the rule for the observance of Easter. To bring the calendar in line with the 325 A.D. Easter, Pope Gregory decreed, with the advice of Christopher Clavius, that the day after October 4, 1582, should be October 15. Then, to avoid a recurrence, Luigo Lilio Ghiraldi (Lilius), a Vatican librarian, suggested that century leap years must be divisible by 400. With this provision, no further adjustment of the calendar is needed for over 3,000 years.

The origin of the term *leap year* can be explained by an example. If a given date, say May 1, falls on a Monday, the following non-leap year it will fall on a Tuesday. However, if the following year is a leap year, the calendar will "leap" over Tuesday and the date will fall on a Wednesday.

DIDYMUS (66 B.C.-10 A.D.) was a grammarian and philologist who endeavored to uphold the standards of the Greek language. He taught in the Library at Alexandria and spent some time in

Rome. He was famous for his great learning and industry. He published a great many commentaries and a very learned treatise on an edition of Homer by Aristarchos of Samothrace.

HERON (fl c 50 A.D.) showed more ingenuity in the application of mathematics than any other writer of his time. Much of our knowledge of the history of Greek mechanics, physics, technology, and geodesy is due to him. His little jet-propulsion steam engine was a familiar picture in physics books. He wrote a three-volume book, *Metrics,* which treated of the measurements of areas and volumes. His formula for the area of a triangle in terms of its sides is Area $= \sqrt{s(s\text{-}a)\ (s\text{-}b)\ (s\text{-}c)}$, with $s = (a + b + c)/2$.*

The fire engine and pumps of Ctesibios are described in his *Pneumatica.* He also wrote on acoustics, discussing pitch as due to the number of vibrations in a given time, pure notes as being exact multiples or simple fractions, harmonious sounds as being simple ratios, and the number of vibrations of vibrating strings in a given time as being inversely proportional to the length of the string. The basis for these statements had already been developed by Pythagoras and Aristoxenes.

ST. MARK (fl 1st century A.D.) was the founder of the Christian church in Alexandria and must have been an important personage on the local scene. He was born in Jerusalem as John, the son of a Jewish matron. Converted by St. Paul, he accompanied Paul on some of his missionary travels and joined Peter and Paul in Rome

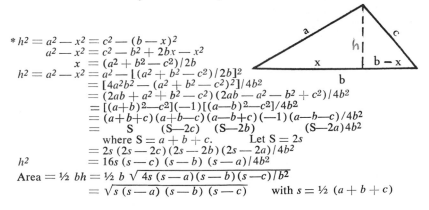

before their martyrdom. It was from his discussions with Peter that he wrote his gospel—about 63 A.D. Returning to Alexandria, he was ordained a bishop. He suffered martyrdom shortly thereafter, caused by his protest against a public procession held in honor of the god Serapis. A cathedral was later erected on the site of his tomb. It was burned during the Arab invasion in 640 A.D. but was rebuilt in 838 A.D. The caliph threatened to plunder the church. In order to save the remains of St. Mark, two Venetian merchants, Buono Malamocco and Rustico de Torcello, smuggled the remains away, in a basket covered with pork, to Venice, where St. Mark's Cathedral was built.

In Alexandria nothing remains but the legend.

MENELAUS (fl c 100 A.D.) lived most of his productive life in Rome. In this period of Greek mathematics, he was one of the most prominent who showed any evidence of genius. He wrote the treatise *Spherics* and was the first to deal with spherical triangles. The first table of chords on record is that of Hipparchos (c 140 B.C.); the next is that of Menelaus.

PTOLEMY, CLAUDIOS (100-170 A.D.), did for astronomy what Euclid did for geometry. For over 14 centuries, his two books *Syntaxis* and *Geographia* governed the thinking in those two fields. Both of these not only summarized all the pertinent information and thinking which had accumulated in the prior centuries, but interpreted it in view of his own observations and ideas.

The *Syntaxis* is known to us only through the Arabic translations. *'H Megala Syntaxis tes Astronomias*—"The Great System of Astronomy"—was translated as *Al Kitab al Megeste* by the Arabs. It was revised in the 9th century A.D. by Al Thabit ibn Kurrah. A Latin version by Gerard of Cremona in the 12th century was the basis of the first complete printed Almagest published in Venice in 1515. It consisted of 13 books. Books I and II treat of various postulates, such as that the earth is considered spherical and in the center of the universe; contain general notions of the celestial sphere, sun, moon, and planets; acknowledge that if the earth would turn on its own axis, it would simplify matters; and give a procedure for forming a table of chords. Book III treats of the length of the year and the theory of the sun. Book IV discusses the length of the month and the theory of the moon, including his own discovery of the inequality of the moon's motion (evection), a most important contribution, and the ability to calculate the position of the moon at any time with errors rarely exceeding 10'. In Book V the construction of his chief astronomical instrument, the astrolabe, is explained. By means of measurements of the moon at widely separated points, the distance of the moon is found to be 59 times the earth's radius—very close. However, the estimated distance of the sun falls short by a factor of about 20. Eclipses are discussed in Book VI. Books VII and VIII constitute a catalogue of 1,028 stars and 48 constellations, which is believed to be mainly a revision of that of Hipparchos. It was intended for an epoch of 137 A.D., but since a precession constant of 36" a year was used instead of 50.26", the star positions were actually representative of the epoch of 58 A.D. The distribution of the stars is as follows: 12 constellations of the zodiac with 350 stars, 21 northern constellations with 361 stars, and 15 southern constellations with 318 stars. Three stars were named twice. Of the constellations, he said: "We employ not the same figures as those before us, as neither did they of those before them, but frequently make use of others that more truly represent the forms for which they are drawn." The theory of planets is discussed in Books IX to XIII, of which more later.

Geographia was concerned mainly with maps and their construction. It developed the idea of conic and modified spherical projection with latitudes and longitudes expressed in degrees, minutes, and seconds. The terms *minute* and *second* are derived from the Latin translation of the text for those divisions: *Partes Minutae Prima* and *Partes Minutae Secundae*. The maps were oriented so that North is at the top and East is to the right. Unfortunately, Ptolemy accepted Poseidonios' figure of 18,000 miles for the circumference, making each degree 50 miles. This meant a foreshortening north and south. Furthermore, reports of latitudes were unreliable and the only data on longitudes were a few reports on the timing of eclipses. Most longitudes were based on estimates by mariners, such as Marinus of Tyre and the Egyptian Admiral Timosthenes of Rhodes.

His plan was to make 10 maps of Europe, 4 of Africa, and 12 of Asia. Although warped, when compared to modern maps, they did represent the information available at the time and continued to be relied upon by geographers until the 15th century. Even the error of underestimating the westward distance between Europe and China by 4,000 miles may have had its benefits. Without it, Columbus might not have ventured forth.

The continuity of the development of planetary theory prior to Ptolemy cannot be traced in its entirety. The Pythagorean school (6th century B.C.) conceived of a series of concentric crystal spheres carrying the heavenly bodies. Plato (428-347 B.C.) developed the doctrine assuming a geocentric system with the stars on a celestial sphere inside of which were seven concentric spheres, one each for the sun, the moon, and the five planets. It was only a very general picture, without any attempt to account for anything. Eudoxos (409-356 B.C.) was the first to make an attempt to represent some of the motions, but it was rather involved; for example, each celestial body was mounted on the equator of a sphere which rotated with its axis atttached to another sphere and this in turn to a third sphere. One sphere was required for the fixed stars, three each for the sun and the moon, and four for each of the five planets. The change in brightness of Venus and Mars, and the fact that certain solar eclipses are annular and others are total, indicated varying distances of these bodies from the earth. This led to abandonment of the homocentric-sphere system of Eudoxos in favor of two systems: movable eccentric circles and epicycles. Heracleides of Pontus is generally assumed to have proposed the epicycle system to explain irregularities in the motions of Mercury in his geoheliocentric model and Apollonios of Perga to have generalized the idea to include the exterior planets. Apollonios seems to have been the first to suggest the eccentric system.

The eccentric-circle system assumed that the planets revolved in a circle whose center necessarily lies somewhere on a line between the earth and the sun. This *center* moved around the earth, obviously, once a year. The period of each planet around this center was equal to its synodic period. In the case of Mercury and

Venus, the orbits were within the orbit of the sun. For the other planets, the circles were so large as to include both the earth and the sun.

In the epicycle system, each planet revolves around the earth on a circle called a deferent. This circle does not represent the true path of the planet but rather the path of the center of a smaller circle around which the planet revolves. For exterior planets, the center of the epicycle moves around on the deferent path with a period equal to the sidereal period of the planet. The period of the epicycle is one year. For Mercury and Venus, the period of the deferent is one year with the center of the epicycle always between the earth and the sun. The period of the epicycle is the synodic period of the planet. The sun and the moon move with variable velocities without becoming stationary or retrograde. These motions could also be represented by epicycles.

Ptolemy made substantial improvement in the theory of the moon, finding it necessary to account for irregularities which were later found to be due to the sun when the moon is in quadrature. This irregularity is called evection. The correction was made by having the epicycle move on an eccentric circle. Although this improved the fixing of the position of the moon, it exaggerated the variation of the distance between the moon and the earth, amounting to a two to one variation in size. This, of course, was not in agreement with the fact.

Aristarchos (310-230 B.C.) suggested the heliocentric system, apparently without fully analyzing its possibilities or adequately presenting the arguments. In any case, the system wasn't received favorably. For one thing, there were still unexplained inequalities which could be accounted for by epicycles—as Copernicus had to do. The Platonists, Aristotelians, and Stoics were unsympathetic to a change in their technique. Then, too, it has been suggested that by this time, the mathematicians had given up hope of finding a true physical system and were wholly concerned with the mechanics of perfecting tables of planetary motions.

One wonders how close science came to avoiding nearly 2,000 years of doubt and struggling with the wrong system.

This, then, was the situation at the time of Apollonios. The system of either movable eccentrics or epicycles could explain retrograde motion. The epicycle was somewhat simpler and gradually replaced the movable eccentric system. Apollonios was apparently noncommittal and there is nothing to indicate he considered the heliocentric system seriously.

Hipparchos (170-120 B.C.) favored epicycles, as it seemed more reasonable that the whole celestial system should be arranged symmetrically about the center, namely, the earth. But he found irregularities, particularly in the motion of the moon, that indicated more information was required. The predecessors of Hipparchos were primarily concerned with explaining retrograde motion and were not aware of irregularities around the zodiac, or considered them minor. The long periods of Jupiter and Saturn didn't help any. At any rate, more data was needed and Hipparchos set about to get it.

Ptolemy's system involved modification and refinement of the epicycle system. To compensate for the elliptical orbit of the earth, Ptolemy resorted to eccentricity of the deferents of the planets. Considerable difficulty stemmed from the assumption that the planes of the planetary orbits were centered on the earth instead of the sun. This required a tilting of the planes of the deferents and epicycles with respect to the plane of the ecliptic, and other corrections. The plan involved enormous labor, but it did represent the motions with fair exactitude. Ptolemy apparently recognized that the epicyclic theory did not pretend to represent the true system but was merely a means for calculating the apparent places of the planets. This it did satisfactorily and it was a very elegant mathematical masterpiece. Copernicus eliminated some of the difficulty by assuming the sun to be the center but he was still plagued with epicycles. The matter was not resolved until Kepler substituted ellipses for circular orbits.

Ancient astronomy essentially ends with Ptolemy, as later writings are merely commentaries and compilations.

DIOPHANTUS (c 246-330 A.D.) was an unexplained genius, one of the greatest Greek mathematicians, and is considered the father of algebra. Little is known of his life, although a little problem is supposed to apply to him: "His boyhood lasted 1/6 of his life, his beard grew after 1/12 more, after 1/7 more he married, 5 years later his son was born, the son lived to half his father's age, and the father died 4 years after his son [his age, 84 years]." He wrote three works of which his *Arithmetica* in 13 books is the most important. It covered the theory of numbers and much of what is now included in algebra and special cases of simultaneous quadratic and cubic equations. He introduced better algebraic symbolism and anticipated progress in algebra by several centuries.

PAPPUS (fl 300 A.D.) wrote a work, *Mathematical Collections,* in eight books, discussing the works of all the great mathematicians of the past and such subjects as proportion, inscribed solids, the duplication of the cube, spirals, the sphere, and mechanics. This is a very important source of the works of Archimedes, Euclid, Aristarchos and Apollonios of Perga.

THEON of Alexandria (fl 375 A.D.) wrote a valuable commentary on Ptolemy's *Syntaxis,* including handy tables explaining sexagesimal computations. His commentary on Euclid was helpful in determining the accurate text of the *Elements.* The statement that the helical rising of Sirius corresponds to the first day of the Egyptian calendar year in 139 A.D., is attributed to him. He was the father of Hypatia.

HYPATIA (370-415 A.D.) was the first woman of note in mathematics. She presided over the Neo-Platonic School in Alexandria and wrote commentaries on an astronomical table of Diophantus and on the conics of Apollonios. She was the last to use the Library, as it and the Museum were destroyed by savage Christian mobs in 389 A.D. She was highly intellectual, dressed simply, conducted herself above suspicion, and attracted many pupils. After Cyril became patriarch, his partisans regarded her as a principal of paganism. In March, 415 A.D., while on her way to school, she was seized and dragged to the Caesareum, then to a Christian church, stripped nude, and hacked to death with oyster shells, and her body was dragged through the streets and finally burned. Christianity treated "pagan" science with attitudes ranging from indifference to frank hostility. Ignorance was exalted as a virtue.

After her death, seven centuries after the founding of the Museum and Library, the curtain comes down on Alexandria as a center of learning—a center which had risen to such heights in the 3rd century B.C.

APPENDIXES

Chronological Table

Partial List of Books Consulted

Index

CHRONOLOGICAL TABLE

B.C.	MESOPOTAMIA	GREECE	EGYPT	B.C.
10,000—	Cave sites from the Old Stone Age in N.E. corner of Iraq			–10,000
7000—	JARMO, earliest settled village Polychrome pottery from Hassuna, Samarra, and Tell Halaf	Oldest settled villages are Nea Nike-media in Macedonia and Elateia in central Greece		–7000
5000—	Multiplicity of temples at Eridu Painted pottery		Traces of Neolithic cultural stages: Tasian, Badarian, Amratean, Gerzean, and Semainion	–5000
3500—	UBAID culture characterized by mud-brick temples, reed houses, terra-cotta figurines, clay nails, and buff or gray pottery with brown or black designs URUK period; picture writing intro-duced with a small tablet from Kish as the earliest example; early stage of ziggurat type of temple; stamp and cylinder seals; red, black, and buff clay nails; pottery gen-erally unpainted; early number sys-tem with a decimal base		Upper and Lower Egyptian kingdoms of city-states	–3500
3000—			MENA, the Thinite, first dynastic king, unites Upper and Lower Egypt (3100) Narmer palette	–3000

	Mesopotamia	Aegean	Egypt
3000— (−3000)	Cuneiform script invented about 3000 Jemdet Nasr period with walled cities; sculpture appears, the outstanding items being the 3-foot alabaster Warka vase and the life-size marble mask of a woman	Numerous Neolithic settlements in Crete with many inhabitants living in caves	Hieroglyphic writing developed; papyrus invented, thereby making the cursive hieratic script practical
2750— (−2750)	Dynasties of Kish, Ur, Uruk, Lagash, and other city-states Royal tombs at Ur contained beautiful gold dishes, ornaments, harp with bull's head, ram in the thicket, and similar items (2600) Cuneiform script reduced in 5 stages from 2,000 signs to about 600 and adopted by neighboring nations and peoples Dynasty of Akkad (Agade) (2334-2154) Sargon I (2334-2279) Earliest reference to Babylon (2300)	Settlers from Anatolia arrive in Cyprus, Crete, and eastern areas of the Greek mainland (2700) Troy II (2600-2300) characterized by pottery and beautiful artifacts excavated by Schliemann	*Old Kingdom* *Dynasties III-VI (2686-2270)* Zoser, the Memphite, Dynasty III (2686), with capital at Memphis Imhotep (2650), architect, physician, and premier Step Pyramid at Sakkarah (2650) Dynasty IV (2600): Khufu (Cheops), Kha-ef-re (Chephren), Men-kau-re (Mycernius) Pyramids and Sphinx at Giza (2600)
2500— (−2500)	Guti invasion (2154-2120) Sumerian revival–Ur III (2120-2004) Ziggurat at Ur; code of Ur-Nammu (2095) Scientific accomplishments: space-value number system with sexagesimal base, tables of multiplication, division, squares, cubes, roots, and compound interest; lunar calendar; constellations depicted on cylinder seals		Dynasty VI, Pepy II (2364-2770)—94-year reign, longest in history *Intermediate Period* *Dynasties VII-X (2270-2160)*
2000— (−2000)		Numerous cities in Thessaly, Boeotia, and west of the Pindus Mountains Beginning of the Palace period in Crete at Knossos, Phaistos, and Malli	*Middle Kingdom* *Dynasties XI-XIV (2160-1788)*

B.C.	MESOPOTAMIA	GREECE	EGYPT	B.C.
2000—	Nineveh founded Reform code of Lipit-Ishtar of Isin (c 1930)		Period of much construction at Thebes; expansion of foreign trade with Nubia and Syria; Nile–Red Sea canal started	–2000
	1st Babylonian dynasty (1894-1595)	Short pictographic inscriptions cut on seals in Crete (2000-1850) First Greek-speaking people (Ionians) enter Greece from north (1900-1600)	Moscow Mathematical Papyrus (1800-1700)	
	Civil Code of Balalama (c 1880)	Cursive form of pictographic symbols in Crete with about 135 symbols, some on baked-clay tablets (1850-1700)	*Intermediate Period* *Dynasties XV-XVII (1788-1567)* Hyksos kings; horse-drawn chariots introduced	
	HAMMURABI (1792-1750); civil code; declares an intercalary month Literary period, largely Babylonian versions of Sumerian tales	Palaces in Crete destroyed (c 1700) and new palaces built	Rhind Papyrus, a c 1650 copy of a c 1850 document; 85 problems involving fractions, simple equations, and mensuration	
	Large numbers of mathematical problem texts Observations of risings and settings of Venus during reign of King Amisaduqa (1646-1626) Dark Ages (1595-1375) during Kassite dynasty rule (1595-1157)		*New Kingdom* *Dynasties XVIII-XX (1567-1085)* Oldest definitely dated glass is from c 1550, although glass beads are much older	
1500—	ABRAHAM leaves Ur for Land of Canaan (c 1600-1500)	Linear A Script with 85 signs in Crete (1600-1400) Crete at height of power	Karnak temple expanded HATSHEPSUT (1495-1475) TUTHMOSIS III (1501-1447), considered ablest of the pharaohs	–1500
		Crete invaded by Mycenaean Greeks (1400); Linear A script adapted to archaic Greek language and now known as Linear B	Luxor temple built during reign of Amenhotep III (c 1400)	

Ugarit cuneiform script with 30 symbols (c 1400). This was one of a number of attempts to form a consonantal alphabetic language in a 6-century period from 1500 to 900.

Tell el-Amarna was new capital of the empire during reign of Akhnaten and Queen Nefertiti (1375-1357)

TUT-ANKH-AMON (1353-1344)

Decans charted before 1300

RAMESES II (1298-1232), builder of temples and monuments; period of great prosperity

MOSES and the Exodus; various dates from 1500 to 1200, the latter date on the basis that Merneptah (c 1225) was the pharaoh of the Exodus

Isin II and other dynasties precede the Assyrian domination which follows after about 900

Mycenae and Tiryns fortified with Cyclopean walls; King Agamemnon

Troy besieged 10 years (c 1200)

ASCLEPIUS, founder or namesake of healing cult

Achaeans settle in Thessaly and Boeotia

Dorian invasion (1100); all Mycenaean citadels destroyed; iron introduced

Large-scale colonization of coastal sites of Asia Minor following Dorian invasion of mainland Greece (1100-1000)

Dark Ages following Dorian invasion (1100-800)

Dorian migration to islands and Asia Minor

B.C.	MESOPOTAMIA	GREECE	EGYPT	B.C.
1000—	*Assyrian Domination (900-626)*	Oldest specimen of Greek alphabet, on island of Thera, 8th century	*Late Egyptian Dynasties XXI-XXXI (1085-30)*	—1000
	Eclipse observations recorded systematically from reign of Nabu-nasir (747-734)	First Olympic game, 776 HOMER composes *Iliad* and *Odyssey* from heroic ballads (8th century) HESIOD (c 750) writes of Grecian myths		
	SARGON II (721-705) founds new capital of Dur Sharrukin (Khorsabad)	Extensive colonization of Italy and Sicily (734-628) TERPANDER of Lesbos (fl 660)		
	Eclipse predicted but not observed on account of clouds (c 670)		Thebes sacked by Assurbanipal (663)	
	ASSURBANIPAL (668-631) collects immense library and works of art at Nineveh	THALES of Miletus (640-546) SAPPHO of Lesbos (fl c 600) ALCAEUS of Lesbos (fl c 600) AESOP of Samos (620-560)		—600
	Nineveh destroyed (612); end of Assyrian empire	ANAXIMANDER of Miletus (611-546) BIAS of Priene (fl 570)	Digging of Nile–Red Sea canal resumed (started in Middle Kingdom period)	
600—	*Chaldean Dynasty (635-539)* NEBUCHADNEZZAR II (604-562); acme of Babylon's wealth and political power; Hanging Gardens; Jerusalem conquered and most of inhabitants deported to Babylon CYRUS assumes kingship in Persia (559)	GLAUCOS of Chios (fl 560) ANAXIMENES of Miletus (585-528) PYTHAGORAS of Samos (580-497) XENOPHANES of Colophon (570-480) THEODOROS of Samos (fl 540) ANACREON of Teos (560-478) HECATEUS of Miletus (550-475) Papyrus available in Greece (550)		

Naucratis built on Canopic mouth of Nile Delta by Miletus as trading city (c 540)

Egypt conquered by Cambyses of Persia (525)

Persian rule (525-332)

DECOMEDES of Croton (fl 520)
Abdera founded (544)
EPICHARMOS of Cos (540-450)
SIMONIDES of Kea (536-469)
Epic poems of *Iliad* and *Odyssey* recited in Panathenaen festivals in Athens after about 535
HERACLEITUS of Ephesus (535-475)
ALCAMION of Croton (fl c 500)
AESCHYLUS of Eleusis (525-456)
PINDAR of Thebes (522-443)
PARMENIDES of Elea (510- ?)
ANAXAGORAS of Clazomenae (499-427)
SOPHOCLES of Athens (495-406)
Miletus sacked and never recovers (494)
EMPEDOCLES of Akragas (492-433)
Persians defeated in battle of Marathon (490)
OENOPIDES of Chios (fl 465)
HIPPOCRATES of Chios (fl 460)
PHIDIAS of Athens (490-432)
POLYCLEITOS of Argos (fl 460)
ICTINUS of Athens (fl 460)
MYRON of Athens (fl 460)
HERODOTUS of Halicarnassus (484-424)
EURIPIDES of Salamis (484-407)
PROTAGORAS of Abdera (481-411)
ZENO of Elea (480——)
PHILOLAUS of Tarentum (c 480——)
Battles of Thermopylae and Salamis (480)
Battles of Plataea and Mycale (479)
Delos Confederation (478)
POLYGNOTOS of Thasos (fl 455)

CROESUS defeated by Cyrus (539)

DARIUS I (521-486) assumes throne; palace at Persepolis; Behistun inscriptions (516)
Persian Empire greater than ever—extends from India to Libya

Nabu-rimanni devises detailed lunar tables (490)

B.C.	MESOPOTAMIA	GREECE	EGYPT	B.C.
475—				—475
		LEUCIPPUS of Miletus (450)		
		HIPPODAMOS of Miletus (fl 450)		
		THUCYDIDES of Athens (471-400)		
		MNESICLES of Athens (fl 440)		
		THEODOROS of Cyrene (470——)		
		SOCRATES of Athens (470-399)		
		METON of Athens (465-385)		
		EUCTEMON of Athens (fl 430)		
	XERXES assassinated (465)	ZEUXIS of Heraclea, Pontus (464-398)		
		ANTIPHON of Athens (fl 430)		
		DEMOCRITOS of Abdera (460-370)		
		HIPPOCRATES of Cos (460-375)		
		BRYSON of Pontus (fl 430)		
		Earliest record of use of letters to denote numerals (Halicarnassus, 450)		
450—		Pythagorean Brotherhood dispersed (450)		—450
		EUCLEIDES of Megara (450-380)		
		ARISTOPHANES of Athens (448-385)		
		Parthenon construction (447-432)		
		TIMOTHEOS of Miletus (446-357)		
		ANTISTHENES of Athens (444-371)		
		ISOCRATES of Athens (436-338)		
		ARISTIPPUS of Cyrene (435-356)		
		Peloponnesian War starts (431)		
		XENOPHON of Athens (430-354)		
		POLYBOS of Cos (fl 400)		
		PLATO of Athens (428-347)		
		ARCHYTAS of Tarentum (fl 400)		
		THEAETETOS of Athens (415-369)		
		DIOGENES of Sinope (412-323)		
	KIDINNU (fl 375)	EUDOXOS of Cnidos (408-355)		
400—				—400

Kidinnu improves lunar tables; eclipses can now be predicted with greater accuracy (350)

Peloponnesian War ends; Thirty Tyrants rule Athens (404)
XENOPHON and 10,000 mercenaries stranded in Persia (400)
EPHOROS of Cyme (400-330)
XENOCRATES of Chalcedon (394-314)
THEODOROS of Chios (fl 380)
PRAXITLES of Athens (390——)
Epidauros theater built (c 390)
Plato founds Akademia (387)
HERACLEIDES of Pontus (388-310)
ARISTOTLE of Stageira (384-322)
PHILIP II of Macedon (382-336)
MENAECHMOS of Athens (fl 350)
PRAXAGORAS of Cos (fl 350)
ANAXIMINES of Lampsacus (380-320)
THEOPHRASTOS of Eresos (372-286)
CALLIPPUS of Cyzicus (370-300)
EUDEMOS of Rhodes (fl 335)
ARISTOXENES of Tarentum (fl 335)
APELLES of Cos (fl 335)
ANAXARCHOS of Abdera (fl 330)
PHILEMON of Soli (361-262)
Alexander the Great born (356)
Temple of Artemis in Ephesus burned (356)
PROTOGENES of Caunos (fl 325)
ARISTABUS the Elder (fl 320)
DEMETRIOS of Phaleron (345-283)
EPICUROS of Samos (341-270)
BEROSOS of Babylon (340—fl 290)
DICAEARCHOS of Messina (fl 320—d 285)
ZENO of Cition (336-264)
Alexander becomes king (336)
Aristotle founds Lyceum (335)

B.C.	MESOPOTAMIA	GREECE	EGYPT	B.C.
335—	Persians routed by Alexander's army at Granicus (334), Issus (333) and Gaugamela (Arbela) (331); Darius murdered by one of his own satraps; Persepolis burned	Alexander invades Asia (334), Egypt (332), Mesopotamia (331), and India Alexander dies in Babylon (323) at 33 AUTOLYCOS of Pitane (fl 300) STRATON of Lampsacus (fl 300) ARCESILAOS of Pitane (316-241) ARATUS of Soli (315-245) CHARES of Lindos (fl 290)	Egypt conquered by Alexander's general, Ptolemy (332); Alexandria founded EUCLID (fl 300) PHILETAS of Cos (fl 300) Hecateos of Abdera (fl 300) ZENODOTOS of Ephesus (325-234) TIMOCHARES of Alexandria (fl 280) ARISTILLUS of Stageira (fl 280) HEROPHILLOS of Chalcedon (fl 280) ARISTARCHOS of Samos (310-230) CALLIMACHOS of Cyrene (310-240) MANETHO of Sebennytus (fl 280) Ptolemy assumes kingship of Egypt as Ptolemaios I Soter, with capital at Memphis (306)	−335
	Seleucia founded by Seleucus (312)			
300—	Antioch founded by Seleucus (301) Zero symbol in common use	CLEANTHES of Assus (301-232) HERMACHOS of Lesbos (fl 270) THEOCRITOS of Syracuse (fl 270) ARCHIMEDES of Syracuse (287-212) Philetaerus usurps Pergamon (283) "Colossus of Rhodes" completed (281) by Chares of Lindos CHRYSIPPOS of Soli (280-206)	ERASISTRATOS of Kea (304-?) PTOLEMAIOS I Soter (306-285) SOSTRATOS of Cnidos (fl 270) APOLLONIOS of Rhodes (295-215) CONON of Samos (fl 260—d 212) Library and Museum inaugurated in Alexandria (285) PTOLEMAIOS II Philadelphus (285-247) List of Egyptian dynasties and kings prepared by Manetho (280) SEPTUAGINTS translate Old Testament into Greek (280) ERATOSTHENES of Cyrene (276-194)	−300
275—				−275

SUDINES of Pergamon (fl 240)
EUMENIUS I (263-241) starts building program in Pergamon

NICOMEDES of Pergamon (fl 225)
ATTALOS I (241-197) defeats Gauls and beautifies Pergamon
MENECRATES of Rhodes (fl 200)
Sosos of Pergamon (fl 200)
Earthquake destroys "Colossus of Rhodes" (224)
CARNEADES of Cyrene (213-129)
Archimedes killed as Syracuse falls to Romans (212)
CRATES of Mallos (fl 180)
APOLLONIOS of Tralles (fl 180)

BOËTHOS of Chalcedon (fl 180)

TAURICOS of Tralles (fl 180)
Antioch at its peak
Library at Pergamon founded by Eumenus I; parchment invented

HIPPARCHOS of Nicaea (190-125)
PANAITOS of Lindos (185-109)
APOLLODOROS of Athens (fl 140)
Polybius taken to Rome as hostage as Third Macedonian War ends (168)
DIONYSIOS THRAX of Rhodes (166-?)
EUDOXOS of Cyzicus (fl 130)
Sack of Corinth (146)
POSEIDONIOS of Apamea, Orontes (135-51)

Pharos built (270); architect was Sostratos of Cnidos
APOLLONIOS of Perga (262-205)
ARISTOPHANES of Byzantium (257-180)

CTESIBOS of Alexandria (fl 200)
SERAPION of Alexandria (fl 200)

ARISTARCHOS of Samothrace (217-145)

AGATHARCHIDES of Cnidos (fl 180)
APOLLONIOS EIDOGRAPHOS of Alexandria (fl 180)
HYPSICLES of Alexandria (fl 180)
ZENODOROS of Alexandria (fl 180)

Ptolemaios V forbids exports of papyrus

PHILON of Bythinia (fl 130)

SELEUCUS of Seleucia (fl 180)

B.C.	MESOPOTAMIA	GREECE	EGYPT	B.C.
	Mesopotamia conquered by Mithradates I; capital at Ctesiphon (140) Arsacid dynasty 140 B.C. to 228 A.D.	Pergamon bequeathed to Rome by Attalos III (133) MITHRADATES VI (132-63) DEMETRIOS of Bythinia (fl 100) ASCLEPIADES of Bythinia (124-40)	ARTEMIDOROS of Ephesus (fl 100)	−100
100—		HERACLEIDES of Tarentum (fl 75) APOLLONIOS of Cition, Cyprus (fl 70) GEMINOS of Rhodes (fl 60) AGESANDROS of Rhodes (fl 60) ATHENADORAS of Rhodes (fl 60) POLYDOROS of Rhodes (fl 60) Sack of Athens by Sulla (86) DIONYSODOROS of Amisus (fl 50) CLEOMEDES of Lysimachia (fl 40) STRABO of Amaseia (64 B.C.—21 A.D.) DIONYSIUS of Halicarnassus (fl 20 B.C.)	SOSIGENES of Alexandria (fl 50) DIDYMUS of Alexandria (65 B.C.-10 A.D.) Alexandria besieged by Caesar and Brucheum burned (48 B.C.) Julian calendar instituted in 46 B.C. Pergamon Library transferred to Alexandria (34 B.C.) Egypt annexed to Rome (30 B.C.)	
B.C. 1 - 1 A.D.		ST. PAUL of Tarsus (1 B.C.—67 A.D.)		B.C. 1 - 1 A.D.
100—	Last astronomical text from Mesopotamia (75)		HERON of Alexandria (fl 50) MENELAUS of Alexandria (fl 100)	−100

100—

200—

300—

400—

THEON of Smyrna (fl 125)

SORANUS of Ephesus (fl 125)
MARINUS of Tyre (fl 150)
Athens beautified by Hadrian (125)
GALEN of Pergamon (129-200)

Seleucia destroyed by Cassius (164)

Sassanian dynasty (228 to 634)

Olympian Games ended by Theodosius (394)

PROCLUS of Byzantium (410-485)

PTOLEMY, Claudius of Alexandria
(100-170)

Rosetta Stone erected in 196

DIOPHANTUS of Alexandria (246-330)
PAPPUS of Alexandria (fl 340)
THEON of Alexandria (fl 360)
HYPATIA of Alexandria (370-415)
Alexandrian Library destroyed by
Christian mobs (390)

Hypatia murdered by mob (415)

-100

-200

-300

-400

PARTIAL LIST OF BOOKS
CONSULTED

Allen, R. H. *Star Names*. Dover Publications.

Aristotle, Works of. Oxford University Press.

Bean, G. E. *Aegean Turkey*. Praeger.

Berry, A. *A Short History of Astronomy From the Earliest Times Through the 19th Century*. Dover Publications.

Blegen, C. W. *Troy and The Trojans*. Praeger.

Bradford, E. D. S. *Companion Guide to the Greek Islands*. Harper and Row.

Brown, L. A. *The Story of Maps*. Little, Brown.

Brown, Robert, Jr. *Primitive Constellations, Researches into the Origin of*, London 1899.

Cajori, F. *A History of Physics*. Macmillan.

Cambridge Ancient History. Cambridge University Press.

Cleator, P. E. *Lost Languages*. New American Library.

Cottrell, L. *The Quest for Sumer*. Putnam.

Denham, H. *The Aegean*. Murray (London).

Diringer, D. *Writing*. Praeger.

Doblhofer, E. *Voices in Stone*. Viking Press.

Dreyer, J. L. E. *A History of Astronomy From Thales to Kepler*. Dover Publications.

Encyclopaedia Britannica.

Encyclopedia of the Classical World. Prentice-Hall.

Friedrich, J. *Extinct Languages*. Philosophical Library.

Greece. Hachette World Guide Book.

Groenewegen-Frankfort, H. A., and B. Ashmole. *The Ancient World*. New American Library.

Harper. *Dictionary of Classical Literature and Antiquities*. Cooper Square Publications.

Heidel, A. *The Babylonian Genesis*. University of Chicago Press.

Herodotus. *Histories*.

Homer. The *Iliad* and the *Odyssey*.

Kramer, S. N. *History Begins at Sumer*. Doubleday.
  Sumerian Mythology. Harper and Row.
Lloyd, S. *The Art of the Ancient Near East*. Praeger.
Mackendrick, P. *The Greek Stones Speak*. New American Library.
Macqueen, J. G. *Babylon*. Praeger.
Mallowan, M. E. L. *Early Mesopotamia and Iran*. McGraw-Hill.
Maxwell, Gavin. *People of the Reeds*. Harper and Row.
Mellaart, J. *Earliest Civilizations of the Near East*. Simon and Schuster.
Morton, H. C. V. *Through Lands of the Bible*. Dodd, Mead.
Neugebauer, O. *The Exact Sciences in Antiquity*. Harper and Bros.
Newman, J. R. *The World of Mathematics*, Vol. I. Simon and Schuster.
Oppenheim, A. L. *Ancient Mesopotamia*. University of Chicago Press.
Oxford Classical Dictionary. Oxford University Press.
Parrot, A. *Babylon and the Old Testament*.
Pausanias. *Description of Greece* (Loeb Classical Library). Harvard University Press.
Payne, R. *Islands of Greece*. Simon and Schuster.
Pentreath, G. *Hellenic Traveler*. Crowell.
Plato, Works of. Tudor Publishing.
Pritchard, J. B. *Archaeology and the Old Testament*. Princeton University Press.
Roux, G. *Ancient Iraq*. World Publishing.
Sachs, A. J. *Late Babylonian Astronomical and Related Texts*. Brown University Press.
Sarton, G. *A History of Science*, Vols. I and II. Wiley.
Smith, D. E. *History of Mathematics, Vols. I and II*. Dover Publications.
Stobart, J. C. *The Glory That Was Greece*. Hawthorne.
Strabo. *Geography* (Loeb Classical Library). Harvard University Press.
Taton, R. (ed.). *History of Ancient and Medieval Science*. Basic Books.

Thompson, G. *Studies in Ancient Greek Society*. Citadel Press.
Turkey. Hachette World Guide Book.
Whelpley, S. *Compend of History*. 1808.
Wolfson, A. M. and A. B. Hart. *Essentials in Ancient History*. American Book.
Wooley, L. *Excavation at Ur*. Crowell.
———. *History of Mankind*. New American Library.
Zehren, E. *The Crescent and the Bull*. Hawthorne.

INDEX

(Casual references are generally omitted)

Clifford N. Anderson's undergraduate and graduate studies were in physics at the University of Wisconsin and in water-power engineering as an American-Scandinavian Foundation Fellow to Norway. The greater part of his career has been in radio system engineering with the American Telephone and Telegraph Company and with the Bell Telephone Laboratories.

In 1923, while with the former, he was engaged in the analysis of considerable radio transmission data obtained in connection with engineering the first radio-telephone circuit between New York and London. It was during this period that he discovered the relation of solar disturbances and abnormal radio transmission, the first to do so.

He has taught engineering physics at the University of Wisconsin, communications systems at Cornell University and solid state devices at the University of Miami. He served as naval officer in both World Wars. He is a Fellow of the American Association for the Advancement of Science and a Fellow of the Institute of Electrical and Electronics Engineers.

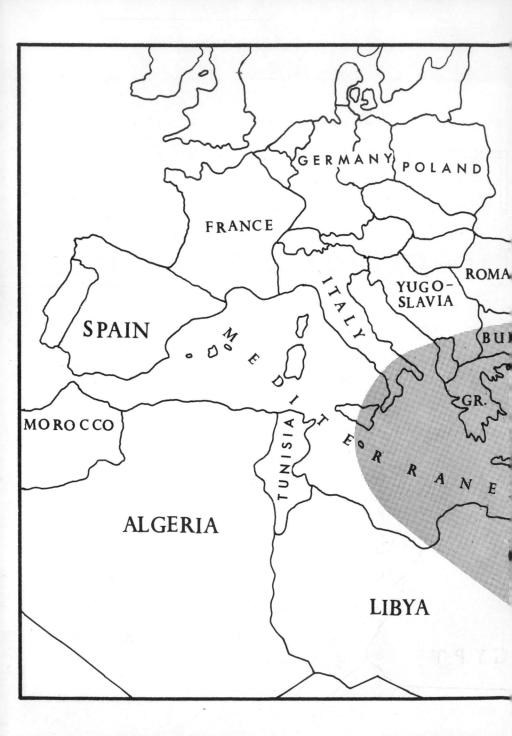